Pr.MAIUS
Control
RM.

The McGraw-Hill Manufacturing and Systems Engineering Series

MAP/TOP Networking

A Foundation for Computer-Integrated Manufacturing

Vincent C. Jones

McGraw-Hill Book Company

New York   St. Louis   San Francisco   Auckland   Bogotá
Hamburg   London   Madrid   Mexico   Milan   Montreal
New Delhi   Panama   Paris   São Paulo
Singapore   Sydney   Tokyo   Toronto

Library of Congress Cataloging-in-Publication Data

Jones, Vincent C.
   MAP/TOP networking.

   Includes index.
   1. Computer integrated manufacturing systems.
2. Computer networks.   I. Title.
TS155.6.J66   1987   670.42'7   87-3630
ISBN 0-07-032806-4

1234567890   DOC/DOC   89210987

ISBN 0-07-032806-4

The editors for this book were Betty Sun and Nancy Young,
the designer was Naomi Auerbach, and the production
supervisor was Dianne L. Walber. This book was set
in Century Schoolbook. It was composed by the McGraw-Hill Book Company
Professional & Reference Division composition unit.
Printed and bound by R. R. Donnelley & Sons Company.

To my three daughters

Contents

Foreword

Standards have been a great contributor to the success of the automobile industry. From standardization of parts and standardization of control device location on vehicles to process standardization, all have had great impact.

In recent years computer technology has had strong influence on all industries, including automotive. In the push by manufacturing companies for international competitiveness, computer-based technology has proliferated. By the late 70s the need to integrate manufacturing processes was recognized. However, the conspicuous lack of standards for communication capability among computers and programmable devices severely limited meeting those needs.

In 1980, General Motors, among others, recognized this significant need for computer communication standards and decided to do something about it. A small group of engineers from seven GM divisions formed the MAP Task Force to pursue the International Organization for Standardization (ISO)—Open Systems Interconnection (OSI) seven-layer communication model. Shortly after, in 1982, a small GM staff group was formed to act as the nucleus of the worldwide effort which was to emerge. I was privileged to head that group. I firmly believed in the potential for "users" to help make standardized computer communications occur. So did others. Most didn't share my optimism about *when* it would occur, but I guess missionary zeal is a powerful tool.

Soon, in early 1984, the MAP Users Group (with the Society of Manufacturing Engineers as Secretariat) was formed. Then the first successful demonstration of MAP occurred at the 1984 National Computer Conference (with the capable help of the National Bureau of Standards and the Industrial Technology Institute of Ann Arbor, Michigan). Seven vendors participated in a GM-sponsored booth. At Autofact '85, 21 vendors helped demonstrate MAP version 2.1. Shortly after, many companies began to implement MAP products. In 1986 the Technical and Office Protocol (TOP) Users Group was formed under the sponsorship of Boeing, and the effort became known as MAP/TOP.

At about the same time it became an international Users Group. Today a World Federation of MAP/TOP users groups exists which represents thousands of users. It is helping to move dozens of countries toward implementation of MAP/TOP version 3.0, the first practical OSI network.

But today as always, knowledge is power. Knowledge is necessary to recognize there are many pitfalls on the road to successful computer-based automation implementation. Every supplier has a solution. A key to success is to select the *right* solution for *your* problem. (Obviously I believe MAP/TOP will help provide that solution in most instances.) The user must be capable of weighing alternatives and making decision to meet needs and requirements. *And* be capable of insuring that what is implemented can be maintained and updated as necessary.

Careful review of this book by myself and several knowledgeable MAP personnel indicates that it contributes substantially to understanding local area network communications based on OSI standards. In addition to describing MAP—its foundations, current status, and future direction—the book is a capable treatise on practical application of MAP/TOP and where they can best be utilized. It also knowledgeably discusses development of implementation strategies.

This book provides the proper background to understand the MAP specification. It accurately portrays MAP's strengths, among which is the international standards base, and covers areas under development which require special planning for later implementation. I highly recommend this as required reading to anyone desiring to add substantial knowledge of MAP/TOP tools to their repertoire.

June, 1987   MICHAEL KAMINSKI
                                                Manager, MAP Program
                                                General Motors Corporation

Preface

Magazines and the trade press are flooded with articles describing MAP/TOP in general terms. Technical journals contain articles discussing the benefits of complementing the fourth bit in the seventh byte of a protocol nobody has ever heard of. In between there appears to be a severe lack of information. This book tries to bridge the gap. My goal is to take the reader from a basic understanding of computers and computer networking to a thorough understanding of the concepts behind open systems networking in general and MAP/TOP in particular. Along the way I have tried to provide some insight into how computer networks really work (as opposed to how they are supposed to) and some of the considerations which must go into developing implementations with true multivendor interoperability.

This book is intended to provide a comprehensive introduction to the world of MAP/TOP. While the primary audience is computer scientists and engineers who are designing computer-integrated manufacturing applications for use over MAP/TOP networks, their managers will find knowledge of the implementation issues involved equally valuable. Students will find the contrasts between the theory of networking and its practice in real life enlightening.

Management-oriented readers should feel free to skim through the technical parts, especially Chapters 5 and 6. Overall, the book is organized into three main sections. Chapters 1 through 4 are general introduction. Chapter 2 and the first half of Chapter 3 can be skipped if you do not plan to read Chapters 5 and 6. Chapters 5 through 8 repeat Chapter 4 in greater detail. Chapters 9 through 12 explore management and technical issues in determining network requirements and specifying, implementing, and managing a network. An extensive glossary is provided for your convenience. Every acronym used in this book is included as well as many terms not used in this book but common in the general networking literature.

There are many people who deserve credit for helping to bring this book about. I am particularly indebted to Laurie Bride at Boeing Computer Services and Mike Kaminski at General Motors who provided the time for their staff to read and critique the manuscript. Among those who contributed were Patricia A. Amaranth, Michael F. Bukowski, Howard A. Fingeroot, Charles Parisot, William J. Riker, Kathleen M. Sturgis, and Gary C. Workman. Thanks also to Gary Blunck of Deere and Company and William Geibel of Kaiser Aluminum for their comments and permission to use their companies as examples.

My thanks to Integrated Computer Systems, Culver City, California, for their permission to use the ideas and illustrations contained in their short course "MAP/TOP: A Comprehensive Technical Introduction and Status Report."

Finally, there are my friends Jim Conrad, Doug Gregory, and Rita Wigglesworth whose excellent comments helped make the text more readable.

Vincent C. Jones

Introduction to MAP/TOP

Welcome to the networking world of MAP/TOP, the Manufacturing Automation Protocol and the Technical and Office Protocols. At first the flood of jargon and acronyms may seem forbidding. You will soon discover that MAP/TOP is not really that mysterious nor difficult once you understand the language being spoken. This book is intended to carry you through the introductory stages to the point at which you can make informed trade-offs and decisions in your plans to implement a MAP/TOP network.

This book is not a substitute for the published MAP/TOP specifications. MAP/TOP is evolving far too fast to be covered by a normally published book. Rather, my aim is to provide the background information to allow you to read the specifications and articles from the current literature, understand what they mean, and, even more important, recognize how they relate to your objectives for using and linking computers.

What Is MAP/TOP?

The term MAP/TOP has been receiving a lot of press since the first demonstrations of multivendor capabilities at the 1984 National Computer Conference. The demonstration of MAP 2.1 and TOP 1.0 in a simulated production environment at AUTOFACT in November of 1985 and subsequent factory floor production installations have proven that MAP/TOP is available today and useful in the real world. The advent of MAP/TOP has had a profound and permanent effect in the development and implementation of computer network technology and distributed computer applications. But editors and reporters vying for readers' attention with claims ranging from "order of magnitude productivity increases" to "the factory of the future is available today," make it hard to distinguish hype from reality.

Compounding the confusion is the term MAP/TOP itself. Its meaning depends on the context of its use. As a networking term, MAP/TOP is simply a name for a suite of networking protocols, a shorthand notation for specifying the networking protocols selected by the MAP/TOP Users' Group. The confusion stems from the use of the same term, MAP/TOP, as the name for the collective dreams of all the potential users. These dreams, or more appropriately visions, range from the elimination of all the point-to-point wiring clutter on the factory floor to total computer-integrated manufacturing (CIM).

Alternatively, the first definition could be considered a particular implementation of a tool while the second is the conceptual reason for the tool. For example, a 1986 Chevrolet Cavalier is a particular implementation of "automotive transportation" while the mobility of American society and the interstate highway system is the result of the availability of the tool "automotive transportation."

The tool analogy carries even further. Many of the arguments both for and against MAP/TOP are manifestations of the screw and glue syndrome—"When the only tool you have is a hammer, every problem starts to look like a nail." In real life, not all problems are nails, and a hammer (or MAP or TOP) is not always the right tool for the job.

The primary purpose of this book is to bridge that gap between MAP/TOP, the networking specification, and MAP/TOP, the computer-integrated manufacturing vision. We will start by describing networking from the perspective of the user of networking services. We will then show the approach MAP/TOP uses to provide some of the desired services (like all network architectures today, it does not provide them all). We will finish by considering how to get from that vision of Computer Integrated Manufacturing to an actual implementation that meets your specific needs.

The vision of computer-integrated manufacturing

Before we get into networking specifics, let us take some time to discuss why we are willing to spend the time and money to implement networking in the first place. What is that vision of CIM that we are pursuing?

Most facilities can be easily divided into three distinct areas: the corporate headquarters, which allocates the money and resources; the factory floor, which actually produces the product; and the manufacturing plant, which provides support functions ranging from new product development to allocation of spare parts for obsolete products to the field. Each of these major areas is composed of numerous departments.

Figure 1.1 shows a typical departmental organization for a manufacturing facility. The factory floor has been broken down into maintenance, scheduling, machining, and assembly departments and the manufacturing plant support services include sales, production control, engineering, and quality assurance. Many of these departments are already using computers for their day-to-day work. Quality assurance has databases, engineering has computer-aided design and engineering workstations, assembly has programmable robots, and machining has numerical control machines. Corporate headquarters has an entire department dedicated to supporting its mainframe computing needs.

```
MANUFACTURING FLOOR - MAP NETWORK

MAINTENANCE DEPARTMENT
   Monitor machine status
   Notify other areas of trouble

MACHINING DEPARTMENTS
PROGRAMMABLE DEVICES
   Direct material handling
   Update machine status information
   Transmit information to assembly
      department

SCHEDULING DEPARTMENT
   Receive orders
   Evaluate machine status
   Modify orders
   Dispatch to production

ASSEMBLY DEPARTMENTS

PROGRAMMABLE DEVICES
   Receive machine parts information
   Assemble to specification
   Update machine status information
```

```
CORPORATE OFFICE
SNA NETWORK
Update production statistics
Update regional inventory
Update quality information
```

```
MANUFACTURING PLANT
TOP NETWORK

SALES
   Order entry

PRODUCTION CONTROL
   Receive inventory status

ENGINEERING DESIGN
   Feedback on part quality
   Generate new prototypes

QUALITY ASSURANCE
   Receive QI and warranty data
   Feedback to engineering
```

Figure 1.1 Sample applications and environments.

The attraction of CIM can be demonstrated best by tracing a simple production engineering improvement through the system. It all starts with a casual remark by a major customer to the president of the company while waiting to tee off at the fifteenth hole: "We could use a whole bunch of your frambus snatchers on our frobish production lines if they could only carry the heavier load." Shortly thereafter, engineering is asked to increase the carrying capacity of frambus snatchers by 15 percent.

Before computer-integrated manufacturing

The engineer sits down at the computer-aided design (CAD) system and calls up the design of the frambus snatcher. Oops, the design is 2 years old and was done on a different, incompatible CAD system. Two months later, after recreating the original design on the new system, our engineer is ready to start engineering. The first discovery is that there was good reason for upgrading to the new CAD system. It shows that under dynamic loading (an analysis capability not available on the old system), the weak link is overstressed, and the frambus snatcher should only be rated at 50 percent of its current rated capacity!

A quick call to quality assurance confirms that the frambus snatcher has developed a reputation for below average reliability in the field, but it will take them several weeks to collect and analyze their data and get back with any failure analysis statistics. Their databases are not designed to supply information in the relationship requested. Rather than wait, the engineer calls a friend in sales support and learns that sales representatives are recommending purchase of spare weak links to all users.

Next our engineer designs a range of alternative solutions. As is usually the case in the real world, none exactly meets the original objective. For example, a simple change in the grade of steel used to fabricate the weak link would eliminate the current failure mode and get the rated capacity to a true 100 percent with minimal impact on materials and fabrication costs. Alternatively, modification of the design of the weak link could increase the rated capacity to 110 percent with a 5 percent savings in materials and fabrication costs. However, the new design would be dependent on a machining capability currently available only on another production line not related to the frambus snatcher line. Reaching the targeted 15 percent improvement would require redesigning the frambus snatcher to eliminate the weak link, a major undertaking, but one capable of increasing capacity to over 150 percent.

Selecting the best alternative is almost totally dependent on the engineer's ability to get information from other departments and functions. Lacking any further guidance, the only choice would be to implement the 150 percent solution. If the 150 percent solution generates only a few percent more sales compared to the 110 percent solution, the default decision could easily be expensive overdesign. A net loss may even occur if the ensuing delay in getting the solution to market exceeded the incremental sales once there. Conversely, it may never have occurred to marketing to ask for 150 percent because they assumed it would require a total redesign and double the cost. Yet having it at reasonable cost would allow penetration of not just the frobish snatcher market (their original goal) but also the snatcher market for finagles and fangles.

Clearly productivity, measured by the ability to make correct decisions at reasonable cost, benefits from useful communications across departmental lines.

The benefit of computer-integrated manufacturing

Compare the previous scenario with the same request, only this time with total communications within and between departments, the vision of computer-integrated manufacturing fully implemented.

Again, we start with our engineer getting a request to increase capacity of the frambus snatcher by 15 percent. This time, although the original design was done on an incompatible CAD system, corporate information systems required migration tools as part of the upgrade to the new CAD system. Using an electronic mail message to request the translation required for the new CAD system, when our engineer comes in to work the next morning, the translated design data is waiting, along with a copy of the bill for the services already approved by the department manager.

Engineering analysis proceeds as before, just 2 months sooner. However, this time the call to quality assurance on the defect in the design of the weak link invokes a far different response. Rather than vague feelings of unease arising out of ignorance, the response is a gentle reminder to get up to date with all the production changes to the design, as quality assurance had discovered the weak link problem from their routine analysis of the first 3 months of warranty data. Although they could not determine why the design was faulty, they had already moved to a stronger material for the link and provided a free field upgrade before the product had been out for 6 months.

After updating the design database, our engineer returns to quality assurance's good graces by optimizing the material selected for the now understood failure mode and reducing the cost of quality and then goes on to develop the two other alternatives already mentioned. The alternatives are summarized in a brief electronic memo to the boss, who passes it on to marketing and production to get their feedback. The decision, when made, is based on the needs of all concerned and addresses all aspects of the problem.

If you think about it, nothing occurred in the CIM scenario that could not have taken place anyway. Indeed, it all should have. So why do we need CIM? Simply to make it easier! Most professionals are more than willing to do a superior job but do not because the time and effort are not worth the payoff. CIM just facilitates the desired communications; it does not force them to occur. Indeed one of the traps of CIM is the electronic equivalent of junk mail. The ease of sending messages, complete with graphs, pictures, and even oral comments to one, a dozen, or even hundreds of people can lead to managers spending half their day sorting through their mail for the occasional message that really does require their attention. It is also vital to avoid mistaking efficiency for productivity. Halving the time required to do a job that does not need to be done may double efficiency but does nothing for productivity.

Real World Examples

One of the earliest examples of CIM based on MAP networking was at Deere & Company. In production since February 1985, their first pilot completely automated the engineering process from initial design through day-to-day production. As shown in Figure 1.2, the integration starts with an engineer who is designing sheet metal parts. While at the workstation, the engineer has full access to designs of parts through a common parts database. Once the part is designed and verified, the design is automatically transformed to the machine tool instruction sequences required, transmitted directly to the sheet metal parts man-ufacturing cell, and fabricated without ever being committed to paper.

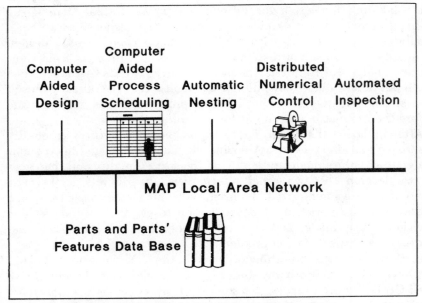

Figure 1.2   Deere & Company's computer-integrated manufacturing pilot.

This arrangement does more than just save the time needed to manually interpret the design and re-enter the information in the proper format for production. It also eliminates re-entry as a source of errors.

An automatic nesting package allows cutting multiple part numbers from a single sheet, facilitating flexible, just-in-time production of low-volume parts. Use of standard networking allows expansion of the system as needs grow without having to start all over again.

Deere & Company's first pilot has withstood the test of time. By the end of 1986, it had expanded to include almost a dozen machine tools and over 40 welders. Their experience has been positive enough to warrant installing a second pilot in 1985 and an additional two in 1986; they plan to add three more in 1987. Indeed, subsequent installations were only considered pilots because of the scale of the applications. MAP was perceived as a minimal risk network choice.

Their focus today is on applications and data. MAP networking is used so they do not have to worry about communications. The challenge is getting the desired databases online and getting the software required to keep them up to date. Tying together all the different databases—finance, personnel, engineering, etc.—does little good if the data is in file drawers. It takes time and effort before people routinely capture the data they need, let alone access it often enough to ensure it is up to date.

Kaiser Aluminum has been another early pioneer in MAP/TOP, installing a MAP 2.0 network in their Erie, Pennsylvania, plant. Their needs were at the other end of the spectrum from Deere & Company's. They needed a system to connect all the different types of plant and administrative equipment, without a need to continually rewire for new equipment additions. Their idea of CIM was the ability to treat the entire plant as an integrated process, accessing all of the available plant information from a single terminal in real time.

Fully implemented by late 1985, any user at an IBM PC/AT terminal anywhere in the plant can, to the extent they are authorized, address any of the central computer operations such as accounting, inventory, order processing, production records, etc. They can access the energy management system to check peak demand, get operational charts, look at problems, or study energy usage impact of specific operations. They can check individual process programmable logic controllers (PLCs) to see how a process is operating or access the process controller for a heat-treating furnace to change set points, reprogram an operation, or just collect operating and maintenance data.

The user can be in engineering, maintenance, quality control, management, accounting, sales, or anywhere else on the network. Engineering can monitor and reschedule operations to reduce peak energy demands. Maintenance can check the programmable logic controller operation for correctness, remotely diagnose problems , and send out the appropriate crews with the parts required. Quality control can verify operational parameters and monitor output quality. Sales can respond to customer inquiries with real-time data on the status of any particular order. Usage of the network continues to expand as personnel learn about the capabilities available and think of new ways to utilize the information made available. Based on the success of the Erie pilot, Kaiser Aluminum is expanding their usage of MAP-based networks to more plants, including much larger ones.

Gains from computer-integrated manufacturing

The highest payoffs from MAP/TOP, as the above examples illustrate, come not from the network itself, but from the integration of the computers used throughout the manufacturing process. The timely flow of appropriate information across departmental boundaries is the true payoff from computer-integrated manufacturing.

Measurements of actual data from Deere & Company, General Motors Corporation, Ingersoll Milling Machine Company, McDonnell Douglas Aircraft Company, and the Westinghouse Defense and Electric Center compiled by the National Research Council[1] are summarized in Table 1.1. Traditional measures used to justify computer-integrated manufacturing show rather poorly. Reductions in personnel costs and engineering design costs were minimal. What was dramatically affected were indirect benefits from the improved communications across departmental lines. Most significant were the gains in product quality and engineering productivity. The availability of significant production and field data to engineers in time frames short enough to allow adjustment of design trade-offs simply makes for better engineering and, consequently, higher quality.

TABLE 1.1 Measured Benefits of Computer-Integrated Manufacturing

Measured range, %	Benefit
5–20	Reduction in personnel costs
15–30	Reduction in engineering design costs
30–60	Reduction in lead time
30–60	Reduction in work in progress
40–70	Gain in overall productivity
200–300	Gain in capital equipment operating time
200–500	Product quality gain
300–3500	Gain in engineering productivity

---

[1]Reprinted from *Computer Integration Engineering Design and Production*, 1984, with permission of the National Academy Press, Washington, D.C.

The perennial cries of engineers and others for timely feedback and control have been proven to be justified. Far from traditional bellyaching, they represent a real need with a measurable payoff. But it is vital to maintain a sense of perspective. Computer networks are not the solution! Rather they are a foundation on which solutions can be built. Networks based on MAP/TOP may not always be the best foundation, but they are available and have been proven effective through numerous pilot projects across many industries. The challenge facing you is to determine if a MAP/TOP network provides a suitable foundation for your needs and, if one does, to structure it to fit.

Think of MAP/TOP as poured concrete. It is the design of the foundation and the setting of the forms that determine the quality of the foundation. If the engineering is not suitable for the ground conditions or the structure, it does not matter that the concrete is top quality; a poor foundation will result. Similarly, if the forms are not set up square, building an acceptable superstructure will be far more difficult, if not impossible. Your job as system architect is similar to the building architect. You must make sure that all the pieces fit together, the foundation is appropriate for the building, and the building is appropriate for the inhabitants.

Chapter

2

Networking Concepts

Before we can talk about MAP/TOP in particular, we need to establish some common terminology. The networking concepts we will be discussing in this chapter are common to all networks, from a punch press and a robot synchronizing their activities to worldwide communications between divisions of an international company. Using a set of generic definitions, common to all forms of computer networks, allows meaningful comparison of the many alternatives available.

First we will explore the more common services required by user applications running in a network environment. Then we will look at some of the characteristics used to describe computer networks and develop consistent definitions for terms such as delay and availability. Finally, we will finish off the chapter with a brief look at some of the different types of computer networks.

Networking Services

Before any rational decisions can be made about what kind of network to implement, we first must know how the network will be used. While we will talk more in later chapters about how to translate user requests into network service requirements, let us start by discussing what kinds of services a network can provide.

To the uninitiated, it would appear from reading through marketing brochures and magazine articles that there are hundreds of different networking services available. Looking closer, however, you will find that almost all are minor variations on a very limited number of themes. The same proprietary nature of networking solutions that forced the development of MAP/TOP is the prime driving force behind the proliferation of service terminology. The same basic service capability will have a different name depending on who developed it, who is selling it, whose brand of computer it runs on (and sometimes even which model within brands), when it was developed (new and improved almost always gets a new name), what features it provides, and what brand or model it connects to!

Approach services the same way you approach buying a car. When you first think about buying a new car, you do not start out with a specific brand and model, along with a list of accessories and options. Instead, you start out with a generic class of service required—family car, sports car, luxury car, light truck, or whatever. From there you refine your selection based on what is available from the various manufacturers in your price range, who has good reliability and service, who provides the features you need, and so forth.

Like motor vehicles, computer networking services also come in generic classes. They are Network InterProcess Communication (NIPC), Remote Process Management (RPM), Network File Transfer (NFT), Network Virtual Terminal (NVT), Remote File Access (RFA), Remote Data Base Access (RDBA), and peripheral sharing. As we shall see, even with the number of unique services reduced to seven, there are still common elements between the various services. At the same time, not all applications need all services. Interactive computer users may find that NFT and NVT are all they ever use. A cell control application may use only NIPC while an automated inspection reporting system may be optimally designed using RDBA.

Network InterProcess Communication (NIPC)

Network InterProcess Communication, as shown in Figure 2.1, is the foundation for all networking services. Its function is exactly what its name implies, a communications service between a process (or program) running on one machine with a second process running on a second machine. The definition includes the degenerate case in which the second machine or even process is the same machine or process as the first. The idea is identical with the operating system's concept of interprocess communication between processes on a single, multitasking machine. Because of this similarity, it is also often referred to as Interprocess Communication or IPC.

In addition to providing the underlying communications for other network services, NIPC is used directly by user application software. A work-cell controller will use NIPC to tell a robot controller program what function to provide next or to inquire about the status of limit switches or the current arm position. An energy management system will use

NIPC for monitoring its far-flung network of sensors and keeping track of critical energy-consuming and heat-producing processes, perhaps even connecting into the job scheduling system to anticipate demands and adjust timings to minimize energy costs. Any time a program on one machine needs to communicate with a program on another machine, the fundamental service is Network InterProcess Communication.

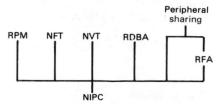

Figure 2.1 Relationships between fundamental network services.

Remote Process Management (RPM)

Before NIPC can provide communications between two processes, it is first necessary to have two processes which are willing to communicate running and available. While it is always possible to have the processes constantly running, the system resources consumed by all the waiting processes quickly become excessive. As the network increases in size, the number of processes is proportional to the number of applications times the number of machines each application can run on. Remote Process Management (RPM) provides an escape from this combinatorial problem. RPM gives a process on one machine the ability to start up a process on a second machine, determine the status of that process as time progresses, and suspend or stop the remote process as required. Again, the services provided are identical to those found on multitasking systems for controlling local processes. The only difference is the need to exercise those functions across an unreliable communications link on a potentially incompatible remote operating system.

Uses for RPM are almost as varied as those for Network Interprocess Communication. Like NIPC, the function is often hidden in the provision of other services. For example, before a Network File Transfer service can copy a file, a cooperating Network File Transfer service process must be running on the machine with the file. In the absence of RPM, the remote Network File Transfer service program must either be started manually at the remote machine or left running continuously just in case it might be needed.

On the factory floor, Remote Process Management may be used by a cell controller to start up the scheduling program on the mainframe as it nears completion of its current task set and will shortly need guidance on what to do next. Conversely, the master scheduling program may start the required processes on the cell controller to perform the tasks required next. Traditional Remote Job Entry (RJE) services are a classic example of Remote Process Management (combined with Network File Transfer). The first "cards" in the job are always job (process) control cards, telling the remote system what processes to run and how to set them up. Similarly, the last card will indicate to the remote system that the job is complete and allocated resources can be freed for use by other processes.

Network File Transfer (NFT)

The most common networking service available to users today is Network File Transfer. While this may seem contradictory given our earlier statement that NFT is built atop NIPC, the key phrase is "available to users." Because of the wide variation in user NIPC needs and the relatively small number of users who are willing to "roll their own" solutions compared to those who simply need some basic capabilities such as NFT, many manufacturers will only build up their NIPCs to the level required to support the limited needs of their other basic services. They will not invest the resources required to build the NIPC up to the level required to make it useful as a general-purpose service. This situation will shift as the industry moves from proprietary solutions toward multiple vendor implementations of international standards. However, until the challenges of testing protocol implementations for conformance and interoperability are conquered, conservative vendors will still prefer the safety implicit in protecting their lower-level services from uncontrolled user access.

The biggest difference between the NFT service and that of RPM and NIPC is its direct availability to users without their needing to write a program to access it. Indeed, unwary purchasers may find that they have purchased one of the many NFT implementations that cannot be invoked from a program but can only be used by a user at an interactive terminal. Such an NFT cannot be used as a building block for more complicated applications.

NFT shares many characteristics with its single machine file copy utility equivalent to which it is often compared. However, there are also many differences. Both vary widely in their ability to manage access to files and convert between various file types and structures. While existing file protection mechanisms are taken for granted by local utilities, it can be more challenging over a network. Just because the user requesting access on the remote machine has the same name as a user on the supplying machine does not mean he or she has the same access privileges or is even the same individual. Operations such as the ability to change the protection on the file are required for NFT but rarely built into the local file transfer utility.

The destination end faces some of the same challenges. For example, is the remote requester of the transfer authorized to access the directory containing the file? Is he or she allowed to overwrite an existing file or create a new one or neither or both? How about overwriting an existing file while another user is reading it? When moving between two machines from the same vendor running the same operating system, the answer is easy. However, when the source and destination systems are different, a more common occurrence as we evolve to multivendor networks, the easy answer of "same as the local copy command" may yield different results depending on which end of the connection you consider local.

Unique to Network File Transfer is the concept of three-party transactions. You will frequently see references in the literature to two-party NFT and three-party NFT. At issue is the maximum number of machines that can take part in a single file transfer. Figure 2.2 shows the different configurations possible in a network file transfer operation. Three distinct roles are involved. There is the producer (source) of the file, the consumer (destination) of the file, and the initiator (requester) of the file transaction. Two-party NFT requires the initiator of the transfer to also be either the producer or the consumer. Three-party NFT places no restrictions on what initiator may request a file transfer between any two machines. That is, three-party NFT can utilize any of the configurations illustrated while two-party NFT can only use those with two machines.

The utility of Network File Transfer ranges far beyond substituting for carrying a magnetic tape between two machines. It is quite justly most famous for allowing movement of files between incompatible file systems, character sets, record formats, and media. IBM Bisync RJE is more commonly purchased to transfer files between incompatible mini-computers (neither of which, typically, sport IBM nameplates) than for its avowed purpose of submitting jobs to IBM mainframes. Even between identical machines, there are many applications in which data in the form of a file needs to be passed from one machine to another. Transferring computer-aided design information from one engineer to another can lead to transferring it directly to manufacturing for archiving and conversion into numerical control programs, which can then lead to transfer (via NFT) directly to the work cell that is building the parts. Even when the information is not normally maintained as a file, if it can be converted to and from file form, it will be moved from machine to machine with NFT.

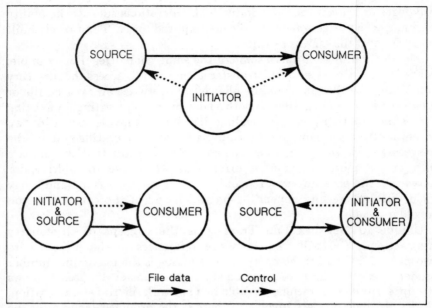

Figure 2.2   Network File Transfer.

Network Virtual Terminal (NVT)

After Network File Transfer, the most popular networking service is Network Virtual Terminal. Where NFT allows free movement of files from machine to machine, NVT provides users with interactive access to any machine from their local machines. Anyone who has ever needed to access services on more than one machine can appreciate the benefits of doing it all from one terminal.

The real power of Network Virtual Terminal comes into play when the machines being accessed use incompatible terminals. Not only do you benefit from the full connectivity of the network, connecting with ease to other machines whether across the room, across the hall, or halfway around the world, but you also get to work with machines that your local terminal could never work with as a locally connected terminal. While using an IBM 3278 mainframe display station to work on a DEC VAX may not be a perfect fit, the only way it can happen at all is through NVT. This is the service Kaiser Aluminum is using to connect their PC/ATs to all the computer systems in the plant.

A closely related service to Network Virtual Terminal is terminal emulation. Terminal emulation is particularly popular when working with small computers such as personal computers and workstations. Superficially, terminal emulation and NVT appear similar. Both allow a local user on a local host to log in as a compatible terminal on a remote host. However, as illustrated in Figure 2.3, they function very differently. NVT is a collaboration on the part of the local and remote hosts to make it appear to the local user that the local terminal was directly attached to the remote host. Terminal emulation, on the other hand, is a collaboration between the local user and the local host to make the local system appear to the remote host as a locally attached terminal on the remote host.

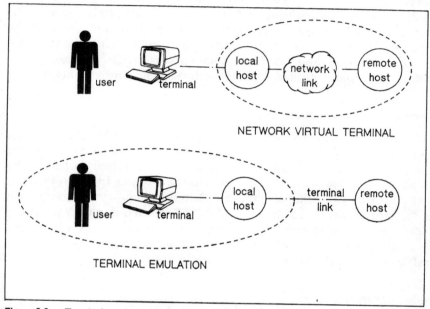

Figure 2.3   Terminal emulation versus Network Virtual Terminal.

Remote File Access (RFA)

As usage of distributed computing grows, three other service needs evolve from the quest for efficiency—Remote File Access, Remote Database Access, and Peripheral Sharing.

Consider a typical use of NFT. Programs and data are kept on a dedicated file-server machine and moved to other machines with NFT as required for processing. This scenario works well until the size of the files moving around starts to grow to the point at which it takes longer to move the file around the network than it does to process the job. Just keeping track of the latest version of a file can become a major chore. When multiple users need to work with the same file on different machines, NFT is no longer adequate.

Rather than moving the entire file around with NFT, the service to use is Remote File Access. A single copy of the file can be maintained on the file server and accessed from remote machines as if it were a local file. Implementing RFA across incompatible file systems can be a major challenge. The file calls on one machine (open, close, create, seek, read a record, write a record, append a record, etc.) all need to be mapped into the file structure of the second machine. Consider the case in which file records as requested by the user are 256 bytes, while the remote system stores its files with 132-byte records. Each file operation of the user can easily translate into multiple remote file system calls, reducing efficiency. Consequently, it will be awhile before we see high-performance RFA capability except between systems that have similar, if not identical, file systems. Of course, even low-performance access to a few thousand bytes of data will usually outperform high-performance transfer of megabytes.

Remote Database Access (RDBA)

The logical extension to Remote File Access is Remote Database Access. Since a typical database query may require many disk reads to find the requested data, RDBA moves the intelligence required to access the database from the requesting machine to the machine in which the data is stored. The requesting machine can then send high-level requests such as "all widgits produced the week of 3/2/87 rejected due to dimension f exceeding allowed tolerance." Not only is response time vastly improved by avoiding RFA delays for each raw disk access request, but the total traffic sent over the network is similarly reduced.

Peripheral sharing

The last of the generic network services is peripheral sharing. The most telling sign of its recent recognition is the lack of a commonly accepted acronym to describe it. While peripheral sharing has been around since the first time a minicomputer user transferred a file up to the mainframe to print it out on the line printer, it is the personal computer and workstation explosion that has led to its recognition as a service worthy of deliberate pursuit.

The range of peripherals to be shared is limited only by the implementor's imagination. Originally limited to disk drives and printers, today's user can share data, disk drives, printers, plotters, tape drives for disk backup, asynchronous dial-up modems, array processors, public data network access, and even IBM mainframe access. Users gain access to devices they could not justify on an individual basis by spreading the cost over multiple users. They gain convenience, efficiency, and quality by being able to select the appropriate tool for the job. They may even gain a better work environment by moving noisy hardware out of their immediate vicinity and spooling jobs rather than feeding sheets of paper by hand.

Network Characteristics

Many terms are used to describe network operational needs. Regrettably, four of the most important ones have been defined so many different ways that it is almost impossible to utilize them without dispute over intent. Who would dare procure a network without specifying the key characteristics of delay, throughput, reliability, and availability? Yet if you were to ask five people to define those terms for you, I wager you would get at least five different answers for each! Rather than mislead you with allegedly definitive answers, let us just look at each separately and discuss the critical factors that can be adjusted and their impact on you.

Delay

Intuitively, delay is the time required for something to come out of the network after it goes in. All the various networking definitions of delay agree on that point. Where they disagree is on when to start timing and when to stop. There are three basic choices available. Timing can start as soon as the first bit enters the network (when the data is "released" by the user) or only after the entire data packet has been accepted by network (at which point the network can verify correctness and start processing it). Similarly, timing can stop as soon as the first bit is delivered by the network to the destination or only after the entire data packet has been delivered. The differences can be significant if the point being measured has a slow data rate compared to the size of the packet. For example, a 1000-byte packet will take over 3 seconds (s) to transmit over a 2400-bit-per-second (bps) dial-up link. Using first-in-to-last-out timing would make the 250-millisecond (ms) propagation delay of a satellite link in the path almost disappear as 3.6 s versus 3.3 s for an all-terrestrial link, a net difference of only a few percent. Conversely, using first in to first out would show up to two orders of magnitude difference in the respective delays for the same two links. Failure to understand how the delay was measured could lead to selection of the 250 ms satellite link over the 3.3 s terrestrial link in a delay-sensitive application.

The third variable in the definition of delay is whether the delay being measured is one way or round trip. A user data terminal interacting with a remote host sees the round-trip delay. However, the network system provider needs to worry about where the delay is coming from and is more interested in one-way delay in order to distinguish network delays from host response time. If nothing else, specifying round-trip delay in a multiple-vendor environment in which no single vendor is responsible for total round-trip delay will normally lead to a finger-pointing exhibition rather than to useful results.

I recommend using one-way, first-in-to-first-out delay whenever you have a choice of definitions, and I will use that definition throughout this book. This definition of delay strictly measures the network component of delay and is independent of the speed or loading on any host machines. Equally important, it is independent of the data rate of the links involved, allowing meaningful comparisons on different-capacity networking schemes. It is not useful in isolation, however. A useful specification for a user at an interactive terminal would have to include not only the network delay as just defined but also the host response time at specific load levels and the ability of the network to push through quantities of data (throughput, discussed next).

Regardless of your choice of definitions, make sure you are consistent so you are not comparing apples to oranges. Be precise about the definition being used and verify that everyone you are talking to is using the same one.

Throughput

One-way, first-in-to-first-out delay only makes up half the specification of network performance. The other key factor is throughput, the sustained rate at which data can be transmitted through the network. Whereas delay will be measured in units of time such as seconds or milliseconds, throughput is measured in units of data per unit of time, most frequently bits per second.

Unlike delay, there is little controversy over when to start and stop the clock. The clock starts when the first bit enters the network and does not stop until the last bit comes out. There are, unfortunately, games in specsmanship played over how to count up the number of bits transmitted. If we look at the stream of bits going over the network link, we will see far more than just the query typed by the user. In a full-powered network such as MAP/TOP, that query will be wrapped in multiple layers of protocols. There will be bytes to detect errors in transmission, bytes to acknowledge data received from the other end, bytes specifying what process on what machine on what network to deliver the query to, and more—lots more. It can take dozens of bytes just to send a simple five-character query! Assume it takes a total of 50 bytes and we are looking just at the throughput of a 10-Mbps link. Rather than the 10

Mbps we expected to see, we only see 1 Mbps of data throughput. And this does not include software processing time required to put on and then remove all those extra bytes, nor any time delays encountered in gaining access to the shared network medium.

The argument over data versus overhead is not always so clear-cut. Consider the throughput of a Network File Transfer service. Do we count the time required to establish a connection with the remote machine? How about the time required to start up the NFT server process there or to create or open the file? Ditto for the time to close the file and release all the associated resources. What about the bits used to specify the file name, directory path, or access rights? There is no intrinsically right or wrong choice. What counts is what you are trying to measure. From the user's view of file transfer performance, only the data bits in the file count. From the network provider's point of view, all bits transmitted regardless of source must be considered in sizing the network. As with delay, the choice is yours. The key is consistency so that comparisons can be meaningful. Probe your sources to determine what definitions are being used. "The usual" is not an adequate specification of the definition in use.

Reliability

Unlike delay and throughput, solid definitions for reliability are available. They have been defined in reliability engineering and have statistical significance. The challenge is not in the definition of standard terms, but rather in the validity of the numbers provided. Reliability in the context of networking can be reduced to two numbers: mean time between failures (MTBF) and mean time to repair (MTTR). MTBF is the average length of time that any particular piece of equipment will operate before failing. MTTR is the average length of time required to get the piece of equipment working again once it has failed. Both are normally specified in hours. Given these two numbers, many useful relationships can be calculated, such as the probability P that a device will fail within a given period of time T:

$$P = 1 - \exp\left(-T / \text{MTBF}\right)$$

The average number of failures F to expect during a given period of time T:

$$F = T / \text{MTBF}$$

Or the percentage of time P on the average that a device will not be functional:

$$P = \frac{\text{MTTR}}{(\text{MTBF} + \text{MTTR})} \times 100\%$$

Statisically significant relationships can be calculated for systems of any degree of complexity. It only requires knowledge of the reliability of the individual components and how failure of any individual component affects operation of the overall system.

The challenge, as any reliability engineer will tell you, is making sure the MTBF and MTTR you are using are relevant to your application. If you are running a three-shift operation, is your MTBF specified for continuous duty or 8-hours-a-day, 5-days-a-week office duty? Does the MTBF assume "perfect" power, while yours is shared with a room full of arc welders? Does the MTTR include travel time for the technician from the nearest field office on the other side of the state? How about the time required to determine which piece of equipment has failed so that diagnosis and repair can begin? Finally, watch out for calculated versus measured MTBF. If necessary, get the help of a reliability engineer to make sure you are working with meaningful data and not being misled by irrelevant numbers.

Availability

Technically, availability A is the percentage of time a given piece of equipment is functional over time and can be calculated as

$$A = \frac{\text{MTBF}}{(\text{MTBF} + \text{MTTR})} \times 100\%$$

As such, it is adjustable by all the techniques used to improve reliability in systems, such as utilizing redundant equipment.

Rather than thinking strictly in terms of reliability, however, I recommend that you think in terms of "mission functionality." What are the jobs that need to be done and what is the availability of equipment capable of accomplishing these tasks? This approach keeps the statistical availability of the various pieces which make up a system in perspective. For example, how many hours can a foreman access the job scheduler during an 8-hour shift? A failure which forces pencil and paper tracking of output for an hour but has no other impact on production is far different from a failure which shuts down the line for the same hour because of an inability to determine what to do next.

Keeping mission functionality at the forefront can also help catch some of the simple oversights that often plague complex systems.

Consider a repair scheduling system for the maintenance department with perfect availability for the access terminals in the maintenance shop. How does the maintenance worker on the factory floor access the terminal that is back at the shop? There is availability according to the numbers and then there is availability that contributes to achieving meaningful objectives.

Mission functionality can also reduce costs. You may not care about the availability of some functions under certain conditions. Who cares about minimizing air conditioning electrical demand when the reactor has lost coolant and all communications are dedicated to preventing meltdown? An extreme example, perhaps. But the point is that not all missions have the same priority, and an ability to trade off one for another can often be beneficial.

Types of Networks

The answer to the question "What type of network do you want?" is a multifaceted one. We will spend the rest of this chapter discussing three different ways networks are classified into types. First we will look at distinction based on geographic size—the question of local versus wide area networks. Then we will look at distinction based on the type of communications service provided—the question of connection-oriented versus connectionless networks. Finally, we will finish with distinction based on the physical connections from machine to machine—the question of network topology.

Wide area networks and local area networks

The nature of data communications provides separation of networks into one of two types. Either all the pieces in the network are located in one facility and can be connected together by a medium provided by the owner of the pieces, or they are located in multiple locations and communications must be provided by a public provider such as the phone company. The former case is a local area network (LAN) while the latter is called a wide area network (WAN).

In a wide area network, since communications must cross the property of others, the communications links are usually provided by common carriers. Often, more cost-effective communications can be obtained from what are called value added network (VAN) suppliers who purchase "raw" data communications links from common carriers and package network services on top of the links. By sharing the links and network hardware among multiple users, better service can be provided to individual users at less cost than they could obtain individually. For many years, because of antitrust regulations, the only public computer data networks available in the United States were VANs such as Tymnet and Telenet. The phone company, AT&T, was effectively barred from the market. In virtually all other countries, the only public data networks were those offered by national post, telephone, and telegraph (PTT) agencies. These networks are all interconnected, and worldwide international service is generally available at reasonable cost.

By virtue of their long-distance orientation, costs in WANs are dominated by the cost of the communications links. Data rates are typically low because of the preponderance of telephone twisted pair as the medium available for communications. A link speed of 56 Kbps is considered high speed. Faster speeds are usually only available in major metropolitan areas or via satellite. In order to maximize the utilization of high-cost communications links, the internal workings of these networks and the protocols they use can be very complex. It is common practice to dedicate substantial computer resources just to squeeze a few percent more data through a circuit.

Local area networks, on the other hand, are just the opposite. Within the confines of your own facility you can install whatever cable plant is most effective for you. Communications links are not restricted to what can run over the cabling the phone company happens to have under the streets. The short distances also allow efficient use of higher data rates. In the world of LANs, a 1-Mbps link is considered low performance. Popular links, such as those used by MAP/TOP, are 10 Mbps. Data rates of 50 Mbps and above have been available for years. At all speeds, the costs in the network are dominated not by the communications link but by the costs of the interfaces used to connect to the link. This is true whether the LAN is a 56-Kbps PBX network or a 50-Mbps HYPER-channel.

In between the LAN and WAN, you will read about a third type of network, the Metropolitan Area Network (MAN). It is possible to get high-speed communications at reasonable cost using cable TV or fiber optic links within a metropolitan area. However, so far there have been no widely accepted implementations or even pilots with promise. For our purposes, we can continue to treat any MAN as either a LAN or a WAN depending upon how it is implemented and what features are critical to our application.

Connection-oriented and connectionless networks

A second key division of networks is into the categories of connection oriented and connectionless. Until the mid-eighties, the two categories were usually referred to as virtual circuit (for connection oriented) and datagram (for connectionless). Although the names have changed, the concepts have not, so do not be confused. Basically, in a connection-oriented network, the network recognizes that all the chunks of data (packets) over the duration of the communications session are related, whereas in a connectionless network, each packet is treated totally independently.

It turns out that whether or not the various packets are considered related has major impact on the service provided by the network and how the user accesses that service. If packets are to be related, there must be the concept of a connection. How else will the network be able to tell when a communications session starts and when it ends? This then requires a means to set up the connection and then tear it down when done. A connectionless network, on the other hand, has no set-up or tear-down overhead. Compensating for it, however, is the need for each packet to carry all the information required to get it through the network. It cannot just reference the appropriate connection and let the network fill in the blanks. As you might expect, wide area networks, in which you are charged for every bit sent, are usually connection oriented. Most local area networks are connectionless to avoid burdening those applications which do not need connection-oriented service with the overhead involved. Applications which do require connection-oriented service from a connectionless network can use an end-to-end protocol to provide it.

Reducing the number of overhead bytes associated with each packet, while sometimes a worthwhile goal in its own right, is not the only benefit to connection orientation. Far more important to the user is the control of errors and sequencing provided. A connection-oriented service will deliver packets to the other end in the same sequence as sent. The receiving user does not need to check for missing packets, out of order packets, or extra packets (either duplicates of packets meant for it or misdelivered packets meant for another user). The sending user knows that all data it sends will be received by the other end exactly as sent. In exchange for the overhead of setting up a connection, both end users are freed from concerns about data integrity and delivery.

A connectionless network merely provides a "best efforts" delivery of packets presented to it. Guaranteed delivery, commonly called "reliable datagram service," is an optional extra. Even with guaranteed delivery, there is no guarantee that packets will be delivered in the same order they were presented to the network. Nor is there any guarantee that they will not be delivered more than once. All the user can be sure of is that with each individual packet the network will do the best job it can to deliver that packet as fast as it can. If sequencing, error control, or delivery guarantees are important to the user application, it is up to the user to add the required level of connection-oriented service to the connectionless service provided by the network. There can be significant benefits to shifting this responsibility to the user besides just reducing the cost of the networking service. Most important is the ability given to the user to adjust the level of sequencing, error control, reliability, etc., to exactly the level required by the application. This avoids the waste of paying for service not required (in the case of needs lower than the level provided by the network) or paying for service which is inadequate (in the case in which the user has to treat the network as a connectionless service because the quality of service provided is insufficient for the application). The key trade-offs involved are summarized in Table 2.1.

TABLE 2.1   Properties of Connection-Oriented and Connectionless Networks

Issue	Connection-oriented	Connectionless
Setup overhead	Yes	No
Sequencing	Sequenced data	No sequence concerns
Error control	Error detection and correction	Typically only on a per packet basis
Delivery	Guaranteed	Best efforts
Addressing	Per connection	Per packet

Network topologies

The third key factor used to distinguish types of networks is the pattern used to connect the various pieces together. We call the various pieces of equipment networked together the nodes and the communications lines connecting them the links. How the nodes are connected by the links determines the topology. The various combinations possible are illustrated in Figure 2.4. Each topology has its advantages and trade-offs. Which is the most suitable will depend on the application and the environment the network must fit.

The complex mesh, Figure 2.4a, is the most common for wide area networks in which it is vital to minimize the cost of communications links and optimize their utilization. To permit communications between nodes which are not directly connected, the network must be able to route packets from node to node as required to connect sender and receiver. This is the topology implied by the terms "store-and-forward packet switching" and "X.25." Since the actual connections will vary with implementation and user needs, the whole mesh is often replaced in diagrams with a networking cloud, Figure 2.4x. This reinforces the transparency of the network internals and focuses the user on the service provided rather than on the details of how it is provided.

The hierarchical tree, Figure 2.4b, is the classical layout for connecting terminals to central host systems. Until the introduction of the IBM token ring in 1985, it was the prime topology used by IBM for networking. Routing decisions are simplified by the regular nature of the topology and top-down master-slave relationships are easily implemented.

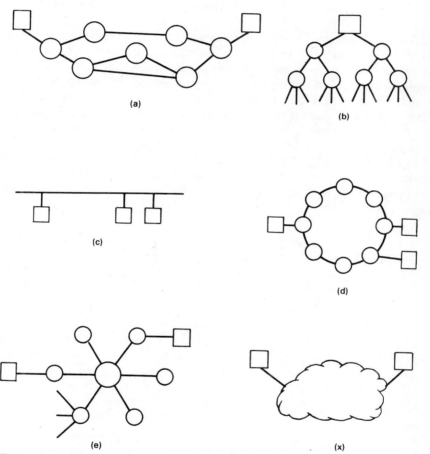

Figure 2. 4   Some network topologies. (*a*) Mesh, (*b*) hierarchical tree, (*c*) bus, (*d*) ring, (*e*) star, and (*x*) generic.

The bus structure, Figure 2.4c, is used by MAP/TOP. It is generally associated with LANs. Since everyone is directly linked to everyone else, there is no need for routing, simplifying network implementation. Since all transmissions are received by everyone, broadcast and multicast capabilities are easily and efficiently provided. At the same time, since adding users does not add to the bandwidth available, expansion capability is finite as each user added competes for the fixed capacity of the medium.

The ring structure, Figure 2.4*d*, is also popular for local area networks. It is an optional topology for TOP. Like the bus, routing is not needed. However, provision must be made to prevent loss of any single node from bringing down the network. This is the topology used by the IBM token ring network.

The star topology, Figure 2.4*e*, has a central switching node to connect an end node to any other end node. Putting all the intelligence required to route from node to node in the central node allows for efficient implementation but at the cost of irreparable loss of the network any time the central switch is unavailable. This topology is most common in PBX networks, where it can take advantage of existing phone wiring.

As you can see, each topology has its advantages, but each has a price to pay for those advantages. In the world of networking today, the choice of topology is usually moot. The actual topology will be determined by the choice of network architecture, which in turn is more often driven by the services the architecture provides to the user rather than topological considerations.

Protocols and Standards

The most important networking concept in today's world is that of layered protocols. Layered protocols are what make today's sophisticated networks possible and what permit us to consider having one vendor's network implementation talk to other vendors.

In this chapter we will start by looking at some of the general characteristics of protocols and the terminology used in the literature today to describe layered protocols. Then we will develop the idea of an open system and show how layered protocols make one possible. We will finish up with a description of the international standard reference model for layered network protocols and discuss some of the groups involved in developing standard protocols which can fit into the standard model.

The Nature of Protocols

Protocols are the rules and conventions used when entities, be they people or computers, need to communicate. When Neil Armstrong first stepped on the moon, millions of Americans watching him on television recognized his hand gesture as A-OK, everything is great. But the protocol was an American protocol, and an almost identical gesture is used in many other cultures (different protocols) to express anger and indignation. You can picture the historic moment being viewed live in Rio de Janeiro, with one viewer asking, "What did he say?" and another responding "I don't know, but he sure is mad about something!"

On a more mundane level, it is just as critical that a business person in a foreign country understand the common protocols in that country. How many business deals have been lost because the visitors unknowingly insulted their hosts or interpreted nodding heads as a sign of agreement when the local custom meant just the opposite? All are examples of the critical need for both parties in a communications session to agree to the same protocols.

Common protocols are even more important for getting computers to communicate. At least people may recognize and compensate for mismatched protocols. How often have you been frustrated by a computer telling you exactly what you did wrong and refusing to act until you fixed it? Compare that to the Queen of England's reaction at a state dinner at which the honored guest from the Far East picked up his finger bowl and drank from it. While the other guests, all Westerners, stared in horror, she calmly picked up her finger bowl and joined him, converting a potential diplomatic disaster into business as usual.

Layering of protocols

Protocols are normally layered to reduce the complexity of each individual protocol to a manageable level. Consider the human example in Figure 3.1. Here, John wishes to express his thoughts of love to Mary. The method he chooses to use is to send a letter. This choice selects a whole series of protocols that John must follow in order to communicate his thoughts of love to Mary. First he must select the means of writing the letter. He could type it, but one protocol says that a handwritten note is much more personal, and therefore more suitable for a love letter.

Having chosen to handwrite it, another protocol suggests what size and style of writing paper he should use, while yet another dictates minimum and maximum sizes for a normal envelope. And John still has not gotten a single thought down on paper! Time to write, but which language (I forgot to mention that John's native language is German, while Mary's is French)? Clearly, the myriad of choices can only be navigated successfully through agreed-on protocols for each layer or function.

The protocols we have been discussing so far are what are called peer protocols. They are agreements between two communicators at the same level at each end of a communication. In addition to communications between peer entities within the same layer, we also need protocols to move from layer to layer. These are called interface protocols and they allow peer entities to communicate by using services provided by lower-layer entities. In the example of John and Mary, John must interface with the postal system to get his letter delivered to Mary.

The postal system interface protocol dictates where to place the address on the envelope, how to distinguish it from the return address, how to request different levels of service (first class, air mail, or special delivery), and so on. Inside the postal system, the letter is again subject

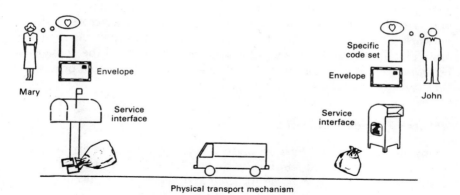

Figure 3.1 A human protocol example.

to peer-to-peer protocols, this time in the mail system layers. The postal system has protocols for moving letters from drop boxes to main post offices to front door delivery. Imagine the confusion if John had to specify the routing algorithms used by the post office to send his letter on its way. Layering the protocols simplifies the job both for John, who instead can concentrate on thoughts of love, and for the post office, which can pick routing methods for efficiency rather than ease of training millions of Johns. Never underestimate the training challenge; the U.S. Post Office must still handle letters without ZIP codes even though the system has been in place for over 20 years.

Computer protocol examples

The world of computers is no different from John and Mary. Communications cannot take place without agreement on appropriate protocols. Since all the protocols must agree for two computers to communicate, the various layers are specified in a "network architecture." From the viewpoint of computer networking, MAP/TOP is a specification of one such network architecture that is selected to meet the needs of manufacturing automation. It is not the only possible selection of protocols, nor is it even a single selection of protocols. Each version number of MAP, be it 1.0, 2.2, or 3.0, is a different selection. Similarly, TOP, SNA, DECnet, and other network architectures specify their own selection of protocols. Sometimes the selections overlap—MAP and TOP are designed to communicate with one another. Sometimes the selections are totally incompatible—connecting DECnet to IBM SNA requires special translating gateways.

There is wide variety in computer protocols just as there is in human communications. There are protocols for the interface between a MAP/

TOP gateway and a packet-switched network, for a terminal user to log onto a remote host, for two cell controllers to converse across a MAP network, or even just for a robot controller to move a particular robot arm. The prerequisite for computer communications, and the challenge being met by MAP/TOP, is to select and implement suitable protocols that can work together to get a job done.

Network Protocol Functions

Protocols in a network perform myriad functions. While many of them are special purpose and will not be discussed until we cover particular protocols, four functions come up time and again in any discussion of computer networking protocols. The protocol functions of error detection and correction, segmentation and reassembly, sequenced delivery, and flow control make possible effective communications between two computers over real-world communications links.

Error detection and correction

The first problem that computer networks all face is that of corruption of data. Real-world communications channels always have ways to introduce errors into the stream of perfect 1s and 0s flowing through them. Errors induced in the data being transmitted can come in numerous ways. The two most common are random loss of an occasional bit, the digital equivalent of "snow" on a TV screen, and the loss of whole clumps of bits, so-called burst errors, as when lightning temporarily wipes out the TV picture entirely. Depending on the transmission medium, the loss could be either inversion of the bit's value (e.g., replacement of a 1 with a 0) or actual loss of the bit (i.e., the stream 11011 becomes 1111).

What type of errors are most common (or even possible) on a link will dictate the protocol used to detect their occurrence and provide for transfer of correct data even in the presence of the error. However, all popular protocols used by computers to ensure reliable transmission share several common traits. They are variations on a technique called positive acknowledgment with retransmission, or PAR. PAR protocols require the data to be broken up into packets small enough to have a reasonable chance of transmission without error. Secondly, PAR protocols require some means of determining if the data contained in any particular packet is good or bad. Given those two capabilities, PAR protocols ensure reliable transmission by retransmitting each packet until it receives acknowledgment from the receiver that the packet has been received correctly. Variations between PAR protocols cluster around how to identify when a packet starts, when it ends, which packet it is, how many packets can be sent without receiving a positive acknowledgment, how to select among multiple possible receivers, and how to determine what packets to retransmit and when.

The need to break the data up into packets leads directly into two of the other common protocol functions, that of segmentation and reassembly and that of sequenced delivery. We will postpone discussion of those aspects until the next two subsections, but I do want to discuss the two main forces which determine what the appropriate size of a packet should be. Each packet, regardless of the number of data bits in it, requires a fixed level of overhead for protocol fields such as address, start and end of packet identifiers, packet ID, and error detection. The larger the packet, the higher the ratio of data bits to total bits transmitted. On the other hand, when transmission errors do occur, the smaller the packet, the fewer the number of bits which must be retransmitted in order to recover from the error. For a given protocol and link error rate, at some point the improvement in efficiency caused by increasing packet size is counterbalanced by the losses caused by retransmitting defective packets.

The actual detection of errors is normally done in one of two ways, by a cyclic redundancy check (CRC) or by a software checksum. (Other techniques, such as longitudinal and vertical parity, have been used in the past but are not seen in modern networks such as MAP/TOP.) A CRC is an excellent error-detection mechanism. Mathematically, it is based on long division, the entire message being treated as a single "infinite" precision binary number, with the remainder from division by a finite number being sent as the CRC with the packet. At the receiving end, the division is repeated and if the results match, there is a very high probability that the received message is identical to the original. By proper selection of the divisor, it is possible to use a 16-bit CRC and be mathematically guaranteed to detect packet corruption meeting any of the following criteria:

- Up to 16 single bit errors

- An error burst up to 17 bits long

- Any combination of errors as long as the total number of bits changed is odd

- Over 99 percent of any other errors that should occur.

In addition to these excellent error-detection capabilities, CRC generators and checkers are trivial to implement in hardware. They only require is a single shift register of the appropriate length and some exclusive-or gates. As a result, link level protocols using CRCs have been popular since IBM invented Synchronous Data Link Control (SDLC) back in the 1960s.

Given all those advantages, you may well ask why anyone would ever use any other error-detection algorithm. The primary drawback to a

CRC is the difficulty of performing the required operations in software on standard computer architectures. Fortunately, in the upper-layer protocols which are normally implemented in software, the problem being addressed by the error check is no longer random bit errors (those are handled by the CRCs at the lower levels) but rather detecting loss or substitution of entire packets. Under these conditions, software check-sum algorithms based on treating the message as a sequence of small integers and adding up their value (usually with some scaling or other simple operations added for robustness) are usually sufficient.

Segmentation and reassembly

We just saw that we need to divide the total data stream into packet-sized pieces in order for error detection and retransmission to be effective. This process is called segmentation. As we move from higher to lower protocol layers, we frequently find that the packet size appropriate for one layer is inappropriate for the next. This leads to a need to break up a packet from one level and send it through the network as several smaller packets. At the other end of the communication, of course, we need to put the little packets back together again to recreate the original-sized packet, the reassembly process.

There are several techniques used to control the reassembly process. We can add a flag to each packet sent, indicating whether or not the packet is the last one required to reassemble the entire original. This technique of using a "more flag" works well for most protocols. As each fragment of the original data packet is received, the more flag is checked. If set (i.e., there is more data to come that needs reassembly), the fragment is combined with any others waiting delivery. A fragment without the more flag set indicates that the original packet is now complete and can be delivered to the next protocol layer.

Sometimes, the sense of the more flag is reversed, so we have a "last segment" flag. The name is different, but the idea is the same. Note that this technique only works if the connection between the peer entities using it is connection oriented. It assumes that there is no need to worry about out-of-order arrival of packets needing reassembly.

If the link between the peer entities is connectionless, the process gets a little more complicated. Now we need a means of indicating not only that segmentation has occurred but also how the various pieces fit together. This can be achieved by actually numbering the individual segments along with the original last segment flag. Now as segments come in, they can be placed in proper order. When all segments have arrived, as indicated by the last segment flag and availability of all the previous segments, the reassembled packet can be delivered up to the next layer.

This process can be carried one step farther to permit transparent segmentation and reassembly by intermediate systems which handle the packet at the same protocol level. This is a common requirement for internet protocols which may need to link networks with different packet-size requirements. Rather than numbering the segments consecutively, each fragment is labeled with an identifier for the original packet plus the location of the first byte of data of the fragment in the original packet (called the byte offset). If an intermediate system must further segment any fragment because it is too large, the byte offset of the extra fragments can be calculated from that of the original fragment. Similarly, adjacent fragments can be combined by any intermediate system if larger packets are desired. In either case, the additional segmentation or reassembly is transparent to the communications. The sending user's system has no idea any such action has taken place, while the receiving user cannot (and need not) distinguish between segmentation by the sender and segmentation by intermediate systems.

Sequenced delivery

The need for sequenced delivery has been mentioned several times. Sequenced delivery is usually attained by using sequence numbers as part of the packet overhead. Sending a sequential identifier with each packet allows the receiving end to acknowledge receipt of the packet to the sending end and determine when to pass on the packet. The packet cannot be delivered to the next higher protocol until all packets with preceding sequence numbers have been received and delivered. The identifier must also be unique for the lifetime of the packet and any packets it might be confused with to allow detection of duplicate and missing packets as well as out-of-order ones.

The need to deal with duplicate and missing packets is a direct outgrowth of using a positive acknowledgment with retransmission (PAR) protocol for reliable transmission in the presence of errors. When a packet is received in error, the receiving protocol can only discard the entire packet. The error detection techniques that are used most often tell us only that an error exists; they do not tell us where in the packet the error is. Consequently, the receiving protocol cannot be absolutely certain that the error was not in the packet identifier itself. This is not a problem for a PAR protocol, as failure to receive an acknowledgment will eventually cause the sender to time out and retransmit the faulted packet.

Duplicates occur when the data packet reaches the receiver successfully and the return acknowledgment is corrupted in transit. The sending side receives the faulty acknowledgment, identifies it as faulty, and discards it. The sending side has no way of knowing that the packet it just discarded was an acknowledgment, so it eventually times out and retransmits the original, correctly received data packet. The receiving side gets the second copy, identifies the sequence number as one it has already received, discards the packet, but does acknowledge it again. If acknowledgments continue to get lost, the sending side will continue retransmitting until either an acknowledgment gets through or it gives up and decides communications are impossible.

Flow control

The fourth common protocol function found throughout computer networks is flow control. Flow control is a natural outgrowth of the common desire to have things work as fast as possible. In the real world, of course, full speed ahead is not always possible. Any computer user knows that as the computer gets loaded down, response times tend to get longer and processing throughput slower. If we want our network to run at full speed when the processor is lightly loaded, we need some way to slow it down when loading builds up. Even when loading does not vary, we can still have mismatches in throughput that require flow control. For example, consider a dial-up terminal user on a 2400-bps modem going through a public data network to access a host with a 56-Kbps access line. The network needs some way to control the data flow from host so that it does not get too far ahead of the terminal line.

There are many ways to provide flow control. They vary in complexity and robustness. The simplest is the oldest, an on/off control for the receiver to use on the sender. This goes back to the days before computers when people used Teletype machines to communicate. The paper tape reader on a Teletype machine was controlled by characters received from the other party. The DC1 character would start the paper tape reader while the character DC3 would stop it. The convention followed into the computer world where terminal handlers which respond to DC1 and DC3 are still found. If the output is coming to the terminal too fast, you just type a DC3 and output will stop until you send a DC1. This technique is simple and effective as long as one side of the transaction is human and capable of recovering from transmission errors. Between machines, the need to handle both lost and spurious flow control characters makes effective implementation difficult.

In the search for flow controls suitable between two computers, the next step was control based on credits. This scheme requires the receiver to give the sender explicit permission to send data before any data can be sent. This makes the implementation simple but still leaves the link vulnerable to lost permission packets. The challenge is to distinguish between a lost permission packet and delays in sending the data authorized by that permission packet. Efficiency is also lost because of the need to send all the permission packets even when the receiver can keep up easily.

Today, modern computer protocols build upon the tools already in place for PAR by using sliding window flow control based on the packet sequence numbers. The window size determines how many packets ahead of the receiver the sender is allowed to transmit. A window size of two would allow the sender to send two packets before stopping to wait for an acknowledgment. If only the first was acknowledged, the sender could go ahead and send one more. If both were acknowledged, it could immediately send two more. As long as the receiver stays ahead of the sender's retransmission timeout, flow can be throttled down as required with no overhead. If the receiver is lightly loaded, it can increase the size of the window. When it starts to slow down, it can just slow down the sender by decreasing the size of the window. If necessary, it can shut the window completely, stopping all transmissions until it is ready to go again.

Protocol Layering

I have already made a number of references to higher-layer and lower-layer protocols, so let us take some time to discuss protocol layering in detail. All computer networks today are based on layering protocols to build up the required services. The particular selection of protocols and how they are put together comprise the network's architecture.

(N) layer protocol model

A complete language has been developed to describe the operation of layered network protocols. It is based on the model illustrated in Figure 3.2. For simplicity, we can choose a layer of interest and call it the (N) layer. The next lower layer is then the $(N-1)$ layer while the next higher layer is the $(N+1)$ layer. Entities within the (N) layer are called (N) layer
entities. Entities can be any identifiable protocol implementation or function. The key concept is that each layer adds value to the services provided by the layer beneath it and offers the improved services to the layer above it. The actual services added will depend on the layer and can range from correction of bit errors induced in the electrical circuit connecting two machines to checkpointing of a transaction in progress to permit recovery from a system crash.

Figure 3.3 shows this in more detail. Here we have zoomed in on just the (N) layer and its immediate environment. The (N) layer protocol entities start with the services provided by the $(N-1)$ layer and commu-

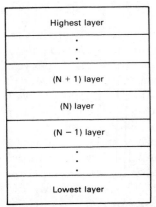

Figure 3.2   (N) layer network model.

nicate with each other to provide the (N) layer services. Although the communication is logically peer to peer between the (N) layer entities, it is actually performed via the services provided by the (N− 1) layer. Successful protocol layering requires defining the services provided by each layer to allow those services to be both reasonable to provide given the services available from the (N− 1) layer and useful for real applications when all layers are combined. It is vital to distinguish between the services provided by each layer and the means used to physically communicate between layers. As we shall soon see, that distinction is the key to building open systems that can communicate regardless of implementation details such as computer language used, operating system calls available, and the type of CPU involved.

Services are implemented as shown in Figure 3.4. The (N) layer accepts the information to be communicated from the (N+ 1) layer above it, adds its own protocol control information to it, and passes it down to the (N− 1) layer for delivery to the remote (N) layer peer entity. In formal terminology, the (N) layer protocol data unit (PDU), composed of the (N) layer service data unit (SDU) and the (N) layer protocol control information (PCI), becomes the (N− 1) layer service data unit, which is then combined with the (N− 1) PCI to compose an (N− 1) PDU, which then . . .

Similarly, on the way back up through the protocol layers, each layer removes its protocol control information from the packet and passes the remainder on up. The fact that one implementation may use procedure calls to pass the data units up and down the layers while another may use message passing has no impact on the ability of the protocols to function and communicate.

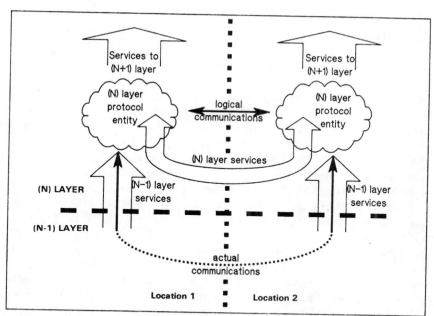

Figure 3.3 (N) layer model, layer detail.

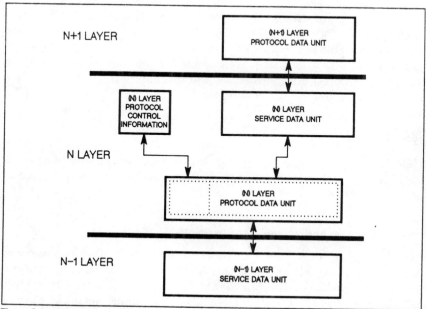

Figure 3.4 (N) layer model, an alternate view.

Open systems interconnection

Open systems interconnection is the "Holy Grail" of computer networking. The ability to take two machines with independently implemented networking software and have them communicate successfully is the raison d'être for the entire MAP/TOP movement. And the key to practical open systems is appropriately layered protocols.

Only two things determine if two (N) layer protocol entities can communicate. The (N) layer entities must agree on the meaning of every bit in the (N) PCI, including any actions associated with each, and they must have a way to transfer the (N) PDUs between each other. The former requires the (N) layer protocol to be adequately defined and properly implemented. The latter requires availability of an (N − 1) layer implementation able to exchange (N) PDUs between the two (N) layer implementations. And what is required for the (N − 1) layer protocol entities to be able to exchange (N) PDUs? That the (N − 1) entities providing the communications service to the (N) layer satisfy the same conditions we just stated for the (N) layer to communicate. This argument continues recursively down the protocol stack until we reach the bottom layer where the bits are physically transported from one machine to the other.

If all layers match up, communications can occur, independent of the specific details of the implementation. This is why modern computer networking protocol standards only specify the provision of services and not the means of accessing them. How the networking services at each layer are accessed has no impact on connectivity and can be left up to the implementor on each machine. What counts is the services provided, for that is what the (N) layer protocols, and ultimately the users and their applications, depend on for communications.

Layer Services

Just as we saw in our discussion of protocols that certain functions seem ubiquitous, so is the case with the services provided by the (N) layer to the (N + 1) layer.

Protocol selection and service access points

When traversing up or down the protocol stack, it is often necessary to select which of several protocol entities at the next layer will be used. This can occur both going down the stack (for example, a transport layer implementation must select which of several available networks to send the packet out on) and going up the stack (as, for example, when the session layer must select which of several user processes should get the packet).

The key to this selection process is a concept called a service access point, or SAP. Consider Figure 3.5 in which we have (N) layer protocol entities selecting among (N + 1) layer protocol entities. Each (N) layer protocol entity knows which (N + 1) protocol entity to deliver each packet to by the (N) layer SAP specified in the packet header. Similarly, each (N + 1) layer protocol entity passes data down to the desired (N) layer protocol entity by going through the appropriate (N) layer SAP.

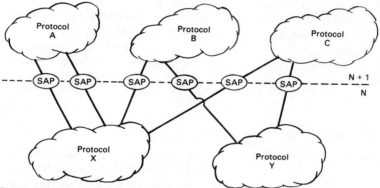

Figure 3.5 Protocol selection via SAPs.

The identification of SAPs need follow only one rule—an (N) layer SAP must uniquely identify the pairing of an (N) layer protocol entity with an (N + 1) layer protocol entity. There may be more than one SAP associated with any single (N) layer protocol entity or (N + 1) layer protocol entity. There may even be more than one SAP identifying the same pairing of protocol entities. At a higher conceptual level, there may be traffic for a multitude of different users all going through the same SAP. However, for any given (N) layer SAP, there must be one and only one (N) layer protocol entity and one and only one (N + 1) layer protocol entity.

Connections and associations

A pair of terms that is frequently confused is connections and associations. The connection service simply establishes a relationship between an (N) layer service access point on one protocol stack and a corresponding (N) layer SAP on another protocol stack. That is, it provides a communications path for an (N + 1) layer protocol on one machine to the desired (N + 1) layer protocol on the remote machine it wishes to communicate with. In the realm of MAP/TOP and other networks based on the International Organization for Standardization's Open Systems Interconnection reference model (the ISO OSI model, coming up in the next section), connections between higher-level protocols directly utilized by users are called associations. The distinction is a fine one, but it boils down to this. If a connection is between protocols which map to machines, it is called a connection. If it is between protocols which map to user processes, it is called an association. As a result, an association at any layer will map one to one with an association at the highest protocol level. A connection, on the other hand, may service multiple associations. In addition, a single association may (although as yet it is very uncommon) utilize multiple connections. Any one-to-one mapping of associations to connections is usually coincidence (there just happens to be only one pair of user application processes communicating over the connection) or convenience (a dedicated connection is desired for performance considerations).

Multiplexing and splitting

The formal terms for the many-to-one mappings of associations and connections are multiplexing and splitting. Multiplexing refers to taking several associations or connections at the $(N + 1)$ layer and putting them all over a single connection at the (N) layer. The usual motivation is to save money by having multiple users share a single connection. The same philosophy is used when multiple terminal users share a single high-speed line using a terminal multiplexer. As long as the multiplexed connection has the capacity to meet the needs of all the users, greater efficiency is the result.

When the mapping is the opposite and a single association or connection at the $(N + 1)$ layer is utilizing multiple connections at the (N) layer, the operation is called splitting. While it is not envisioned as a required function in MAP/TOP networks, you may run into it in other networks, particularly those linked by "voice-grade" common carrier circuits. Before the advent of high-speed modems able to exceed 4800 bps on a dial-up phone line, it was not uncommon to have dial-up back up of leased lines which used splitting over multiple dial-up lines to maintain the required data rate. Even today, in those areas not blessed with digital data phone service or its equivalent, it can be the only way to obtain links capable of reliable operation above 10 to 20 Kbps. In local area networks, where performance is limited by the processing time required for the protocols rather than by the speed of the links available, splitting is counterproductive and is not used.

Data transfer

There are several different aspects to the service called data transfer. To begin with, there is normal data transfer consisting of taking an (N + 1) layer PDU presented at an (N) layer SAP and delivering it to the (N + 1) layer protocol at the corresponding remote (N) layer SAP. But there are also variations on data transfer. (N + 1) data can be transferred as part of the process of establishing or releasing an (N) layer connection. An ability to send expedited data may be provided, using a high-priority path not bound by the flow controls exerted on normal data transfer. The ability to provide flow control and sequencing are often an integral part of providing the data transfer.

In the process of transferring data, the (N) layer may also need or want to use packets whose size differs from those handed down from the (N + 1) layer. The breaking up of large packets into smaller ones is called segmenting. If the opposite impact is desired, either of the two techniques illustrated in Figure 3.6 can be used to convert multiple small (N + 1) layer packets into larger (N) layer packets. Concatenation takes multiple PDUs from the (N + 1) layer and combines them into a single SDU at the (N) layer. Blocking, on the other hand, takes multiple (N) layer SDUs, adds PCI to each, and combines them into a single PDU for processing by the (N − 1) layer. Each technique has its advantages and disadvantages. Concatenation can only be used if the (N + 1) layer protocol does not depend on the preservation of PDU identity over the (N) SAP connection. Blocking preserves that information but does so at the cost of extra overhead at the (N) layer.

Error control

The two primary aspects to error control are error detection and notification of the results of that detection. Error detection includes all the topics we discussed about how protocols provide a reliable data transfer function. Error notification recognizes the need for the (N) layer protocol to inform the (N + 1) layer of the results of (N) layer's error detection efforts. For example, once data is successfully transferred by the (N) layer, the (N) layer can inform the (N + 1) layer so that the higher layers can proceed to any next step which had to be held pending delivery. More important [since any (N + 1) layer protocol would never trust the word of an (N) layer protocol but would only proceed after direct confirmation of receipt by its (N + 1) layer peer], the (N) layer can inform the (N + 1) layer of any errors that the (N) layer is incapable of recovering from so that the (N + 1) layer can decide on the best approach to continued communication. This may be retransmission of the lost packet without waiting for the (N + 1) layer retransmission timer to expire or perhaps using knowledge (such as available alternate paths) not available to the (N) layer protocol to complete the communication.

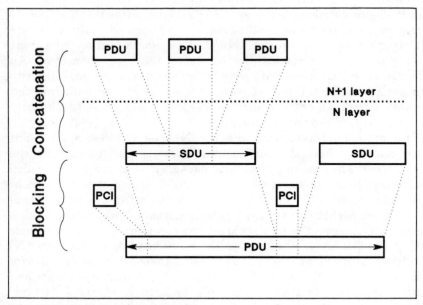

Figure 3.6   Concatenation and blocking.

Reset

When all else fails, it may be necessary for an (N + 1) layer protocol or a peer (N) layer protocol to grab hold of an (N) layer protocol and reset it to a known state. This is particularly true in the case of detection of an unrecoverable error condition or when the controlling protocol otherwise has reason to believe the (N) layer protocol is not performing correctly. Because the existing state information in the protocol being reset is lost, this action can result in lost or duplicate packets and should not be considered lightly. Normally resets are required only when machine or link failures have occurred or when a machine is powering up (in effect, recovering from the most cataclysmic of machine failures, being turned off).

The ISO OSI Reference Model

We now have almost all the tools we need to actually start discussing networking. We have terminology to describe how applications make use of networking (NIPC, RFA, etc.), we have terminology to describe how a network performs (delay, throughput, etc.), we can describe how the nodes making up a network are connected (bus, mesh, etc.), and we have the terminology to break up protocols into layers and describe how they interact to provide services. We are only missing the guidelines to tell us how to do the actual layering of the various functional protocols required to make up a network. These guidelines are provided by the International Organization for Standardization in their international standard, ISO/7498—"Information Processing Systems—Open Systems Interconnection—Basic Reference Model," or the ISO OSI model for short.

The ISO work on open systems interconnection started in 1977 with the formation of Subcommittee 16 to develop an architecture for open systems interconnection. That committee resulted in the publication of the ISO seven-layer reference model in 1979. That document worked its way through the standardization process until it finally was approved in 1984 as an international standard.

The reference model itself actually serves two purposes, and it does both very well. First, it provides a common basis for the coordination of computer network standards development. MAP/TOP and many other networks would not be practical without it. Secondly, it provides a means of placing existing network implementations and standards in perspective. This allows meaningful comparisons between networks with radically different architectures and definitions, such as between IBM SNA and DEC DECnet.

The reference model does this by defining seven layers of protocols, the services provided by each layer, and the functions performed at each layer. (A layer can provide a service by passing up that service as provided by lower layers, whereas the functions of a layer are those service enhancements actually performed by a particular layer.) These functions and services are defined generically, with no implementation specifics. The idea is more one of specifying where different kinds of services and functions should be placed rather than specifying for each layer the specific functions and services to be included. The ISO OSI reference model does not specify services and protocols. Misunderstanding over this point, more than anything else, delayed its ratification as an international standard. The ISO OSI reference model is not an implementation specification. It is a reference framework for the development of protocol specifications and standards.

Although the ISO OSI reference model is an international standard and as such would seem fixed and inflexible, it is really a living document. Even before it was formally approved, addenda were proposed and working their way through the system, extending its applicability and refining the definitions in the light of experience with the model in the real world of implementing networks. Additional addenda will continue to be proposed. Some will make it into standards status, others will not. All will continue to follow the guidelines set down by the original subcommittee, interpreted in the light of new knowledge.

The ISO OSI model layers

The ISO OSI reference model has seven layers. Starting from the bottom of Figure 3.7 and working up, layer one is the physical layer, layer two is the link layer, layer three is the network layer, layer four is the transport layer, layer five is the session layer, layer six is the presentation layer, and layer seven is the application layer. Outside the seven layers are management and control functions. Users of network services are not included in the model, which only deals with intersystem connectivity.

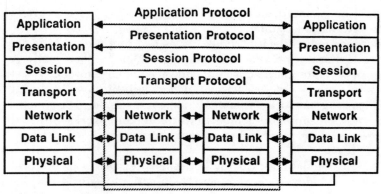

Figure 3.7 The ISO OSI layers.

Physical layer

The physical layer is the bottom-most layer in the model. In many respects, this layer is where the rubber meets the road. It is the layer at which any bits which need to get from one machine to another actually get moved around. Any two machines connected by a physical channel are considered to be adjacent whether they are side by side in the same room or on two different continents connected by a dial-up telephone link.

Specifications for implementation of any layer always cover procedural and functional characteristics. Unique to the physical layer is specification of electrical and mechanical requirements as well. While other layers, particularly those at the lower levels, can frequently benefit from hardware assists, the physical layer is the only layer which cannot be implemented solely in software. At some point, physical hardware is required to transfer those bits from one node to the next.

Link layer

Starting with the link layer, all upper layers exist to expand on the services provided by lower layers. In the case of the link layer, also commonly referred to as the "data link" layer, the key service added is error control. The physical layer, being part of the real world, is subject to errors. The link layer upgrades the service provided by the physical layer from a direct physical link between two nodes to a reliable, error-free link between physically connected nodes.

In the case of a connectionless link layer service such as MAP/TOP uses, the word reliable assumes a new meaning. In a MAP/TOP network, the link layer protocol guarantees that any packet received by an adjacent node will be free of any errors. However, to make that guarantee, it will not deliver any packets which may contain errors. This alters the dictionary definition of reliable to mean only that *if* a packet is delivered, it will be error free. MAP/TOP leaves it up to a higher protocol layer to extend reliable to include delivery guarantees.

Numerous other functions can also be provided by the link layer. It can provide for addressing which of several nodes on a shared physical link will receive the data. Segmentation and flow control are also common. The key is if a function applies strictly to the transfer of data across a physical link directly connecting two nodes, it belongs in the link layer if it is not already built into the physical layer.

Network layer

We now have a "reliable" communications link between physically connected nodes. What about when the nodes which need to communicate do not have a direct physical link? That is the purpose of layer three, the network layer. It combines the individual links provided by the physical and link layers into a communications network. It performs routing of packets as required to provide data transfer between nodes whether or not they have a direct physical connection. In a network where all nodes are physically connected, such as a simple MAP local area network, the network layer often degenerates into a null layer. Null layers are common in network implementation. Many network architectures do not even try to provide the full range of functionality provided by the ISO OSI model. They can be implemented faster and with better performance by leaving out unused services.

You do want to be careful that you do not get carried away leaving out layers, however. Early local area network users soon discovered that although their networks individually consisted entirely of adjacent nodes and hence did not require a network layer, as soon as they wanted to communicate between nodes on two different networks, they needed the network layer back to link their multiple networks. Most of the work going on in the network layer today is related to internetworking rather than traditional packet switch networking. As a result, sometimes you will see attempts to rename the network layer the internetwork layer or to divide it into two layers, a network sublayer and an internetwork sublayer. The trend today is toward recognition that while the protocols in the network layer may have multiple names, the underlying function remains the same.

Transport layer

The transport layer provides much the same function for the network layer as the link layer did for the physical layer. It takes the end-node-to-end-node service provided by the network layer concatenation of physical links and makes it transparent and reliable. Transparent means that users of the transport service do not need to be concerned with the type of network or links involved. The transport will provide whatever segmentation and reassembly are required to fit the data over the network. It will add to the services provided by the network whatever error checking, flow control, sequencing, etc., that is needed to raise the level of service provided up to that required by the user.

The transport layer is where the packets dropped by a connectionless link layer will be detected and retried. Although not required by the model, most transports used for data transport are connection oriented. The only exceptions are in special applications such as voice or telemetry where timeliness of delivery is more important than completeness of data and occasional drop outs are tolerated in order to keep up the flow.

Additional services which can be provided by the transport can include expedited service, where limited amounts of data can be transferred quickly without being subject to normal flow controls, and multiplexing, where multiple transport connections will be established over a single network connection (assuming the network service is also connection oriented). Of course, a connection-oriented transport would also provide for connection establishment and release.

The most important aspect of the transport layer, however, is not what it does but rather where it resides. The transport and higher layers are outside the traditional "network cloud." They are always within the domain of the end-node machines. This makes transport the lowest layer that the user can specify without worrying about what the data communications vendor requires for connection to their service. For the public data network user, the transport layer is the first opportunity for users to specify their needs rather than settling for whatever is available.

Session

The session layer has an interesting history. When the ISO OSI model was first published, a lot of people wondered what it would be good for. The functions proposed for it were scattered throughout the layers of contemporary networks. Unlike all the other layers in the model, there simply were no networks with a corresponding layer in existence. This confusion is often reflected in articles published in the early 1980s and even in some today. I think this is because the session layer's prime purpose is not so much a specific function, like the other six layers, but rather to serve as a changer of perspective. The session layer is where the view of a communications transaction changes from the lower layers' concern with connecting two machines to the higher layers' concern with communications between two user processes.

The distinction at first may seem like splitting hairs, but the impact is real. It allows physical through transport to concentrate solely on providing a useful communications channel from one end-node machine to another without worrying about how it is to be used or what the process model is on either end machine. To the presentation and application layers above, all details of the provision of communications can be safely ignored. The application layer can simply state "give me this level of service at this cost" and let the session layer handle all the details. The result has been simpler, more efficient transport layer specifications and an ability to go beyond basic communications services and start looking at providing networking services in the session layer that previously were only dreamed of, such as data checkpointing and crash recovery.

Presentation layer

Almost the exact opposite of the session layer, nobody has ever been in doubt about the function of the presentation layer. If we go back to our human protocol example, it is the presentation layer which handles converting John's German to Mary's French. The presentation layer's sole function is to make the data at one end understandable to the other end. In the world of computers, this can be as basic as converting from the ASCII character set used by a DEC VAX to the EBCDIC character set employed by an IBM 3090. On the factory floor, it would free the cell controller from the need to know how each of the machines controlled by it expresses a dimension of 1 in. The presentation layer would take the cell controller's representation of the data, perhaps a 32-bit floating point number, and convert it to whatever form was required by the machine controller addressed, perhaps an 8-bit integer or a character string. The presentation layer makes the representation of data (provided there is a one-to-one mapping) a nonissue for the application layer.

Application layer

The topmost layer of the ISO OSI reference model is the application layer. This is the layer that user programs and processes accessing the network talk to. It is the interface to the open systems' environment and the only access point available to users. The other six layers exist solely to support the services provided by the application layer. Here is where you will find all the services we discussed in Chapter 2, NIPC, NFT, RFA, etc. The majority of the protocol development work being done today is occurring in this layer of the model.

Management and control functions

Outside the scope of the seven layers, but critical to the operation of any network, are the management and control functions. The very function of the various layers makes a network prone to disastrous failure if some means of monitoring the operation is not available. Consider the link layer, for example. Its prime purpose is to make any failures at the physical layer invisible to higher layers. That means that a user on a deteriorating phone line will not have any indication of trouble until the line is so bad that it cannot support any communication. The goal of network management and control would be to identify the problem before it affects the user and allow corrective action to be taken in a timely, rather than panic-stricken, way.

The biggest challenge to network management and control is the need to continue to function even when layers are broken. This requires communications paths between management agents on different nodes which are not dependent on proper functioning of all seven layers. While the ISO OSI reference model recommends using all seven layers whenever possible, it does recognize the need for special-case solutions. However, beyond recognizing the need for management and control, it says very little.

Linking ISO OSI networks

While not actually part of the ISO OSI reference model, a natural outgrowth is a variety of ways to link networks together to expand their size or connectivity. The mode of linking is defined by the layer at which the link performs. In the OSI environment, links make sense at four layers: the physical, link, network, and application.

A link at the physical layer (see Figure 3.8) is called a **repeater**. It operates at the physical layer only, typically restoring signal amplitude and timing. Totally transparent to all the layers, repeaters can only be used to link identical networks in which all seven layers match. The most common use is in local area networks to extend and interconnect baseband segments.

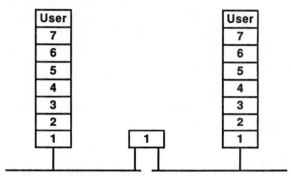

Figure 3.8 Repeater architecture.

Moving up a layer, a link at the data link layer (Figure 3.9) is called a **bridge**. Bridges provide network expansion by connecting two physically distinct networks at the link layer. They rely on the use of identical data link protocols across the network, including any link addressing and frame size limits. Since the connection is at the link layer, the physical layers may be different. In a MAP/TOP network, for example, bridges are used to connect carrierband segments to a broadband backbone and to connect between broadband channels. Intelligent bridges can keep track

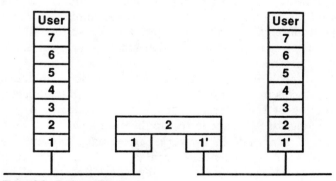

Figure 3.9 Bridge architecture.

of what addresses are on what segment and only transmit packets that have sources and destinations on opposite sides of the bridge. This serves to isolate local traffic and reduce the total network traffic to much less than the sum of all the traffic on each subnet.

A network layer connect (Figure 3.10) has two names. It can always be called an intermediate system, but if capable of routing packets between multiple networks, it can also be called a router. Services provided can include path selection, message relaying, and alternate routing. There are no restrictions on the interconnected link or physical layers (aside from being compatible with the network layer, of course). Intermediate systems are the preferred method for linking MAP and TOP networks. Use of intermediate systems instead of bridges in this application permits optimizing frame sizes for the different media used and simplifies address administration. Because frames are specifically addressed to the intermediate system rather than transparently passed through as with a bridge, the different networks connected do not require common address administration to avoid conflicts.

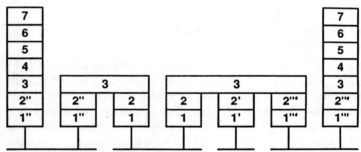

Figure 3.10   Intermediate system architecture.

Connections between networks are normally not made at the transport, session, or presentation layer. Commercially available networks today either match from the network layer on up (for example, MAP and TOP) or they do not match at all. Networks that do not match at all can still be linked by using a protocol conversion gateway (Figure 3.11). Protocol conversion protocols are added to connect the incompatible application layer protocols of each network. The ISO model includes these additional protocols in the application layer. Although technically incorrect, the function of the interconnect protocols is clearer if you think of them as an eighth layer above the application layer.

Gateways between incompatible networks are usually difficult to implement and limited in functionality. Even so, they are common in multivendor networks because outside of a few special cases such as ARPA/DDN and MAP/TOP, total mismatch of all layers is the norm rather than the exception. The protocol conversion gateway maps the features of one network into whatever corresponds in the second network. The architecture of each side of the gateway will be whatever is required to match the proprietary network on that side. They are normally required to connect a MAP/TOP network to a non-OSI network and are the most common way of connecting just about any network to IBM.

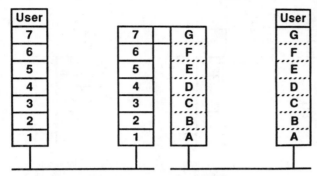

Figure 3.11   Protocol conversion gateway architecture.

A Simple Example of Layered Protocols in Action

Let us look at what it takes to implement a usable network using layered protocols in accordance with the ISO OSI model. Consider the small network in Figure 3.12. For the sake of a simple example to follow, assume that a numerical controller (NC unit no. 21) completes the task it is currently assigned. Since it does not know what to do next, it notifies its cell controller (CC no. 2) that it is free and awaiting a new task. The cell controller has nothing queued up, so it refers the request to the factory management program that is running in the factory host computer. The factory management program checks the job scheduling program to determine the next job to schedule on NC unit no. 21 in work cell no. 2. Finding that the next task is a different one from the task just completed, the factory management program retrieves the appropriate program file for NC unit no. 21 and sends it to CC no. 2, the cell controller for the cell. Back at CC no. 2, the cell controller accepts the file containing the program for NC unit no. 21 to execute, converts it to the format required by NC unit no. 21, and downloads the program to NC unit no. 21 for execution.

Within this overall operation, let us narrow our focus even more and examine just what it takes to do only one of the transactions involved, copying the file with the NC program in it from the host down to the cell controller. You may be surprised at how complex even a "simple NFT"

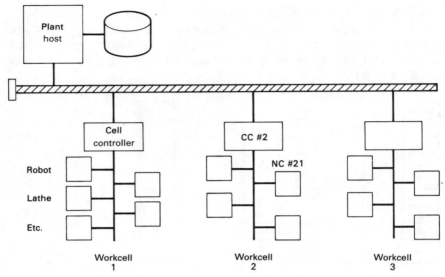

Figure 3.12   A simple network application.

can be. Although we will be discussing the process in terms of a MAP 2.1 network implementation, the degree of complexity is typical of most modern general-purpose networks; only the details differ.

Two perspectives

One way to look at the file transfer operation is from the viewpoint of the pieces of hardware involved. Figure 3.13 shows some of the typical MAP network components which might be involved in putting together our scenario. At the host end of the transaction, we have a host minicomputer. Since the data is in a file, there is a disk drive to hold it and a disk controller interface to access the disk drive. A stand-alone network interface unit is used for the actual connection of the host into the MAP network. An input/output (I/O) card is required to talk to the network interface unit using a proprietary protocol over a custom cable. The other side of the network interface unit is an RF connection to the broadband trunk cable.

Broadband trunk cables are heavy, shielded coaxial cable. Normally the cable is of the semirigid variety in which the solid aluminum shield on the cable also serves as a built-in conduit. Depending on the design of the system, it may range anywhere from 1.2 to 3 centimeters (cm) (about 1/2 in to over 1 in) in diameter. To make the connection between the network interface unit and the trunk cable, flexible drop cables are connected into taps on the trunk cable. This drop cable is usually flexible, 0.6-cm (1/4-in) coaxial cable similar to that used to hook a television set to a video cassette recorder.

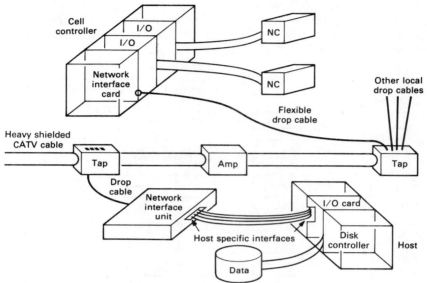

Figure 3.13   The physical perspective.

At the receiving end of the file transfer, the cell controller will also connect to a drop cable. In this case, I assumed that a board level network interface unit, which mounts in the cell controller's card cage, is used instead of a separate unit.

Looking inside the boxes in Figure 3.14, we see a very different perspective. In addition to a pair of seven-layer network protocol stacks, one for each end of the connection, we have the user processes above each and the physical connection, discussed above, between the two stacks. Let us trace the file transfer through the ISO OSI layers as used in MAP 2.1 and see what they really do. For simplicity, we will start with the steady state condition of an error-free data flow across the network.

Layer functions in the data flow phase

We start at the application layer on the host side. Assuming that the file being transferred is too big to send as one packet, the application layer segments it into protocol data units appropriately sized for the session layer. According to the ISO OSI model, the application layer hands its protocol data units (PDUs) to the presentation layer, not the session layer. However, in practice the presentation layer is indifferent to PDU size, and any limits on PDU size will be enforced by the session layer. Besides, MAP 2.1 does not use the presentation layer and packets are handed directly to the session layer from the application layer.

The only session layer functions used by MAP 2.1 are associated with connection establishment and release. During steady state data flow, it serves as a straight pipe between application and transport, slowing the flow of the packet only long enough to add the necessary addressing for its peer session process on the other end to deliver it to the correct application process.

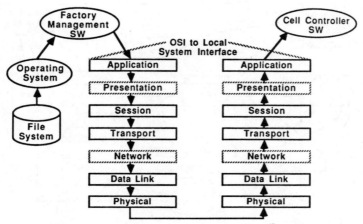

Figure 3.14   The OSI perspective.

The transport layer is where the process starts to get interesting. First, if the session PDUs are too large, the transport layer must segment them down to the size required by the network layer or negotiated at connection establishment with its peer transport on the cell controller. It then adds the necessary headers and other information to allow its peer at the cell controller to verify that all packets have been received, put into proper sequence, and delivered to the proper session entity. If any data packets have been received by the host transport from the cell controller transport, it may also choose to "piggyback" the acknowledgment for those received rather than send an explicit acknowledgment packet.

The transport layer has more to do than putting together the protocol control information (PCI) to be sent with the PDU (protocol data unit). In order to recover from loss of a PDU in the network, it must save a copy of it and set a timer to retransmit it if an acknowledgment is not received in time. If the PDU is being retransmitted, the transport layer needs to keep track of how many times it has tried to send the particular PDU and take other steps if limits are exceeded. (Taking other steps normally means do whatever is standard operating procedure when a connection is determined to have died.)

Our example network is self-contained and does not require any internetworking services, so the network layer is a straight pipe similar to session. On MAP 2.1 networks, full network layer functionality is only required if both ends of the connection are not on the same LAN or if the transport layer is not segmenting the PDUs it hands to network small enough for the link layer.

The link layer functionality in MAP 2.1 ensures that only error-free packets get through the network. To do this, a 32-bit cyclic redundancy check (CRC) is calculated and appended to the PDU. No record keeping is required since the link layer is connectionless, and it is up to the transport layer to detect and retransmit lost packets. The link layer will also put an address on the PDU so the cell controller can recognize that the packet is addressed to it when it sees the packet on the LAN.

Finally we get down to the physical layer. Since MAP 2.1 is a broadband token bus, media access control must wait until the host holds the token. Once in possession of the token, the host can broadcast the packet onto the network and physically get the bits from the host to the cell controller.

Now that we have the bits on the cell controller, we need to work our way back up the protocol stack. The link layer listens to all packets broadcast on the network. Any without valid CRCs are immediately tossed. Those that pass the bit error test are then examined to see if they address the cell controller. Any that do not are discarded. Those valid packets that are addressed to the cell controller are cleaned of all link level PCI and passed up to the network layer.

Since we assumed a pass-through network layer on the sending side, the receiving side does the same, passing the link packets straight up to the transport layer.

Transport examines each packet received and sends an acknowledgment for each one that is valid. After scheduling the transmission of an acknowledgment, the transport can check to see if the packet is a duplicate of one already received and discard it if it is. Received packets are put back into order. If session PDUs were segmented, the transport reassembles them for delivery to session. The session PDUs are delivered up to the session layer in order, with no errors, duplicates, missing, or out of sequence PDUs after removing all transport PCI.

After bubbling up through the session layer and null presentation layer, the application layer converts the PDUs into local file format and writes the data into the file.

Other layer functions

Before any data can flow through the network, the layers must first go through the connection establishment phase. The process starts with the factory management software on the host requesting the file transfer service from the local application layer. The application layer must set up an association with its peer application layer on the cell controller in order to fulfill that request. However, setting up that association requires a communications path between the peer entities, which is provided to the application layer by the presentation layer. The presentation layer then must go through the same process, requesting the session layer to set up an association between itself and its peer at the cell controller's presentation layer. In our example, this process continues until we get to the network layer. Since the network, link, and physical layers in MAP 2.1 are connectionless, no connection establishment phase is required and communications can occur immediately.

At each stage, the (N+ 1) layer service will negotiate with the (N) layer for the desired level of service. This is not a give and take style of negotiation but rather a two-stage handshake. The (N+ 1) asks for everything it would like, the (N) layer responds with what it can provide, and the (N+ 1) layer must decide whether to take it or give up. For example, consider the question of PDU size at each layer. The application layer wants the biggest packets possible to minimize overhead. So it requests 10,000-byte packet service from presentation. Presentation does not exist, so session fields the request. Since segmentation is not provided at session layer, session passes the request down to transport. Transport receives the request and recognizes that it exceeds its largest size. Before responding to session with its maximum PDU size of 2500 bytes, however, it first checks with network. The network layer does not want to segment, so it checks with link, which responds that 1412 bytes is the best it can do. Network so informs transport, which then proceeds to set up a connection with its peer transport on the cell controller. The two transports then negotiate peer to peer, with host transport asking for a 1390-byte PDU exchange (1412-link limit less network and transport PCI requirements). The cell controller, being short on memory space for buffers, responds with a 256-byte limit. To make this example interesting, let us assume that the implementation of transport on the host is limited in its segmentation capability. Host transport does some quick calculations and determines that the largest SDU it can handle segmenting into 256-data-byte PDUs is 2048, so it reflects to session that the best it can do is 2048 bytes. Since our MAP 2.1 session does not include segmentation service, it subtracts the number of bytes it needs for PCI from the 2048-byte transport SDU size and passes the remainder up to presentation and thence to application. The file transfer application has the option of telling the user it cannot do it or doing its own segmentation to the less efficient (for file transfer) block size offered by session.

Now that we have established the basics of negotiation, let us look at what each layer does. The application layer negotiates down the stack for an appropriate association with its peer on the cell controller. Having established that association, the sending side will open the appropriate source file while the cell controller peer will set up to write the appropriate file, verifying first that the host has the appropriate permissions to write over whatever is already there.

The session layer will field the application layer's request for an association since the presentation layer is null. It does that by mapping the requested association onto a transport connection and negotiating with transport to determine who will provide the services requested. Since the MAP 2.1 session layer is minimal, the negotiation actually consists of a request from session for the requested services from transport. Of course, since MAP 2.1 is a consistently designed network architecture, transport will respond with an acceptable answer.

The transport layer decides locally how to provide the requested services, sets up a connection to the requested peer transport if one does not already exist, and finalizes negotiations. All counters, timers, and sequence numbers required by the connection will be initialized and buffers allocated. The network, link, and physical layers, being connectionless, have no idea a connection is being established and treat all packets as they do during steady state data flow.

Once the transport connection is established, the session layer can utilize it to set up the appropriate association with its peer. Working back up the protocol stack, the application finally has an association it can use to negotiate file transfer details with its peer and all layers reach data flow phase.

After the file transfer completes, we enter the release phase. This is the reverse of the establishment phase, less most of the negotiation. The application layers agree that the file transfer is complete, close any files still open, and release any other resources associated with the association. One of those resources is the association itself, so the session layer can do the same (release any resources associated with the association). However, before it does so, it needs to make sure both peer application processes are done and all data has been delivered. Similarly, the transport connection can be released if it is not being used by other associations. While normally negotiated, the release process is also used unilaterally as when one side of a communications dies and the other needs to clean up and recover.

ISO Standardization Work

MAP/TOP network specifications are based on internationally accepted standards whenever any are available. The International Organization for Standardization (ISO) is the primary source of standard protocols suitable for inclusion in MAP/TOP and is becoming more dominant as time goes on. Since MAP/TOP capabilities and implementation requirements will be constantly evolving as technology advances, an understanding of the standardization process, particularly as practiced by ISO, is vital. Only by tracking the progress of relevant standards can the normal user hope to stay ahead of MAP/TOP plans for change.

The International Organization for Standardization

The International Organization for Standardization (ISO) is a voluntary, nontreaty organization. As such, its standards are really only recommendations for standard practice. However, in several European countries, its standards have been given the force of law, so do not be misled into thinking that just because membership is voluntary, the outputs do not count. They do.

Membership in ISO is limited to the principal standards group from each country. For example, the member for the United States is the American National Standards Institute (ANSI), Canada's is the Standards Council of Canada, and Britain's is the British Standards Institute. Each of the member groups may then turn around and delegate the actual standards-making work to other national standards groups. For example, in the United States, ANSI has assigned the task of developing local area network standards to the Institute of Electrical and Electronics Engineers (IEEE). We will look at the LAN standards IEEE has developed and is working on in the last section of this chapter.

The ISO standardization process

All ISO standards, be they for networking, screw threads, or solar energy, follow the same development process. When the need or desire for a standard is recognized, a working group will be formed in the appropriate committee or subcommittee. The developers will work together and produce a document which contains all the features which they believe necessary for the desired standard. This document, intended for circulation within the working group, is called a working draft (WD). It is typically rough and unedited, but it is the earliest documentation available with any degree of stability associated with it. At this stage, a standard number has not yet been assigned, and major changes can easily occur before the concept being standardized ever gains approval.

The second stage occurs when the working group has reached internal consensus and is ready to expose its ideas to the world at large. At this point, the proposed standard is registered with the ISO Central Secretariat and receives an official standard identifying number which it will keep permanently. Documents which have received a number and are ready for circulation to all participating nations for balloting are called draft proposals (DP). In general, a document in DP stage is far more stable than any in WD stage. While it is still risky to do so, vendors seeking an edge in the market will sometimes start to implement the standard in this stage. The primary risk is that change will be required to gain approval from all balloting nations. Some standards receive major comments sufficient to return them to the committee for a retry with a second draft proposal. Theoretically, there is no limit to the number of draft proposals required before advancing to the next stage. Sometimes, the state of the art is advancing too rapidly to be captured in a standard. Disagreement between the working group and one or more of the national member groups (or their designee) can also cause an excessive number of draft proposal voting cycles.

The next stage, draft international standard (DIS), is reached when all comments of the member bodies have been incorporated and the document is ready for final balloting. While a DIS is probably not yet written in the official ISO editorial style, only minor technical problems should remain to be resolved. Implementing a DIS is generally safe and is common practice in computer networking.

Once all the changes have been made, the DIS can progress to approved international standard (IS) status. This is the final version of the basic standard. It will be technically and editorially correct and available in all three official ISO languages: English, French, and Russian. At this point, the only reason to be hesitant about implementation is if the standard may not be suitable for the intended application. There is no need to be concerned with any changes. The standard is not going to get any more stable.

You are probably wondering how a standard can keep up with technology if it is considered unalterable upon reaching IS status. While basic standards have only four stages to their life cycle, there are two more types of documents encountered in the world of ISO standards.

The term draft addendum (DAD) is used to describe a proposed supplement to an IS or a DIS. It consists of new subject matter relating to the basic standard. The supplement can either extend the coverage of the base standard or provide alternate means of achieving the desired aims of the base standard. The potential implementor must be cautious as DAD is used to describe supplements in both DP- and DIS-equivalent stages of development. Once the supplement is fully approved and has all the characteristics of an IS, it is called an addendum (AD).

Network standards status

Literally dozens of network-oriented standards are working their way through the ISO standardization process. Lower layers of the ISO OSI reference model have numerous standards available for implementation. You have a choice of several local and wide area networks standards at DIS or IS which include full specification of layers one through three (physical, link, and network layers). Transport and basic session standards are equally solid.

The higher-layer protocols and services, however, are just reaching stability. The first few ISO application and presentation layer standards to reach DIS status only did so in mid-1986. Network management is probably the least developed of all. Aside from the framework, which is in DIS, the first network management protocol standards did not even reach DP until late in 1986.

Other major standards groups

There are many groups around the world involved in developing networking standards. The biggest in the networking world, along with ISO, is the International Telegraph and Telephone Consultative Committee, more commonly called CCITT (Comité Consultatif Internationale de Télégraphique et Téléphonique). Unlike ISO, CCITT is a treaty organization under the auspices of the United Nations to provide the standards required for international communications. Membership is made up of the post, telegraph, and telephone (PTT) branch of the governments of member countries. The United States, lacking a governmental PTT, is officially represented by the U.S. Department of State. CCITT recommendations are published every 4 years. Each edition is color coded to identify the year of publication; for example, the 1984 versions of the standards are the "Red Books." CCITT data communications standards are identified by a capital letter (X for digital, V for analog), a period, and a unique integer. For example, the international standard for public data networks is X.25 while that for 9600-bps two-wire modems is V.32. Other standards activities in CCITT use other letters for their standards. For example, the integrated services digital network standards are part of the I series.

Regionally, the European Computer Manufacturers Association (ECMA) has been around since 1961. It is made up of 15 ordinary (voting) members, all manufacturers of data processing equipment in Europe, and seven associate (nonvoting) members. Its primary claim to fame in computer networking was its action to break the deadlock in the IEEE 802.3 local area network committee by promulgating its own Ethernet-like local area networking standard, ECMA-80. Like ISO, ECMA is a nonvoting member of CCITT. ECMA standards can be recognized by the prefix ECMA in front of the standard number.

Also international in scope, although dominated by its U.S. membership, is the Institute of Electrical and Electronics Engineers (IEEE). Officially an industry group, it is active in standards development in many areas of electrical engineering and computers. It is currently the standards organization for local area networks to the point at which ISO has incorporated their LAN standards verbatim, only changing the covers to include the ISO standard designation. IEEE standards are identified by the prefix IEEE in front of the standard number. No hyphens or other joiners are used, for example, IEEE 488, an instrumentation bus standard, or IEEE 802.4, the MAP local area network media and media access standard. Because IEEE gets its numbers from the committee or subcommittee developing the standard, you must be careful when interpreting the status of any committee's output. Some committees, such as IEEE 802.6, have been meeting for years but have yet to produce a viable standards proposal. Others, such as 802.3, continue to produce new standards, all of which are lumped under the IEEE 802.3 banner.

In the United States, the two biggest players (not considering IEEE) are the Electronic Industries Association (EIA) and the National Bureau of Standards (NBS). The EIA has developed several hundred standards, all identified by the prefix RS (for recommended standard). Perhaps most famous for its modem interface standard, RS-232, EIA is developing the RS-511 manufacturing messaging standard, supported by MAP for factory floor device messaging.

The National Bureau of Standards (NBS) is responsible for developing standards for the U. S. government. They are the source of Federal Information Processing Standards, more commonly referred to as FIPS pubs. Their role in MAP/TOP goes far beyond the impact of FIPS pubs on the commercial market. In 1983 the NBS organized a series of workshops for implementors of OSI networking protocols in which the original protocols for MAP were identified. This work led to the 1984 NCC networking demonstrations. The workshops continue today, providing a forum for the bit-by-bit decisions on options and specification ambiguities. The minutes of these workshops form an integral part of the MAP/TOP specification.

All the organizations fit together as shown in Figure 3.15. Under the pressure of users (such as the MAP/TOP community) demanding quick development of networking standards, ISO and CCITT are letting ISO take over the development of data communications and networking standards. Coordination between ISO and CCITT then allows the integration of ISO standards into the CCITT standards as appropriate, without forcing users to wait for the 4-year cycle before being able to benefit from standards development. All the groups (and more) that we have discussed in this section provide input into the standards. In effect, ISO is serving as a clearinghouse and coordinating agent for the development of computer networking and data communications standards.

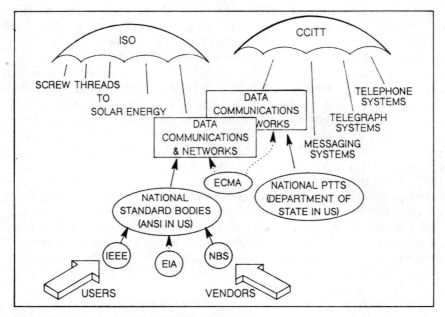

Figure 3.15   How the standards organizations fit together.

The IEEE 802 LAN Standards

While ISO has numerous committees that are hard at work developing higher-layer standards, most of the work at layers one and two for local area networks is being done by the IEEE Project 802. Figure 3.16 shows the organization of the nine working groups that make up the IEEE Project 802. These are identified by the added decimal after the 802 number.

At the top and encompassing all the 802 standards is the 802.1 work on architecture, management, and internetting. The goal of 802.1 is to provide a common, consistent method of addressing, internetworking, managing, and utilizing any 802 local area network. 802.1 describes a common interface to the layers defined in IEEE 802 that hides the differences between the various lower-layer approaches. Except for the network management aspects, the 802.1 standard has been stable.

Network management appears to be reaching consensus with the release of revision L (they started with A!) of the 802.1 draft proposal.

IEEE 802.2 describes a common logical link control protocol for all 802 LANs. Originally, 802.2 consisted of two protocols, type 1, connectionless service, and type 2, connection-oriented service. Type 3, single-frame service, was added in 1986 to meet the needs of time-critical applications. We will discuss these more in Chapter 6.

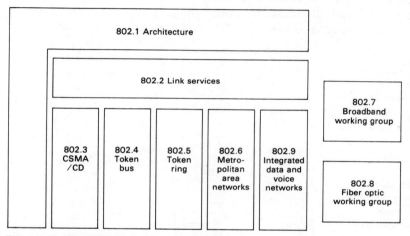

Figure 3.16 The IEEE 802 family of standards.

IEEE 802.3, 802.4, 802.5, and 802.6 each describe a particular approach to local area networking. Each of these standards specifies two things: a means of regulating media access and the actual physical requirements (electrical signaling, cable used, connectors, etc.). The media access control sublayer has been an enigma for ISO. It has some characteristics that belong in the physical layer and some that fit in the link layer. As shown in Figure 3.17, it really spans both layers. To avoid conflict with the ISO OSI model, it was placed in layer two, the link layer. Revision of the ISO OSI model to specifically address media access control is under way, and by the time you read this it should be safely ensconced in the physical layer. This eliminates the confusion you will see in the literature of the mid-eighties where there are two IEEE LAN standards specified for the link layer, with one of the two split to also include the physical layer.

As for the standards themselves, 802.3 was derived from the original DEC-Intel-Xerox Ethernet specification. It specifies a carrier sense multiple access with a collision detection method and a number of physical signaling methods and media (baseband coax, broadband coax, and baseband twisted pair). The first version developed, a 10-Mbps baseband coax implementation providing an upward growth path from existing Ethernet installations, has been approved as ISO 8802/3 and is the standard used for TOP.

MAP users are most concerned with IEEE 802.4, the broadband token bus LAN standard. Originally broadband only, 1986 saw its physical specifications expanded to include direct rather than radio frequency signaling on limited dimension broadband cabling, a technique given the name carrierband. Standard data rates range from 1 Mbps to 10 Mbps. The 5-Mbps broadband version has been approved as ISO 8802/4.

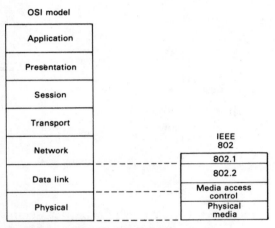

Figure 3.17   IEEE 802 in the ISO OSI model.

IEEE 802.5 is the "standardized version" of IBM's token ring. It consists of a token passing ring access method and baseband signaling on the twisted pair (both shielded and unshielded) at data rates of 4 Mbps and 16 Mbps. Note that it does not standardize any other layers of IBM's token ring networking. While it will allow users to share token ring wiring among vendors, it does not guarantee that they can communicate.

The last of the four IEEE 802 physical layer (including media access, of course) standards is 802.6, the metropolitan area network. While this committee has not yet published any standards, they have made numerous contributions to our understanding of the needs of networks that are too large to use standard LAN designs, yet small enough geographically (tens of kilometers) for high connectivity at high bandwidth to be feasible. Originally, this committee looked at using cable TV as the distribution medium; today they are investigating fiber optics.

The 802.9 working group on integrated data and voice networks is the latest addition to IEEE Project 802. It was chartered in November 1986 to develop an interface standard for desktop devices to use to connect to IEEE 802 LANs and Integrated Services Digital Networks (ISDNs). Media are restricted to twisted-pair wiring carrying both voice and data.

The two remaining IEEE 802 committees are technology consultants to the physical layer committees. 802.7 concentrates on the needs of broadband networks and develops recommended practices for broadband LANs, including unified design specifications, frequency allocation planning, and a guide on how to design, install, certify, and maintain broadband systems. 802.8 serves a similar consulting function that is looking at fiber optics networks.

Recap of Key Concepts

The dream of open systems interconnection (OSI), in which any machine from any manufacturer can just plug into a network and communicate with any other machine, is not as far fetched as some might lead you to think. After all, we can do it today with telephones and CB radios, so why not with computers? The key to OSI is layered protocols. With the ISO OSI reference model as a framework, OSI networks such as MAP/TOP are attainable and practical now.

At the same time, we must recognize how closely tied MAP/TOP is to the ISO standards work in data communications. Realistically, MAP/TOP is pushing the state of the art in standards development. The 3.0 release of MAP/TOP was delayed over a year waiting for the required standards to stabilize. Many forces shape the development of standards; MAP/TOP is neither the only force nor the most powerful. That it has come so far, so fast, is a credit to the users who have demanded OSI and have been willing to pay for it.

4

The Genesis of MAP/TOP

The previous chapter's discussion on open systems interconnection would seem to imply that there are no challenges left in computer networking. However, availability of open systems requires more than just a reference model. It requires well-defined protocol standards and a large enough market to justify the investment by vendors in the implementation of those standards. The dual nature of MAP/TOP, split between being a network architecture specification of protocol standards on one hand and a movement toward computer-integrated manufacturing on the other, is not accidental. Both aspects are critical prerequisites to success.

In this chapter, we will look at the real world MAP/TOP is struggling to influence, and the motivations driving its development. This is crucial to understanding what MAP/TOP is designed to do and recognizing areas in which it may not be appropriate. We will see how the symbiotic relationship between MAP and TOP works and how other industries are considering taking advantage of MAP/TOP's success. We will look at the stack of protocols the original MAP and TOP task forces put together for MAP 2.1/TOP 1.0, the first generally useful version of MAP/TOP. We will conclude with a discussion of the successive generations of MAP/TOP, how they relate to one another, and some of the key forces driving usable open systems today.

The Political History of MAP/TOP

Before we can talk intelligently about what MAP/TOP is and where it is going, we really need to understand where it came from. Standards are not something that occur automatically whenever someone perceives a need. Ben Franklin established the first city fire department in Philadelphia in the 18th century. Fire hose couplings in the United States were not standardized until 1904 to allow one city to help another when fighting fires. In 1948 the United States, Britain, and Canada finally agreed on a common standard for screw threads. The rest of the world took a separate course and developed an incompatible set of metric screw thread standards. Even where safety and health are directly affected, standardization can be slow. Traffic signs and signals varied from state to state in the United States according to whatever plan was adopted by the individual state legislatures. It was not until 1927 that the United States adopted a national standard. Worldwide, the shift to internationally recognized traffic signs is proceeding very slowly. Nations still cannot agree on which side of the street cars should be driven.

The development of computer networks is following the same pattern. In the absence of accepted standards, each individual manufacturer has developed its own proprietary networking architecture and protocols. IBM has SNA, DEC has DECnet, Burroughs has BNA, HP has Advance-Net, Gould has Modway, Allen-Bradley has Data Hiway. Name any computer or machine vendor and you will find it has its own network architecture. Even within a vendor, you will find that some machines cannot talk to others. That was the environment in the late 1970s when General Motors, Boeing, and other major companies started integrating the computers in their plants. GM leads the user rebellion.

General Motors was in a real predicament. Computer-integrated manufacturing plans could not be based on a proprietary network because no single vendor could come close to meeting the wide-ranging needs. At the same time, the multivendor environment required to meet equipment needs made off-the-shelf communications impossible, as no two vendors communicated decently. Roger B. Smith, chairman of GM, summed it up beautifully in August of 1984:

> We are limited in the manufacturing efficiency we can achieve by the Tower of Babel that exists among robots and other computer-aided programmable devices. Only about 15 percent of the 40,000 programmable devices in GM plants now can communicate outside their own processes. That is because each uses vendor-unique communications methods. It's as if each of these machines were speaking its own language—French, Italian, Russian, Chinese, Hungarian, or whatever. They need an interpreter. And that interpreter comes in the very costly form of custom hardware and custom software needed to interface between different processes.[1]

It did not take GM until 1984 to realize problems existed. By the end of the 1970s, over half their automation budget was going into the custom

---

[1] *Mechanical Engineering*, June 1985.

interfaces between incompatible machines. Unlike most manufacturers, GM was big enough to do something about it. In 1980 GM formed a task force, which included representation from computer and programmable device manufacturers, to develop communication standards. This required a major investment by GM in the definition and certification of a suitable network. The network architecture developed was the General Motors' Manufacturing Automation Protocol, now known as MAP 1.0. GM formally adopted the MAP plan on October 23, 1982, and issued an ultimatum. Any vendor wishing to do business with GM in the future must implement networking with MAP.

The response by computer vendors was underwhelming. GM wanted generally available, competitively priced multivendor networking. What they got instead was high-priced, custom-implemented specials developed just for bidding on GM contracts. Even the world's largest corporation did not have the clout to move mainstream vendors from business as usual with proprietary networks.

Boeing fights a similar battle

The Boeing Company began developing an architecture for internal networks in the late 1970s. The result of their work was the Boeing Network Architecture (BNA), a subset of IBM's Systems Network Architecture (SNA) suitable for interconnecting the multivendor data centers the company had distributed around the United States. While General Motors was struggling with islands of automation on the factory floor, Boeing was faced with similar problems automating the office and engineering functions. By 1980, Boeing had 45 mainframes, 400 minicomputers, and nearly 20,000 workstations and terminals from more than 85 different vendors.

Even after a management edict cutting the number of allowed vendors down to six, the objectives of BNA had to be kept to a minimum to make progress possible. They can be summarized in three rules:

- Avoid duplication of material and manual data entry between computers.

- Always think of computers as integrated systems; there are no stand-alone devices.

- Do everything possible to protect existing investments, especially in software.

The architecture was expanded in 1982 to integrate some of the office computers with the data centers. Then in 1984 it was expanded again to connect the manufacturing operation with the office computers and data-processing centers. But like General Motors, Boeing needed generally supported open networking. As long as the networks were one-of-a-kind specials, there could never be the range of services and the common availability that is required to make the computer-integrated office a reality.

NBS provides the missing link

Major manufacturers like GM and Boeing were not the only computer users looking for open systems networking. The U.S. National Bureau of Standards (NBS) was looking for a means of encouraging vendors to develop open systems to meet the networking needs of the U.S. government. At the same time, vendors were faced with a dilemma. Even if they were convinced that a market existed for open systems based on standard protocols, the protocol standards available did not guarantee interoperability. There were incompatible options allowed, and critical details were still subject to interpretation. This meant that two vendors could both implement "open systems based on standards" and their systems would be no closer to interoperability than they were with proprietary networks.

The Institute for Computer Science and Technology section of NBS attacked the problem by organizing and sponsoring the Open Systems Interconnect Implementors' Workshops. First started in 1983, their original goal was a feasibility demonstration of open systems at the November 1984 National Computer Conference. Attendees at these meetings selected the protocols to be used and worked out the implementation details required to allow interoperability. Boeing, General Motors, and other users were actively involved. Boeing cosponsored the office network demonstration with NBS while General Motors sponsored the demonstration of the factory floor network. The first demonstration of a local area network based on OSI protocols in the United States was a success.

The NCC show demonstrated more than just computer networking technology. It also demonstrated the support of vendors and users for OSI networking and its future. Participants in the Implementors' Workshop were unanimous in their desire to continue the workshops beyond the NCC show. Only one change was requested. Future workshops should be oriented toward developing salable products rather than demonstrations. Boeing and General Motors agreed to sponsor an OSI product demonstration at a future conference showing significant increases in functionality. The question of how to deal with the relationship between MAP and OSI networking in general led to the idea of an office-engineering version of MAP. The MAP steering committee asked the Boeing delegates if their company would lead that effort and provide a focus for its development. Boeing accepted and the TOP movement was begun.

The growth of MAP/TOP

While the NBS Implementors' Workshops were proving that OSI networks were feasible, General Motors continued to work to show that OSI networks could be profitable for vendors as well. Seeking out other manufacturers who had similar computer integration problems, GM showed them how the benefits of general availability of MAP would be worth the pain required to force vendors to make it generally available. With the help of McDonnell Douglas, GM recruited Ford, Chrysler, Deere, Kodak, and other companies inside and outside the automotive industry to form the MAP Users' Group in March 1984. That users' group has since grown to include membership by hundreds of manufacturing companies and related users' groups around the world. Nor has the impact been lost on computer and controller vendors. Virtually all have announced commitments to add MAP compatibility to their mainstream products.

The success of the MAP Users' Group approach to user-defined product specifications led to the formation of the TOP Users' Group in December 1985. The two users' groups merged and the first MAP/TOP Users' Group meeting was held in May 1986. The close cooperation that led to the successful demonstration of MAP/TOP in a simulated production environment at the 1985 AUTOFACT show continues today. The MAP and TOP task forces work together on common concerns and the NBS Implementors' Workshops continue to provide a neutral forum for resolving implementation issues.

MAP/TOP design objectives

The MAP Specification, Version 2.1, dated March 31, 1985, is explicit about the motivation of the early MAP designers:

> The driving force behind the General Motors MAP effort is the need for compatibility of communications to integrate the many factory floor devices. These devices are now provided by many different vendors, and it is our continued intention to use many vendors in the future. It is GM's goal to provide an environment for multiple vendors to participate on a standard communications network.
>
> It is the intention of the MAP task force to promote a multivendor network environment. In order to reduce risks and provide vendor incentive, MAP specifies existing or emerging national, international, and/or industry standards.
>
> The MAP architecture is based on the International Standards Organization (ISO) reference model for Open Systems Interconnection (OSI). Particular standards that are appropriate for our industry are specified for each layer.

Although responsibility for MAP/TOP development has expanded beyond the confines of GM, three key design objectives have not changed. First and foremost, the purpose of MAP/TOP is to bridge the islands of automation. MAP is building bridges on the factory floor while TOP builds them in office and engineering. Together, MAP/TOP builds bridges from factory floor to office to engineering to parts suppliers to banking and more. The selection of computers, workstations, or machine controls should not be dictated by which machines can talk to which. Network communications as easy to hook up as electrical power, telephone, or compressed air will make multivendor solutions to meet factory floor requirements commonplace rather than a high-cost, custom-designed option.

The second key objective is actually a desired outcome of the first. Users would like to see multivendor networking as a commodity product. The ability to pick and choose networking solutions the way you purchase steel, paper, or brake shoes today promises real financial benefits. Imagine common, compatible networking available in a competitive, low-cost mass market like that existing for personal computers. However, like the personal computer market, if what you need is not the standard, you are going to find your options severely restricted.

The third key objective is an implementation consideration. The MAP/TOP task force does not want to be in the protocol development business. It is far more effective to let the experts on the standards committees do this demanding and extremely detailed work. However, in seeking standards that meet their needs, MAP/TOP users must be willing to trade off efficiency for acceptance. Whether MAP/TOP is the correct choice for you depends on your application. Participating and investing in MAP/TOP development can help you ensure that the network defined is a good fit with your needs.

The MAP 2.1/TOP 1.0 Protocol Stack

We have already spent time discussing protocols in general and making random references to MAP 2.1/TOP 1.0. So let us take a look at just what MAP 2.1 and TOP 1.0 consist of and why they are such a significant milestone in the development of MAP/TOP. I have commented several times on the dual nature of MAP/TOP—that it is both a dream of CIM and a network architecture specification to build that dream upon. MAP 2.1/TOP 1.0 is the first version of that architecture specification suitable for use outside of General Motors. MAP 2.1- and TOP 1.0-compatible components and computers have been available since 1986 and are working their way down the learning curve. The functionality provided is minimal but enough to get many jobs done, albeit not necessarily as efficiently or as conveniently as many proprietary solutions. But if you want to use multivendor solutions, you at least have an alternative to writing your own network software.

Let us take a quick look at the services and capabilities which make up MAP 2.1/TOP 1.0 (Figure 4.1). This is only a cursory look to provide reference points for our more detailed examination in the next few chapters. We need an overview of the whole to see how the pieces fit together and how the changes in the different levels to get to MAP/TOP 3.0 are meant to work.

LAYERS	MAP 2.1 PROTOCOLS	TOP 1.0 PROTOCOLS
Layer 7 Application	ISO FTAM (DP 8571) File Transfer Protocol Manufacturing Messaging Format Standard (GM MMFS) Common Application Service Elements (MAP CASE)	ISO FTAM (DP 8571) File Transfer Protocol
Layer 6 Presentation	NULL ASCII and Binary Encoding Only	
Layer 5 Session	ISO Session (IS 8327) Kernel and Full Duplex Functional Units Only	
Layer 4 Transport	ISO Transport (IS 8073) Class 4 only	
Layer 3 Network	ISO Connectionless Internet (DIS 8473) Optional use of X.25 as a subnetwork under ISO 8473	
Layer 2 Data Link	ISO Logical Link Control (DIS 8802/2) (IEEE 802.2, Type 1, Class 1) Optional use of X.25 requires appropriate link and physical layers for X.25	
Layer 1 Physical	IEEE 802.4 Token Passing Bus Media Acess Control and IEEE 802.4 Token Passing Bus	ISO CSMA/CD (DIS 8802/3) CSMA/CD Media Access Control 10 Mbit/second Baseband Media

Figure 4.1   MAP and TOP common core of protocols.

Application layer protocols

MAP 2.1 provides three user services at the application layer: a network file transfer capability called FTAM, a simple interprocess communications capability called CASE, and a manufacturing-specific interprocess communications capability designed to make up for the lack of a presentation layer called MMFS.

The first, FTAM (File Transfer, Access, and Management) provides file transfer capabilities. It is based on a now-obsolete draft proposal version of ISO FTAM and illustrates one of the dangers of implementing to draft proposals. They do change. The MAP task force recognized the

risk at the time and deliberately chose to limit capability in order to
minimize implementation cost. They needed a file transfer mechanism
implementable in 1985. ISO FTAM and its supporting protocols were
not standardized until 1986. The functionality chosen was the minimum
required to transfer a file from one machine to another. None of the
remote file access facilities in ISO FTAM were included. The protocol
was also modified to link directly to session services. This eliminated
dependency on the ISO presentation layer protocols, which were also
still in the developmental stages.

Common Application Service Elements (CASE) is also based on the
ISO protocol of the same name, this time derived from working draft
documents. The capabilities specified are the minimum possible, providing for connection setup and release and full duplex data transfer.
Late in 1986, ISO changed the name of CASE to association control
service elements (ACSE). Although the name will be different in
MAP/TOP 3.0, the function will be the same.

The third service, Manufacturing Messaging Format Standard
(MMFS), pronounced Memphis, was developed by GM specifically for
MAP 2.1. It is an extremely powerful protocol for communications with
numerical control, programmable logic control (PLC), and robotics
applications. It provides all the features missing in MAP 2.1 because of
a lack of presentation and sophisticated session services. Its prime
disadvantage, however, is its very power. It is incompatible with the 3.0
and later versions of MAP which use the presentation and session layer
services in accordance with the ISO OSI model. Users of MMFS who
need to upgrade to the corresponding MAP 3.0 protocol will have to
rewrite their applications to the extent they utilized any of the powerful
features of MMFS not included in the MAP 3.0 replacement.

Two other protocols written by the MAP task force are provided to
allow the network to run and stay running but are not actually used by
normal users. These are a directory service for mapping meaningful
names to machine-usable addresses and a minimal network management
protocol to allow control of network operation and diagnosis of failures.

TOP 1.0 specifies MAP FTAM only. While the lack of MMFS makes
sense (how many office workers regularly converse with robots?), network management and directory services are essential for widespread use
and should be required anyway.

Presentation level

MAP 2.1/TOP 1.0 does not include a presentation protocol. As a result,
no changes in data representation are possible (except as provided by
MMFS). This restricts FTAM to simple text files and raw binary octet
stream files. Users of CASE must handle their own data conversions.

Session layer

Session services consist of the session kernel and the full duplex function unit. The session kernel provides for orderly setup and release of connections (the ability to close a connection without the loss of data). The full duplex functional unit provides for two-way simultaneous communications only. No provision is made for controlling two-way alternate (half-duplex) or one-way (simplex) interaction. No ISO-defined options such as synchronization, activities, or segmentation are supported.

Transport layer

The MAP 2.1/TOP 1.0 transport is the ISO-compatible subset of NBS Class 4 transport. It provides for connection establishment and release and for both expedited and normal data transfer. Removed from the NBS specification to allow ISO compatibility are datagram support, graceful close (provided by ISO OSI at the session layer), and status of connection reporting.

Network layer

MAP 2.1/TOP 1.0 has two services at the network layer. Internetting is provided by ISO connectionless internet protocol. This is the full ISO standard and optional functions such as padding, source routing, security, priority, quality of service maintenance, and route recording may be requested. The optional functions may not be required, however. The inactive subset of ISO connectionless internet is allowed under certain conditions for simple, isolated networks.

Also supported at the network layer is X.25 public packet switched networking for a wide area network connection between geographically separate MAP/TOP local area networks. This connection is minimal in MAP 2.1/TOP 1.0. It does not permit usage of the many optional features normally provided by X.25 suppliers. Standard X.25 services must be duplicated in the transport layer because the X.25 virtual circuit service is treated as a connectionless link.

Link layer

IEEE 802.2 class 1 service is used as the link layer protocol. This provides a multipoint peer-to-peer connectionless protocol well matched to the needs of ISO class 4 transport and ISO connectionless internet. The 48-bit option for address field length is required. The intent is for every node in every MAP/TOP network to have a unique link address of

its own, allowing easy movement of hardware from network to network
and the linking of networks via repeaters and bridges without concern
for addressing conflicts.

Physical layer

This is the other layer in which MAP and TOP differ in order to better
meet the needs of users. MAP is based on IEEE 802.4 broadband token
bus running at 10 Mbps. The 5-Mbps MAP networks frequently referenced in articles existed because of the early unavailability of 10-Mbps
modems from more than one vendor that could talk to one another.
Multivendor certified 10-Mbps modems did not become generally available until late 1986, and the 5-Mbps modems were permitted as an
interim measure.

TOP specifies IEEE 802.3, carrier sense multiple access with collision
detection, on a 10base5 cable. This is the Ethernet equivalent form of
IEEE 802.3, chosen for ease of migration from existing Ethernet-based
networks. The 10base5 cable specifies a data rate of 10 Mbps using
baseband signaling with up to 500 meters (m) between repeaters.

Development Directions

MAP and TOP network specifications always have a version number
associated with them. For example, the previous section just described
the architecture of MAP 2.1/TOP 1.0. The version numbers are defined
to indicate the compatibility of different MAP versions. The major
version number (the integer part of the specification number) specifies
major compatibility classes of MAP/TOP specifications. Different
MAP/TOP versions with the same major version number can communicate with each other, though normally restricted to the capabilities
available if both had the same version number as the lower of the two.
Thus a MAP 2.2 implementation could communicate with a MAP 2.1
node but only with MAP 2.1 capabilities. The minor version change from
2.0 to 2.1 to 2.2 signifies added capabilities that are backward compatible
with each other. Between major version numbers, such as 1.0 to 2.0 to 3.0,
the compatibility is limited to the ability to share the same broadband
cable (for 1.0 to the others) or share the same 802.4 network channel (for
2.X with 3.X). TOP 1.0 is the exception. Its compatibility corresponds to
MAP 2.1.

MAP 1.0

MAP 1.0 actually refers to the second version of the original MAP
specification, released April 18, 1984. It was a major rewrite of the
original 1982 specification and added several appendices explaining how

it was supposed to work. It was installed in a very limited number of GM plants and was demonstrated at the 1984 National Computer Conference (NCC). This conference is often credited with changing the perception of MAP from being an onerous GM procurement specification to its current status as the foundation of computer-integrated manufacturing.

MAP 2.0

MAP 2.0, published on February 2, 1985, moved MAP over to standard protocols for all the lower layers. Installed in a few GM pilot installations, it is known today simply as the starting point for the 2.X compatibility class. Like MAP 1.0, it has never been commercially available.

MAP 2.1

MAP 2.1 marks the first "real" MAP specification. Consisting of compatible extensions to 2.0, it added the missing pieces of directory service and network management that allowed the implementation of useful networks. The 1985 AUTOFACT demonstration was implemented to this specification, allowing many of the "missing pieces" to be discovered and ironed out before any major vendors had nonconforming products in the marketplace.

The MAP 2.1 errata, about 200 pages long, documents all the fixes made to get the AUTOFACT demonstration to work. Considered a correcting and clarifying of the original printing, it is not known to contain any technical changes except for clarification of ambiguities and matching what was actually implemented at AUTOFACT in 1985. The MAP 2.1 errata have since been published as the MAP 2.1.A specification and incorporated in a combined release as part of the MAP 2.2 specification document.

TOP 1.0

The original TOP specification was sponsored by Boeing Computer Services and first published in November 1985. TOP 1.0 was designed to allow access to MAP networks from office and technical computers, an early deficiency in MAP recognized at the 1984 NCC demonstration. TOP 1.0 provides file transfer to and from MAP 2.1 systems connected via bridges or intermediate systems. No enhancements are planned that would be compatible with MAP 2.X.

MAP 2.2

Designed to provide a compatible growth path for MAP 2.1 networks, MAP 2.2 adds several key cost and performance enhancements to MAP

2.1. Originally scheduled to be published in early 1986, it suffered multiple delays as one little problem after another needed to be fixed before release. While frustrating, most of the delays were caused by conservatism on the part of the developers as they tried out different parts of the specifications before committing to them. Since there will not be a major multivendor demonstration for 2.2 like there was for 2.1 or will be for 3.0, this conservatism was justified even though it delayed release until fall of 1986.

The big changes in MAP 2.2 are the carrierband alternative to broadband and the Enhanced Performance Architecture (EPA). Carrierband has the potential to halve the cost of connecting to a small MAP segment but has been the source of many of the delays as engineers at Kodak found some corner cases which did not fit the specification. The EPA provides for real-time network response. The miniMAP extension to EPA allows a network connection requiring minimal memory and hardware for very low-end controllers, sensors, and the like. We will discuss the EPA and miniMAP in the next section.

MAP 2.2 also includes a new appendix on application level naming and addressing and more detail on bridges and their use in MAP. Other items originally planned for MAP 2.2 have been postponed until the MAP 3.0 release.

MAP 3.0

MAP 3.0 marks the incompatible leap from the draft proposal protocol subsets used in MAP 2.X to international standard protocols for all seven layers. This has been the target of the MAP/TOP/OSI movement from the first. Progression through a series of 3.X releases can be foreseen as capabilities such as security, concurrency control, and database are developed, refined, and added to the standard. However, for the first time in the history of MAP, its future is not overshadowed by plans for an incompatible move to a next generation.

Delays in the development of stable international standards have directly affected the availability of MAP 3.0. Originally scheduled for publication in mid-1986, the MAP/TOP 3.0 specifications were not ready for publication until June 1987. Commercial availability of products based on MAP/TOP 3.0 is expected in 1988 following an exposition of MAP/TOP 3.0 products planned for early in the year. Rather than a feasibility demonstration of prototypes as was done for MAP 2.1/TOP 1.0, it will feature actual products functioning in simulated work environments.

While many users may be disappointed by the delays affecting MAP 3.0 availability, most will find the services provided well worth the waiting. The MAP 3.0 service selection is superior, even compared to many proprietary networks. The experience of early pioneers with MAP 2.1 and TOP 1.0 has been put to good use. Their experience has not only affected what services were selected but also how they are provided. Included in 3.0 will be standard programming interfaces to services so that user applications implemented on one machine can be easily moved to others.

All services in MAP 2.1 except MMFS are available in MAP 3.0. FTAM is enhanced with remote file access features and improved file management. The interface to CASE is extended to allow access to more of its capabilities. Network management and directory services are also expanded but not as much as desired because the international standards for them are still under development. The only major incompatibility from the user application perspective is the move from the MMFS standard for manufacturing messaging to RS-511. This move has the potential to force applications writers who do not plan ahead to literally throw out their MAP 2.1 applications and start over if they want to migrate to MAP 3.0. How to avoid this unpleasant situation is covered in Chapter 5.

Major new application services for MAP 3.0 are Computer Graphics Metafile (CGM) and Initial Graphics Exchange Specification (IGES) for graphics data exchange. Inside the network layer there are improvements to the routing specifications and more efficient use of X.25 links. Finally, a broadband cable plant planning, installation, and maintenance guide has been added.

TOP 3.0

The TOP partner for MAP 3.0 is TOP 3.0. Only the second TOP release, it has been designated TOP 3.0 to emphasize the partnership of MAP/TOP 3.0. Like TOP 1.0, TOP 3.0 differs from its MAP partner only where absolutely necessary to meet the unique needs of office workers and engineers. For example, supported cable plants are IEEE 802.3 and 802.5 as well as 802.4 and the factory floor-only Manufacturing Messaging protocol is not included. Common MAP/TOP 3.0 protocol specifications ensure smooth communications between office and manufacturing floor. MAP 3.0 application layer services included in TOP 3.0 are FTAM, CGM, IGES, network management, and directory service.

TOP 3.0 is the first release of TOP that can effectively implement fundamental office services. Unlike TOP 1.0, TOP 3.0 will include services not found in MAP. Basic Class Virtual Terminal (VT-B) allows interactive remote computer access. X.400 Message Handling Systems (MHS) provides electronic mail service. Office Document Architectures (ODA) for characters, graphics, and facsimile in processible, formatted, and processible formatted form allow complex documents to be generated, shared, and modified by multiple users.

Network connectivity is enhanced by the addition of media alternatives to 10base5 802.3, including broadband 802.3 and token ring 802.5. User applications portability is provided by specification of the Graphical Kernel System (GKS) for two-dimensional graphics. TOP 3.0 elevates TOP from its original status as a subordinate of MAP to a full-capability office network which can justify its own existance. Outside the manufacturing world, it meets the needs of service and retail industry users ranging from govenment agencies to insurance and banking. Inside or outside the manufacturing world, it provides an OSI alternative to the proprietary and de facto multivendor networks currently required for office automation.

Enhanced Performance Architecture

The Enhanced Performance Architecture (EPA), a reaction to the complexity of the ISO OSI seven-layer architecture, was introduced in MAP 2.2. Founded on the premise that the protocol overhead of presentation, session, transport, and network layers is incompatible with the needs of real-time control and low-cost, minimal function controllers, the EPA eliminates them and directly connects the application layer to the link layer. While this may seem extreme, it works if the link layer protocol is upgraded to a confirmed single-frame service. (Single-frame service used to be called "reliable datagram service" before ISO replaced the datagram-virtual circuit terminology with connection-connectionless.)

The key that makes the EPA functional is a simple restriction; the source and destination application layer peers must be on the same LAN segment and therefore able to communicate directly at the link level (i.e., they must be adjacent nodes). Since they are adjacent, the network layer is not required for routing, so it may be discarded. If we provide a reliable link level service (as is done in EPA), there is no need for the transport layer to duplicate that capability, so we may discard that layer. As currently used in MAP/TOP, all the session layer does is map application associations onto transport connections. Since we are keeping the architecture simple, we can do away with multiplexing multiple associations onto a single connection and can discard the session layer as well. This is not a real loss, as low-cost nodes will probably only have one application entity to associate with in the first place. Finally, because of the tightly coupled application environment, the expectation is that the transfer syntax used to communicate is well known by both applications. This allows elimination of the presentation layer.

Putting it all together gives the architectures in Figure 4.2. MAP/EPA on the left would normally be the cell controller, while the miniMAP architecture on the right would be used in the low-cost controllers.

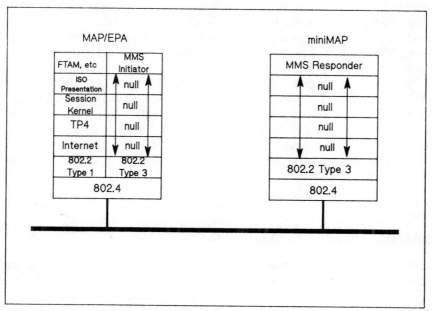

Figure 4.2   MAP/EPA.and miniMAP architectures.

MAP/EPA

The MAP/EPA architecture provides the best of both worlds (except possibly cost). The EPA side provides rapid response time for short, high-priority messages while the MAP side retains all the normal capabilities of MAP/TOP. Useful wherever there is the memory and computing power available to support both stacks, the architecture provides easy connection to existing Proway plant networks as well as supporting low-cost miniMAP nodes on the same LAN segment.

The protocol makes sense on cell controllers, robots, large PLCs, and numerical controllers. For process control cells, it makes sense for only the cell controller to support the MAP/EPA architecture, providing low-cost in-cell communications and a gateway for miniMAP nodes to communicate outside the local cell. The architecture is compatible with both broadband and carrierband cabling systems.

MiniMAP

The miniMAP architecture is just the EPA side of the MAP/EPA architecture. It provides rapid responses for short, high-priority messages. However, that is all it provides. Aimed at the needs of dumb devices such as sensors and low-end controllers for simple, low-cost connection, it provides just that to adjacent miniMAP and MAP/EPA nodes only. A MAP/EPA gateway is required to communicate outside the local segment. MiniMAP is almost always associated with carrierband cabling for minimum cost.

Chief disadvantages, aside from the limited connectivity, are the 1024-octet maximum message size and limited network management support. On the other hand, it does connect easily to existing Proway networks. Most important, of course, is price. Primary usage will be in small, cell-sized networks for process control. It is not a general-purpose solution, however, so trying to use it as one will be frustrating and probably unsuccessful.

Other OSI Efforts

Lest anyone think that the MAP/TOP Users' Group is the only force driving the development of open systems, I would like to finish this chapter by mentioning some of the other organizations contributing to the development of MAP/TOP today.

National Bureau of Standards

The National Bureau of Standards (of the United States) does more than just develop standards for the U.S. government. They also run the Workshop Series for Implementors of OSI Protocols mentioned in the beginning of this chapter. These workshops meet every few months and bring together future users and potential suppliers of OSI networks. The process they follow is to start with the specifications given in various standards and to develop an understanding of what the protocols really need to do. The output is agreement on implementation and testing particulars, such as which options will be used, resolution of ambiguities in translating the abstract specification into a concrete implementation, and how to test two implementations for interoperability.

Participation in the workshops is strictly voluntary, and no corporate commitment is associated with participation. However, some events associated with the workshops do require commitment, for example, the

1984 National Computer Conference demonstration of office multivendor networking and the 1985 AUTOFACT demonstration of MAP and TOP.

The implementation agreements reached at the workshop are an integral part of the MAP and TOP specifications. For example, the TOP 1.0 specification precedence in the event of incompleteness in protocol option or parameter specifications is first the MAP 2.1 document (for common protocols), second the NBS OSI Implementors' Agreements, and last the ISO protocol specification(s) themselves.

The implementation agreements are used outside of MAP and TOP as well. NBS has developed the OSINET, a cooperative network for implementors to use for test development, prototype testing, and demonstrations. Protocols covered by implementation agreements are listed in Figure 4.3. New protocols are added whenever there is sufficient interest.

ISO File Transfer, Access, and Management
CCITT 400 Series Recommendations for Message Handling
    Facility
CCITT and ISO Directory Service Protocol
ISO Session Protocol
ISO Transport Classes 4 and 10 and Connectionless Protocols
ISO Connectionless Internetwork Protocol
Network Dependent Convergence Sublayer Protocol between
    X.25 and ISO Connectionless IP
CCITT Recommendation X.25
X.25 Packet Layer Protocol to Support the Connection-
    Oriented Network Service
Private Subnetworks
IEEE 802.2 Logical Link Control
IEEE 802.3 CSMA/CD Access Method
IEEE 802.4 Token Bus Access Method

Figure 4.3 Protocols covered by NBS OSI implementation agreements.

Corporation for Open Systems

A nonprofit organization with a planned annual budget of over $10 million, the Corporation for Open Systems (COS) has been called the most significant development for OSI since publication of the ISO OSI model. Although it was not officially formed until January 1986, the 17 founding companies had been meeting for at least a year before, planning its organization and objectives. Initially membership was limited to North American manufacturers and OEMs of networking products. However, by the summer of 1986, it had expanded to include users and companies worldwide.

The basic purpose of COS is to promote United States support of ISO OSI and Integrated Services Digital Network (ISDN) standards so that different brands of computers can communicate with one another and to establish a single, consistent set of tests and certification methods to ensure that they actually do. They plan to concentrate first on CCITT X.400 (message handling) and ISO FTAM. Their goals are to establish and demonstrate testing capability for those two protocols, refine the NBS implementation agreements to make interoperability easier to attain, and develop a practical test methodology to confirm that inter-operability. This is expected to lead to the availability of "production" test facilities for FTAM and X.400 by 1988, allowing member companies to offer "guaranteed interoperable" FTAM and X.400 products.

Clearly these goals parallel those of the MAP/TOP community. The intent is not to duplicate the MAP/TOP effort but rather to expand it with the development of testing capabilities for the general-purpose protocols useful to all computer users. Interoperability of FTAM and X.400 also provides interoperability of supporting layers, such as pre-sentation, session, transport, and network. This allows the MAP/TOP teams to concentrate on the unique aspects of their specifications, such as manufacturing messaging and product data exchange.

European efforts

Europe has generally been far ahead of the United States in developing open systems. The reasons are many and varied. National pride in national companies competing with IBM leads to national requirements for open systems with the force of law. Government ownership of post, telephone, and telegraph offices provided government-sanctioned incentives for using X.25 public data networking. Support for open systems and standards in general has been stronger there than in the United States.

Examples of the kinds of efforts going on in Europe to promote open systems are the Intercept Strategy and the European Programme to Harmonize the Use of Standards. The Intercept Strategy was developed by the Department of Trade and Industry of Britain. Originally published in 1983, it is intended to identify and promote draft standards as they evolve. It is also aimed at broadening the range of standards development to application areas not currently covered. The European Programme to Harmonize the Use of Standards is focused on OSI standardization. Its goal is for every European country to publish identical functional standards, eliminating local differences from country to country and simplifying the task of providing compatible communications throughout Europe.

Recap of Key Issues

MAP has grown far beyond its initial status as a General Motors procurement specification. Partly as a result of that growth its progress is slowing considerably. It still remains the prime example of a successful user-driven standard and has radically changed the view of the standards community toward users. As a user yourself, you must keep in mind that MAP/TOP reflects the needs of General Motors, Boeing, and all the other users and vendors contributing to its development. It is up to you to ensure that it meets your needs. This can be either passive—verifying that the standards meet your needs before you select them—or active—joining the MAP/TOP Users' Group and working to shape the standards as they evolve to meet your needs as well.

5

Application Layer Services

The preceding chapters have been devoted to developing a general understanding of networking and MAP/TOP in the context of the ISO OSI reference model. Now that we have the "big picture" it is time to zoom in on the details of MAP/TOP. In this chapter we will examine the specific services accessible to the user and application writer. We will concentrate on the capabilities available in MAP 2.1 and how they evolve with the move to MAP/TOP 3.0. Chapter 6 will describe the intermediate layers as defined in MAP/TOP, while Chapters 7 and 8 will look at the physical layer specifics of MAP and TOP, respectively.

Common Application Service Elements (CASE)

The ISO Common Application Service Elements provide the basic network interprocess communication services needed by typical application layer services. The fundamental capability provided by CASE is association control, the ability to link up with a process on another system and communicate effectively. A key extension to CASE, called Commitment, Concurrency, and Recovery (CCR), provides for automatic recovery from any crashes or other catastrophes that occur in the process of utilizing an association.

Association control

The core service provided by CASE is association control, also called CASE Kernel or Association Control Service Elements (ACSE). It provides the ability to set up a communications association between two processes independent of the location or implementation of either. This is the minimum network interprocess communications capability required to develop distributed applications on diverse, autonomous computers. Association control provides the mechanism to allow application processes to communicate in a meaningful way. It ensures that the two application processes are the ones which actually want to communicate and that they are doing so in a relevant context.

Association control provides the means of identifying the remote application process by name. While the presentation layer ensures that data representations are understandable by both application processes, it is up to association control to make sure that they are meaningful by maintaining the context for interpreting the data at each end. That is, the presentation layer provides an ability to transfer times and dates and numbers, and the association control keeps track of whether the time and date sent is part of a transaction setting the time to start an operation or should be interpreted as part of a command updating the local time.

Consider a Numerical Controller (NC) driving a milling machine. When communicating with the cell controller, association control assures that the NC is talking to the application process in the cell controller for milling machines. Both must agree on the same coordinate axes and dimensional units. The association control between the cell controller and a factory floor host would be more challenging. Here the two parties must agree that they are talking milling machine data and not lathe or robot commands. If lathe data needed to be exchanged as well, an association for the lathe context could be set up to prevent possible confusion.

Commitment, Concurrency, and Recovery (CCR)

Association control provides the base-level common application service elements. However, many applications share common needs above and beyond simple association control. The most common of these is the need to recover and reliably complete transactions interrupted by system failures. This need is met by the CASE optional extension for Commitment, Concurrency, and Recovery.

Aimed at meeting the needs of applications such as distributed database, remote job control, and transaction processing, CCR provides the facilities required for synchronizing distributed operations. Chief among these are coordinated logging and backup. By sharing synchronization points, the application processes at each end can agree on how far to back up in the event of a failure and can safely restart operations after a system crash at either end or inside the network.

The underlying objective for CASE is to provide those application-level capabilities required by most applications. This relieves the standards developers and implementers from the drudgery of reinventing the underlying services required to provide each high-level service. As applications develop in sophistication and complexity, we can expect to see additional protocols added to the standards arsenal to handle the common elements of required services.

MAP 2.1 CASE

MAP 2.1 specifies a subset of ISO CASE association control to provide a user-accessible general-purpose network interprocess communications facility. The subset defined is intended to ensure upward compatibility of applications written to utilize it. The application implementor should be able to isolate the application from protocol changes in CASE as the standard evolves and new capabilities are added. This includes the transition from MAP 2.X to MAP/TOP 3.0. MAP 2.1 includes a recommendation on the application interface to CASE to help ensure compatibility with planned enhancements.

The MAP 2.1 CASE restricts the user to four CASE services. These are association establishment, normal release of an association, abnormal release of an association, and information transfer. Association establishment provides for setting up the association between two application processes. Both normal and abnormal release of an association provide a means of terminating an established association. The difference is that a normal release insures that no information is lost in the process, whereas abnormal release can result in loss of information in transit. The reason for having abnormal release is to handle those situations in which cooperation of both sides cannot be counted on, as when the network connection between the two processes is lost or the application process on one machine has crashed and cannot be depended upon to complete the necessary handshaking to ensure data integrity before releasing the association. Information transfer itself provides a straight pipe down to session layer (there is no presentation layer in MAP 2.1).

MAP 2.1-recommended CASE function calls

While MAP 2.1 does not specify an actual interface to MAP 2.1 CASE, it does recommend one based on 12 function calls defined in the programming language C. Contrary to popular belief, using C to develop an application does not automatically provide for portability from machine to machine. However, as a commonly available system programming language, C aids application portability provided the code is designed, written, and tested to be portable. The recommended interface is interesting because it clearly shows how the services specified by the CASE service standard are mapped into functional protocol implementations:

ACTIVATE **(name, service).** The ACTIVATE call is required before any other CASE functions are called. It allocates resources within the CASE implementation for the particular user process issuing the call. It allows the user process to identify itself by name (or an alias) to the MAP/TOP network. The SERVICE parameter is for future expansion. Currently the only service available is data transfer service. The actual resource allocation is done based on the operating system's unique process ID for the process and is implementation dependent. That, combined with the lack of a "deactivate" function, means that the only way to modify the initial declaration is to kill the user process and start over with a new user process.

CONNECT **(destination, service, options) and** ANSWER **(service, info, timeout).** These two calls provide the ability to set up an association. To function, the calling user process must issue a CONNECT that matches an ANSWER issued by the destination user process. Either call may be issued first; however, only the ANSWER call has a timeout that is programmable.

The ANSWER call tells the MAP/TOP network that the user process is available for an association. The MAP 2.1 interface restricts the user process to only one outstanding ANSWER at a time. The SERVICE and TIMEOUT parameters are self-explanatory. The only available service is data transfer. The timeout is how long to wait (forever is a valid option) for a remote process to issue a CONNECT to associate with you. The INFO parameter is the interesting one. This is a catchall for any useful information provided by the calling user process. It includes the name (or alias) used by the calling process, the name the caller thinks you have, the name of the context desired, and a password in case you want to verify access.

The CONNECT call performs a number of functions. It starts by using the directory name service to find the complete network address for the destination you specified in the NAME parameter. You can also provide the fields (your name, context desired, the name of the process you want to associate with, and any password required) to be passed on to the called user in the INFO structure as discussed above for ANSWER. Note that MAP 2.1 CASE does not provide any context services, so the context field is ignored.

From the viewpoint of the ISO model, the CONNECT call causes the construction of an association request PDU, issues a session connection request primitive including the association request PDU as user data, and waits for the response. Before issuing the session connection confirm primitive, CASE will analyze its peer's association response PDU (returned as user data with the session connection response) and update the user process INFO structure, along with informing the user process of the outcome (success or failure) of the association request.

DISCONNECT **(channel) and** ABORT **(channel).**   These two function calls illustrate the two different ways of terminating an association or connection. DISCONNECT provides a subset of what is commonly called a negotiated, or graceful, close. A full-featured negotiated close is like bringing a telephone conversation to a close. One person will say there is nothing left to discuss. The other party to the conversation can disagree, asking further questions or expanding on the current answers. Only after both parties agree they are done do they hang up. The MAP 2.1 interface does not allow the peer user to disagree with hanging up. Indeed, MAP 2.1 requires the peer user to immediately stop talking, even if in the middle of a transaction requiring multiple sends, and hang up. What the MAP 2.1 version does guarantee is that any data already turned over to the network for delivery will be delivered before the association is dissolved.

The ABORT function call, on the other hand, does exactly what its name implies. It causes immediate, unconditional termination of the association. Any messages in transit or awaiting delivery are discarded, and resources tied to the association aborted are freed up. Using our telephone analogy, it is like hanging up without saying goodbye first. The action is immediate and irrevocable. While all user programs must be written to handle the other side aborting, as a network problem could force the underlying layers to abort both ends of the association, it is usually cleaner to use DISCONNECT to terminate an ongoing association. Exceptions would be when you do not have time to wait for your remote peer process to respond or you have reason to believe that the remote peer process is hung and never will respond. In either case, any data or messages sent that have not been explicitly or implicitly acknowledged by the remote user process must be regarded as potentially lost. The ABORT command invalidates the message integrity guarantees that are normally provided by the connection-oriented CASE data transfer service.

SEND **(channel, size, end, data, timeout) and** RECEIVE **(channel, size, info, data, timeout).**   The actual data transfer is provided by the SEND and RECEIVE function calls. As in the DISCONNECT and ABORT calls above, the CHANNEL tells CASE which association the function call refers to. The END (of message) parameter in SEND allows the sending of stream data.

The user can build a long message to send to the remote peer without the overhead of passing a single huge message buffer to CASE. Instead, longer messages can be built up piece by piece and delivered as a logical unit to the remote peer, which can then accept the message piece by piece at its own pace, without losing the knowledge that it is all one message.

The SIZE parameter refers to the number of octets of data in a SEND call or the desired number of octets of data in a RECEIVE call. The INFO and DATA parameters in the RECEIVE call are pointers to data structures that can be used to return information (the end of message flag using INFO and the data itself using DATA). The usage of pointers as parameters is an artifact of the C language used to define the interface, not a communications requirement for ISO CASE.

CHKIO **(channel, action, info)**, WSEVENT **(event, timeout)**, WANDEVENT **(events, timeout)**, WOREVENT **(events, timeout), and** CHKEVENT **(event).** MAP 2.1 also defines asynchronous versions of the CONNECT, ANSWER, SEND, and RECEIVE functions. These allow the user process to continue with other processing while the network is carrying out the requested actions. Control and monitoring of these asynchronous tasks is provided by the above five function calls. CHKIO allows the user process to determine the status of any particular action (CONNECT, ANSWER, SEND, or RECEIVE). WSEVENT, WANDEVENT, and WOREVENT provide the ability to wait for a particular event to occur, wait until several events have all occurred, or wait until any of several events have occurred. The last function call, CHKEVENT, is provided to allow the user to determine what events have occurred, especially after a wait using WOREVENT.

Moving to MAP/TOP 3.0 ACSE

The MAP 2.1 interface specification for CASE places a number of requirements on the using application process. MAP/TOP 3.0 includes a more extensive applications interface to ACSE. It does not impose any restrictions on the user application other than those already in MAP 2.1. All services provided by the MAP 2.1 interface are available from the MAP/TOP 3.0 version. The main change in the MAP/TOP 3.0 interface is access to ACSE capabilities that a 2.1 application must provide for itself. However, a 2.1 application ported over to 3.0 can continue to provide for itself and to ignore the added capabilities of the 3.0 interface.

Let us look first at those considerations that will not change, even with a move to MAP/TOP 3.0. First and foremost, security is an application responsibility. MAP 2.1 CASE provides an optional password field that the remote application can use to verify the identity of the calling process. Perhaps in MAP/TOP 3.X we will see some simple authentication mechanisms. Even then, any application that really cares about the identity of using processes will still provide its own security. The protection provided by ACSE is not designed to withstand deliberate subversion.

Two other considerations which will not change are the need for a user process to be able to handle an abort indication from ACSE and the ability to have multiple incarnations of the same application process. The former we discussed above in the paragraph describing the ABORT function call. The latter is a natural outgrowth of the UNIX environment assumed in a C-language definition.

An upgrade of the user application interface to ACSE will eliminate several restrictions currently in the MAP 2.1 definition. In the association establishment phase, MAP 2.1 has no provisions for an application to refuse a connection request. If the application does not want to associate with a remote process, it can only clear the channel by answering the request and then releasing or aborting the channel. With MAP/TOP 3.0 this will no longer be required. The user process will be able to refuse an association based on the identity of the calling party or for any other reason. Of course, there is no reason why an application must refuse to answer a call rather than continue in the manner of MAP 2.1, answer, and hang up. Also involved with the association establishment phase is the inability of a MAP 2.1 CASE interface user to have more than one application title associated with the user for the life of the user's process. This restriction, too, should go away in 3.0.

When and if commitment, concurrency and recovery are added to MAP/TOP, several other restrictions in MAP 2.1 CASE will be eliminated. In the MAP 2.1 CASE interface, data is always treated as a stream, and once it is delivered to the user process, it is no longer controlled by CASE. The only way one user process can know that the other user process has completed a transaction is by explicit or implicit acknowledgment from that other user process. Any rollback or resynchronization in the event of failure is strictly up to the user applications. The addition of CCR will provide tools to coordinate rollback and resynchronization. The availability of negotiated and nonnegotiated checkpoints means that the network service will preserve data even after delivery to allow backing up to the last agreed-upon checkpoint if a failure should occur.

File Transfer, Access, and Management (FTAM)

The only service included in MAP 2.1 which does not specifically require the user to write programs to use it is network file transfer. This facility, based on ISO FTAM, allows the user to take a file on one machine and copy it onto another machine. This could be the transfer of a new part design from engineering to an NC machine on the factory floor, reprogramming robots over the network rather than hand carrying new programs with a bubble memory loader, or distributing work orders from corporate headquarters to the various manufacturing divisions. Network file transfer can be used anytime information in the form of a file on one machine (or information that can be put into file form) needs to be moved to another machine. The file can be a program, production data, work orders, sales orders, or anything else.

ISO FTAM

ISO FTAM (File Transfer, Access, and Management) reached draft international standard status late in 1986. As the name implies, the standard covers not only the needs of network file transfer but also those of remote file access. The protocol is based on the concept of a "virtual file store." The FTAM protocol on the user's machine maps the user's requests, specified in terms of the user's local machine's file system, into the network standard representation of a file system, the virtual file store. The FTAM protocol at the other end, where the file actually resides, then translates the network standard file requests into the system-dependent file operations required to physically access the file. While this may seem unnecessarily complex (why not just map directly from the user's file system to the server's file system?), it keeps the protocol finite as we increase the number of user and server file systems supported. Each system implementing FTAM needs to implement only two translations, one from virtual file store to local and a second from local file store to virtual, regardless of how many other FTAM implementations on disparate file systems are on the network. The alternative, usually seen in proprietary implementations because it provides higher performance, is an implementation nightmare that increases with the square of the number of file systems to be supported.

Like most ISO application protocols, ISO FTAM depends on ISO presentation services and ISO ACSE/CCR for its implementation. Indeed, the dependency is so strong that all three were put out to ballot together so that any changes required in one could be reflected in the other two as necessary.

The full ISO FTAM provides a truly machine-independent network file transfer service. A file can be moved from one machine to another without loss of structure or data content as long as the receiving machine is capable of representing the structure or data. This is not always the case. For example, UNIX has a very simple file system that supports only two file types, binary (a stream of octets with no structure other than total number of octets) and ASCII (text lines of arbitrary length, delineated by new lines). The UNIX file system has no way of preserving the structure of a file with records composed of 128 binary words with 36 bits in each word. Similarly, a machine which only supports 32-bit single-precision floating point numbers will degrade data originally consisting of 64-bit double-precision floating point, which it has no way of representing meaningfully.

The remote file access capability provided by FTAM is intended for those applications which do not need or want to move the entire file but rather want to leave it in place and just access it as if it were a local file. This may be due to a desire to keep all users working with the same data, as with several designers sharing common parts data, or to physical restrictions on local storage, as with small machines accessing large files or shop floor machines in an environment too harsh for magnetic storage media to survive.

The specific access capabilities provided by FTAM are those normally used when working with files. The user can retrieve, overwrite, or insert data anywhere inside an existing file. Similarly, the user can append data to an existing file or delete one. Combined with the ability to create files and manage files, discussed in the next paragraph, a user can do just about any operation on a remote file that is available locally. Even if the translations to and from virtual file store are not the most efficient on a record-by-record basis, many applications can be performed more efficiently overall than if it were necessary to move large files around the network and keep them all up to date.

The final aspect of FTAM is that of file management. ISO has included in this category such capabilities as creating new files, specifying their attributes, inspecting and changing file properties, naming and renaming files, and controlling ownership and access rights. The classification of a function as access, transfer, or management makes little difference to the user. It is the combination of the three to provide the capabilities normally associated with a local file store that counts.

MAP 2.1/TOP 1.0 FTAM

The TOP 1.0 FTAM is the MAP 2.1 specification, which is based on the second draft proposal for ISO FTAM (ISO 8571) and the NBS Implementation Agreements for Open Systems Interconnection Protocols. It provides for file transfer and limited file management only. Only two types of files may be transferred: raw binary, consisting of a stream of binary octets with no embedded structure, and simple text, consisting of variable length lines up to 250 ASCII characters (7-bit printable characters only) with each line terminated by an ASCII carriage return and line feed pair (not included in the 250-character limit).

Within the contextual limitations, the user can create or delete a file on a remote system, transfer a local file to an existing remote file entirely replacing any data already there, transfer a remote file to an existing local file entirely replacing any existing data, and read the attributes of a remote file. While this may seem like minimal capabilities compared to the current FTAM standard, it is enough to get a file from one machine to the next. For example, one procedure to copy a local file up to a remote host would be to read the attributes of the destination file on the remote host to see if it already exists, create an empty file with the desired attributes if the destination file did not exist, and finally perform the actual transfer of data.

File attribute agreements

The specific capabilities of MAP 2.1 FTAM are given by the NBS/OSI implementation agreements covering Phase 1 FTAM implementation. These cover features ranging from valid file names to how to tell the length of a file. The only extension required by MAP 2.1 is that "transferred" files must be stored so as to be accessible by local users (provided, of course, that they have appropriate access permission) and that local files be transparently available for transfer (again, subject to any security provisions). Since this is our first contact with the implementation agreements, let us look at the kinds of issues they cover.

File name.   The ISO FTAM minimum range for a file name must be supported. This consists of from one to eight characters from a specified (and fairly limited) character set. No maximum length or specific format is required; therefore, implementors are free to extend the file name structures supported to include any local features (e.g., directory trees, passwords, longer names, additional valid characters, multipart names, etc.). Although extensions are allowed, they are not required. An implementation may reject any extensions beyond the minimum requirement.

Access structure.   The only file structure supported is unstructured. No concept of record structure is provided.

Presentation context.   Two presentation contexts are supported, one for text and the other for binary data. Text format is that defined by VARCRLF. It consists of variable-length lines with each line terminated by a carriage return and line feed pair of symbols. All lines must be terminated and none may exceed 250 characters (not including the terminator pair). The use of carriage return or line feed symbols is forbidden except as part of the terminator pair. The ISO 646-character set (a 7-bit ASCII definition) will be used.

The binary presentation context is a totally transparent one. The file is considered a single stream of octets, with no structure or meaning attributed to it. Any interpretation of the meaning of individual or groups of octets is strictly up to user applications. In other words, whatever bits go in at one end come out at the other.

File size. Even though there is no file structure supported, the definition of file size follows the ISO FTAM three-part specification. It consists of a definition of unit size in octets, specification of the number of units, and the difference between the exact size and that determined from the size and number of units. The specification of future file size is optional (a potential problem with file systems which preallocate file space).

Requested access. The file activities which are supported in the definition of file access are read, replace, read attribute, and delete. Note that there is no ability to write or change file attributes. The burden is on the implementor to provide for reasonable defaults that allow a transferred file to be useful.

User considerations

If you plan to develop applications based on MAP 2.1 FTAM, you need to be aware of a number of side effects of the specification of FTAM for MAP 2.1. These affect how your application accesses FTAM and what the limitations on that access are.

The only FTAM which can communicate with MAP 2.1/TOP 1.0 FTAM is MAP 2.1/TOP 1.0 FTAM. Between MAP 2.1 FTAM implementations, there can also be minor differences. Even though the specification requires that FTAM requests not be refused if an NBS/OSI implementation agreement optional parameter is not present, the defaults assigned in the parameter's absence will depend on the particular implementation. Since all MAP/TOP specification and NBS agreement optional parameters are required to be supported if requested, it is safest to specify all options rather than leave it up to the local implementation to default them. In other words, do not assume that the FTAM implementation on all machines will make the same default assumptions that the FTAM implementation you developed the application on originally made.

Two key missing capabilities in MAP 2.1 FTAM are concurrency and failure recovery. There are no provisions for controlling access to a file by multiple users except for whatever local controls are in place. Two users can write the same file with neither learning that only one of them succeeded (the other was overwritten by the second writer). This will affect applications which need to read the file, modify it, and then write out the new version. Like some of the operating systems it must run on, MAP 2.1 FTAM has no provision for locking the file. A second user can read the file (before the first user has written it out), modify it, and write its new version right over the changes made by the first user.

Failure recovery, the other key missing feature, means that the impact of any failures is unpredictable. If a failure occurs while a file transfer is in progress, there is no telling what state the destination file is in. It could be nonexistent, it could be completely transferred. More likely it will be somewhere in between. The exact state is up to the implementor of FTAM on the particular machine and the capabilities of the local operating system. The NBS OSI implementation agreements strongly recommend (but do *not* require) that at a minimum the file be left in a state in which further remote operations are possible. However, even that may not be true. You will need to verify implementation details with all FTAM vendors involved in the application to determine what steps your application can use for recovery. Even then, for application writers who cannot guarantee the environment they will be running in, you need to assume the worst and have a strategy for dealing with a file which you can neither access nor delete. That is, one which is consuming the file name you want to use but not letting you use it.

MAP 2.1 to MAP/TOP 3.0 migration

MAP/TOP 3.0 uses the ISO DIS FTAM, which is implemented above ACSE and presentation services. Although still not full ISO FTAM, MAP/TOP 3.0 does add file access and additional file management capability. Applications which use MAP 2.1/TOP 1.0 FTAM should migrate easily, as all the old services are included in the MAP/TOP 3.0 version. Except for changes in the access interface, the biggest difference is that applications will no longer have to do everything for themselves (although they still have the option of doing so). There are more file types available, so file format conversions by the user application will be required less frequently. The same is true of presentation contexts. Users will not have to provide as many of their own character set transform routines or worry about converting binary number representations or any of the other functions the presentation layer can handle automatically. However, rollback and recovery were not included in MAP/TOP 3.0 and will continue to be a user-application responsibility.

Do expect to see a strong push to upgrade to MAP/TOP 3.0. The added capabilities make possible many applications which would have to be programmed using CASE in MAP 2.1. First and foremost is the addition of remote file access capability, but that is not all. The ability to move data smoothly between machines with different representations will have a major impact, particularly in the international applications which require extensions to ASCII to allow for characters not used by English speakers such as ü, ç, or é.

The addition of remote file access capability increases the desirability of concurrency control, an optional feature for MAP/TOP 3.0. One of the prime reasons for providing remote access is to allow multiple users to share a single central file. If that sharing requires updating and writing in addition to reading, there may be no choice but to require the concurrency option. Until concurrency can be controlled by the FTAM protocol, distributed data applications development is far more difficult.

Manufacturing Messaging Format Standard (MMFS)

So far, we have discussed two very generic user services, CASE/ACSE and FTAM. The third, and last, user service available in MAP 2.1 is just the opposite. MMFS, the Manufacturing Messaging Format Standard, is designed specifically to bridge the communications gap between work-cell controllers and programmable machines. It is a protocol which speaks the language of numerical controllers, programmable logic controllers, and robots. It allows the user to work in terms like "X axis high limit switch" rather than "bit 6 of byte 3" as would be required using CASE for the same task.

The MMFS protocol is unique in another respect as well. Unlike the other two user protocols in MAP 2.1, it was written by the General Motors MAP task force rather than based on existing standards. This was not because of any feelings of "Not Invented Here" on the part of the MAP task force but rather because there were no suitable standards even being worked on that could meet General Motors' needs. As a result, the protocol is an orphan, a temporary standard unique to MAP 2.X.

The purpose of MMFS is to transfer digitally encoded information between factory floor devices. It is a very versatile standard, suitable for use in many applications that require machine-independent process-to-process communications in the context of factory floor operations. It is actually more than just an interprocess communications facility; it defines a messaging language as well (remember, MAP 2.1 does not include a presentation layer, so the functions normally provided at layer six had to be built into MMFS). MMFS defines both the form and the meaning of messages, including both presentation and application layer functions. The only assumption made by the protocol designers was that a reliable transport service was available. The result is a very powerful protocol with the potential to cause severe migration problems in the move to MAP/TOP 3.0 for those who do not plan ahead. We will discuss how to minimize these problems at the end of the next section, where we discuss the protocol replacing it in MAP 3.0, RS-511.

MMFS syntax

The MMFS syntax is built upon the concept of a message. The two basic building blocks which can be used to make up messages are "fields" and "data streams." Fields are further broken down into two parts: the identification and the content. The content of a field represents a single piece of data, such as a 16-bit integer or a string of 80 characters, up to a maximum size of 127 octets. The identifier of a field indicates the nature of the field, such as a diagnostic code or the contents of a memory location. Fields cannot contain other fields as their contents. Data streams are similar to fields except they carry no identification (they are content only) and their content can be very long (up to 10^{300} octets). The content can be a large single unit of data or multiple units of data of the same type.

Fields and data streams are combined into messages using special kinds of fields called groupers. Groupers are recursive, so a grouper may build a group of groups, as well as of fields and data streams. Messages must always start with a message grouper since they are, in fact, a group. In a like manner, data streams must be preceded by a special field called a data stream grouper, which specifies the length of the data stream in octets.

The overall structure of a message is shown in Figure 5.1. Here we see that the first field in the message is the message grouper, which can be a simple octet count, a count of the number of groups, or what is effectively an open parenthesis which will be closed by a matching "close parenthesis" grouper to end the message. The field preceding a data stream, as already mentioned, must be a data stream grouper. Looking inside an individual field, we see some more options for extensibility. The first octet of any field must be the first octet of the field identifier. If the high-order bit of that first octet is a 0, it is a one-octet field identifier, and the remaining 7 bits specify the field type. If the high-order bit is a 1, the low-order 7 bits of the octet are the octet count for the actual field identifier which follows. The field content follows the last octet of the identifier subfield and is evaluated the same way: If the high-order bit of the first octet is a 0, the remaining 7 bits make up the value; otherwise, they determine the number of octets making up the contents subfield.

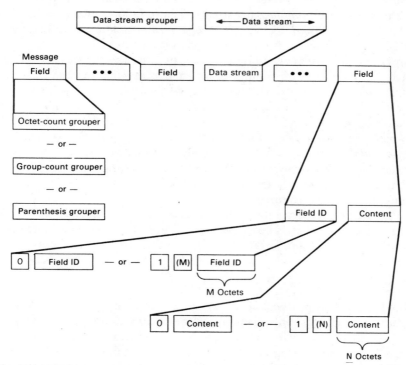

Figure 5.1 MMFS message syntax. (*By permission of General Motors. Reproduced from GM's* Manufacturing Automation Protocol—A Communication Network Protocol for Open Systems Interconnection Version 2.2, *August 1, 1986*.)

Semantics

The semantics of MMFS is the assignment of actual field identifiers and values to specific meanings in the context of a MMFS "conversation." Because of its origin as an all-things-for-all-users protocol, the semantics of MMFS are extremely rich (if you need them) or complex (if you do not). To simplify discussion, the MMFS specification represents all defined fields with two-, three-, or four-letter mnemonics. The number of letters used is significant. Two-letter mnemonics represent a class of fields, all sharing the same identifier but distinguished by their contents subfield. For example, the parenthesis grouper has the mnemonic PG. Open parentheses has content subfield value 0, while close parenthesis has content subfield value 7F (hexadecimal). Similarly, an unsigned integer field has the mnemonic UI, and the contents subfield is the value of the unsigned integer. In general, the contents subfield can be expected to contain either data (such as an unsigned integer) or a function code (a limited set of valid values, such as with the parenthesis grouper).

Three-letter mnemonics are used for those fields which have a limited set of codes allowed for their content subfield. The three-letter mnemonic specifies which function code is in the content subfield (as well as implying the identifier subfield). For example, the parenthesis grouper with the content code signifying open parenthesis has the mnemonic POP while the one with the content code that signifies close parenthesis is PCL. Another term associated with three-letter mnemonic fields is that of "action field." Action fields are the MMFS equivalent of transaction components. Fields identified in the MMFS specification as action fields must only be used in transaction sequences so that responses can be associated with their corresponding requests. Examples of action fields are file transfer requests, message size negotiation, and numerical control commands.

Four-character mnemonics are reserved for user-defined fields. Any nonstandard semantics must use these. There are 256 user-defined fields defined, called US00, US01, US02 . . . USFE, and USFF.

Conformance classes

The full MMFS protocol is an extremely large and complex implementation. Since small controllers and other devices could never be expected to implement the entire protocol, well-defined subsets are included. The first level of subsetting is based on context. Then, within each context, are several conformance classes ranging from minimal capability up to all possible commands in the context.

There are three contexts defined for MMFS: numerical control applications, programmable controller applications, and robot applications. Although originally the task force thought contexts might be necessary to eliminate ambiguity as the standard expanded to include other needs, today they function only as subsetting guidelines. Further development is unlikely, as the standard is considered a dead end and will not be included in MAP 3.0. Its MAP 3.0 replacement, RS-511, can be used to replace MMFS in applications if the applications are kept simple enough. We will discuss how to ease the migration from MMFS to RS-511 in the next section.

Each context is further subdivided into four conformance classes, numbered 0 through 3. Minimum capability is designated as conformance class 0, with each higher number indicating the addition of more capability. Higher-conformance classes include all capabilities found in lower-conformance classes, allowing negotiation downward in case one machine has a lower conformance class than another. Not all conformance classes have been specified in the defined contexts. In fact, in two of the three defined contexts, there is only one conformance class explicitly defined, conformance class 0. The third context, robot applications, defines conformance classes 0, 1, and 2. Definition of conformance class 3, the full context, is left as an implicit definition, a dangerous mode of operation in a dynamically evolving specification (which MMFS no longer is) because what was conformance class 3 before an update may not communicate with conformance class 3 after an update.

Manufacturing Messaging Service (RS-511)

RS-511 could be called the protocol with many names. It is known by its name—Manufacturing Messaging Service—by its initials—MMS—by its document number—EIA 1393A (given it by the Electronic Industries Association, the first group to try to develop it into an accepted standard)—and by its EIA standard designation—RS-511.

RS-511 started out as an effort to develop a Computer Numerical Control (CNC) protocol by the Electronic Industries Association. The General Motors' MAP task force convinced EIA to expand the scope of the RS-511 effort to include programmable logic controllers and robots. Part of the agreement was that EIA could build on the MMFS protocol specification provided the standard was upgraded to follow the ISO OSI standards, including changing the syntax to that specified by ASN.1. The hopes of the MMFS group back in 1984 are reflected in the preface to the MMFS appendix of the MAP 2.1 specification.

> Recently, the Electronic Industries Association (EIA) Committee IE-31 voted to adopt all of MMFS and to reissue it, in a somewhat changed and enhanced form, as draft standard 1393A. This EIA standard will supersede MMFS when it is approved. At that time, the messaging language specified in this appendix will cease to be the official MAP messaging language, and the EIA standard will be implemented. Until that time, however, the messaging language specified in this appendix is considered to be a close approximation to the future EIA standard, especially at the conformance class 0 level.

Little did anyone realize at the time just how "changed and enhanced" the EIA version would be. EIA 1393A has gone through six draft proposals and is not scheduled to reach standard status until late 1987. The only useful remaining compatibility with MMFS is at the conformance class 0 level, and even that can be lost if application design and implementation are not migration oriented.

Principles of operation

Manufacturing messaging service is an example of what ISO used to call a Specific Application Service Elements protocol, or SASE. Compared to a CASE, Common Application Service Elements, which meets general needs common to many applications, a SASE builds upon the foundation provided by CASE to meet the needs of a specific application. In the case of RS-511, the specific application is manufacturing messaging. In addition to providing generic services such as send data or set up an association, RS-511 supports manufacturing and factory floor oriented messaging as specific as "stop robot" and "spindle speed override."

General operations and semantics useful for almost all industries are defined. Individual industry associations are expected to define industry specific operations, semantics, and conformance requirements. To gain approval of all interested parties, RS-511 attempts to meet all the needs of all possible users. As a result, it defines a multitude of functions and options, making it an extremely complex protocol. Once the standard is approved, the challenge will be to extract useful subsets that make sense on the factory floor in controllers with finite processing power and memory.

The MMS protocol architecture (Figure 5.2) is similar to the CCITT X.410 remote operations protocol, developed for electronic mail and messaging. X.410 is based on the concept of initiators and agents (called responders in MMS terminology). The initiator requests the remote agent to take an action. In response, the agent takes the action and reports the result to the initiator. This protocol is an asymmetric "master-slave" style protocol rather than the more balanced, peer-to-peer relationship we are used to seeing. Its advantage for MMS is the ability to concentrate implementation complexity in the initiator, usually running on a more powerful controller, and keep the responder implementations simple for low-powered NC and PLC effectors.

The syntax used for RS-511 messages is ASN.1. While ASN.1 is similar to that of MMFS in function, it differs substantially in form. We will discuss ASN.1 in the next chapter when we cover the presentation layer.

RS-511 services

RS-511 provides a wide range of services to the user. However, they can be categorized into eight areas: memory exchange, context maintenance, device control, operator communication, events, journals, file system, and coordination. Let us look at each area.

Memory exchange is a very basic service. It allows the initiator to read or write memory locations in the responder machine. It seems simple until we look at all the options. The read or write can be performed immediately or delayed until a specified event occurs. The memory locations can be specified by machine address or by variable name. More than one variable or memory location can be read at a time, including mixtures of various data types ranging from integers to booleans to ASCII strings. Variables may be local to the particular initiator or responder association or global to the entire machine. The variations are unlimited.

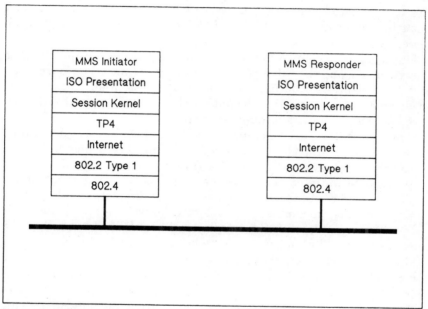

Figure 5.2 MMS protocol architecture.

Context maintenance sets up and maintains the context shared by initiator and responder. Named references to any of the memory exchange parameters, events, journals, semaphores, or file system identifiers can be defined or deleted as desired. This allows each responder on the controller to work in a context unique to the task it is performing, which meets the needs of the task it is performing, without affecting other responders that are also in action.

Device control is one of the most important contexts to maintain. Device semantics are defined by each industry association, and obviously initiator and responder must agree on the context they are both operating in. It would not do for the initiator to issue an emergency stop command in the robot context and the responder to interpret it as a control point override in the process control context of the furnace it was controlling.

Operator communication is provided by what is effectively a simple virtual terminal capability. The initiator can ask for input from specified devices such as a keyboard, touch screen, or bar code reader and output data on a specified device such as the display screen.

A wide range of event-driven activities are definable. Conditions defining an event are programmable, including alarms, one-shot triggers, and regular scans. Priorities may be assigned, and actions such as reading a variable, starting or stopping journaling, or even scheduling jobs can be performed based on occurrence or lack thereof. Summary reporting commands are also provided for tasks such as reading all currently active alarms.

Journals can be defined to keep track of programmed events, the time they occurred, and the value of variables at those times. The journal can be a limited-size first-in-first-out queue or an essentially infinite (i.e., on-line mass storage) buffer. The initiator can read the journal as desired based on time of entries or number of entries.

Numerous file system operations are defined. The responder can be instructed to down load a file into a region in the responder's memory (remote program load) or to get a file from a third party (which may or may not be the initiator). The initiator can perform numerous operations on the responder's file system such as reading directories and opening, closing, reading, renaming, and deleting individual files. These file operations are not intended as a replacement for FTAM but rather as a convenient extension to provide some basic services.

Finally, RS-511 provides numerous services for coordinating activities. Job scheduling tends to be industry specific. Although some functions such as selecting a local job file are general purpose, others such as different types of job starts and stops make sense only in specific contexts. Semaphores are provided to allow safe sharing of critical resources and interlocking of related job or batch streams. Status reporting ranging from self-test results to industry-specific, device-specific status items (step in progress, current recipe, etc.) round out the available capabilities.

The power and flexibility available to the writer of RS-511 applications are limited only by the writer's imagination and the computer power available. As was the case in MMFS, conformance classes are required in order to keep the size of RS-511 responder implementations down to something that will fit into a controller at reasonable cost. Keeping the application simple will be particularly important in the early days of MAP 3.0, before enough implementations and cross testing have been done to work the incompatible edges off the lesser-used aspects of the protocol.

MMFS to RS-511 migration

There are major differences between MMFS and RS-511. Although RS-511 started out as MMFS, it has changed so much along the way that users who do use MMFS must design carefully to avoid throwing out their software and starting all over again when the time comes to upgrade from MAP 2.1 to MAP 3.0. The two standards are not even editorially similar. RS-511 has been revised extensively to match the editorial style required for publication as an ISO standard. This makes it difficult to recognize the many similarities that still remain.

There have been major changes to the content of the messaging language. MMFS was originally designed to function over a minimal connection-oriented transport. It provides facilities for segmentation, syntax definition, and flow control that RS-511 assumes are handled by the lower layers. There are no fields to provide those functions in RS-511. Applications written for the higher-level conformance classes that utilize these facilities will need to be rewritten if not completely redesigned.

The situation is much brighter for applications written to utilize the 0-level conformance classes. Changes at the 0-level conformance classes are generally minor. The functionality of the conformance classes will be changed slightly but should have little impact at the 0 level. For example, the NAM field in MMFS specifies that the next field, which must be a character string, is the name of a file. The equivalent field in RS-511 includes the name of the file as the value of the field. These kinds of differences can be handled during migration if the application is coded so that all calls to MMFS are made indirectly through subroutines which then call the MMFS interface. That way, as long as the functionality is still available in RS-511, it is only the interface subroutine library that needs to be rewritten instead of making massive changes throughout the application when the time comes to move from MAP 2.1 to MAP/TOP 3.0.

The following guidelines will help insure that the MMFS functionality used is still there when it is time to move to RS-511. First of all, stay within conformance class 0. Yes, those extra capabilities will make your application much simpler to write, but they will come back to haunt you when you decide to upgrade. Furthermore, even at the 0-conformance level, keep it simple. In particular, limit any message to at most one action, keep your data unit sizes small (so no segmentation is required), and avoid groups.

The easiest solution to the migration challenge is to wait for MAP 3.0 and implement directly in RS-511. If your schedule can wait until at least 1988, skipping MAP 2.X will save converting over. Of course, this is the classic next-computer-generation dilemma. Only you can balance the benefits of waiting for the next generation with the gains from implementing today with hardware and software of known quality, reliability, and performance. Even MAP vendors are not immune from vapor-ware introductions. Full-page magazine ads and four-color marketing brochures are much easier to produce than are fully functional, interoperable networking software.

If you do decide to implement first in MAP 2.1 or 2.2, plan now for the revisions required when you upgrade to MAP 3.0. This is no time for software engineering shortcuts. Modularity and good design documentation are vital. And make sure all your vendors are committed to upgrading to MAP/TOP 3.0 on a schedule that is acceptable to you.

Network Directory Service

The next two services we will be discussing are quite different from the previous four. Network directory service and network management are not utilized directly by normal applications the way ACSE, FTAM, or RS-511 are. Rather, they are services required to make the network functional and to keep it functioning.

Network directory service provides a critical translation function. The network protocols deal with addresses in machine-readable form. For example, each connection on an 802.4 token bus is addressed by a 48-bit binary address, while the machines themselves have 22- to 34-hexadecimal digit internetwork addresses so they can be uniquely identified from all other machines in the world. The network directory service allows us to refer to machines and the services available on them using descriptive names, such as "the cell controller for work cell no. 2" or "the FTAM service on that cell," without concern for how these descriptive names map to the actual addressing requirements of the network.

OSI naming and addressing

Before we look at how the directory service itself works, let us take some time for a closer look at naming and addressing. As we have already seen, there is a need for two different classes of addressing. At one level, we need addresses that are efficient for the protocols running on the machines in the networks, addresses which pack the most information in the smallest number of bits to minimize overhead. On the other hand, network users and applications running over the network need names which are meaningful and are not tied to hardware or implementation specifics. Imagine the confusion if your name changed anytime you moved and got a new phone number or if changing from a rotary to a Touch-Tone phone required you to get a new phone number.

ISO recognized the dual nature of the usage of names and defined two classes of network names, primitive and descriptive. A primitive name is one uniquely assigned by a naming authority to a particular entity. It is an arbitrary label attached to the object, and the user need not know how the name was derived. A telephone number used to dial a call to London from New York is just such a primitive name. The caller does not need to know that the first three digits provide access to AT&T international services or which digits are the country code and which are the city code. By dialing the correct sequence of digits (using the primitive name) the caller can always connect (barring system errors, of course) to that particular phone in London, identified by its primitive name.

Descriptive names, on the other hand, are what people like to use, even when it comes to phone numbers. ISO defines a descriptive name as an unordered list of assertions about an object, in which each assertion defines a set of objects. Using our phone number example, the descriptive name for the same phone might be customer service at Harrods Department Store, London, England, phone number 12-1234. Unlike a primitive name, a descriptive name need not denote a single unique object; it may denote many objects (customer service at Harrods, London, England, denotes multiple phones) or no objects at all (customer service at Harrods, Moscow, USSR, is an empty set). Descriptive names may also include primitive names, such as the "local" phone number in the first example of a descriptive name.

So what is this mystical naming authority that all primitive names come from? A naming authority is any entity (a person, machine, organization, or whatever) that can provide a unique name upon request and guarantee that name is not in use anywhere in that entity's naming domain. The naming authority is not responsible for how the name is used. It can even partition its name domain and delegate the handing out of names to subauthorities. Phone companies do this all the time—in the United States, the area code is used to partition the country into regions, while within each area code, the 3-digit exchange codes are used to partition the larger domain down to local phone companies, which in turn hand out the final, unique phone numbers.

OSI usage of names and addresses

Within the ISO OSI reference model, addresses are used three ways. They are used to distinguish between various (N) layer entities supporting different (N) layer protocols or sets of (N) layer protocols. They are used to distinguish among the (N + 1) entities bound to (N) service access points to allow reestablishment of communications in the event of connection failures. And they are available to accommodate as yet undetermined security and management requirements. Perhaps just as important, they are not used to distinguish among aspects of protocols such as quality of service or software versions, between connection-oriented and connectionless operation, or between hardware components.

ISO has chosen to develop standards only for application entity names and network service access point addresses. This allows clear specification of the service desired (from the application entity title) and the end system it is running on (from the NSAP address), yet retains maximum flexibility for local implementation choices. A system can be designed around these two addresses and use the addressing in the other layers in whatever way makes the most sense. Note, however, that while the addresses for other layers are locally selected and their values are not standardized, the representation used for those values frequently is standardized.

Figure 5.3 shows network addressing as defined in ISO 8348 Addendum 2 to the Network Service Definition Covering Network Layer Addressing. The address is made up of two major parts, the Initial Domain Part (IDP), which specifies the naming authority responsible for issuing the name, and the Domain Specific Part, which is the primitive name provided by that naming authority. The delegation of naming authority is simplified by the two-part substructure of the Initial Domain Part. ISO has claimed for itself the "ultimate naming authority" role and assigned the first part, the Authority and Format Identifier, to the major international naming authorities. The second part, the Initial Domain Identifier (IDI), is then provided by the authority identified in the AFI, using the format specified in the AFI.

The standardization of application entity names is not as well defined. Through 1986, the two groups in ISO who could have been doing the job, the upper-layer group and the management group, were still debating who should have the responsibility. Each wanted the other to do it. As a result, the job might end up being done by the Directory Service designers. They are striving for a single unified directory service for all OSI objects, from NSAPs and application entities to robots, files, and bank accounts. This goal requires uniform naming conventions for all levels, which they may try to provide themselves if they cannot get them from other sources to include in the directory service.

MAP 2.1/TOP 1.0 network addressing

Three network address formats are defined for MAP 2.1/TOP 1.0 (Figure 5.4). The difference is in the network identifier, which describes which set of interconnected local area networks is referenced in the address. The three formats provide three levels of independence from address conflicts. The simplest is the single location network identifier, useful when the network is self-contained at a single location. Multiple sites are easiest to connect using the middle format. This allows full control over the assignment of network identifiers by the network owner. However, it does require that all networks which communicate have an agreement over how to assign unique network identifiers. The third format is for those networks for which the required cooperation between communicating networks is not available. This format uses the internationally assigned CCITT X.121 addresses obtained as part of an X.25 network connection to ensure unique network identifiers for all connected networks.

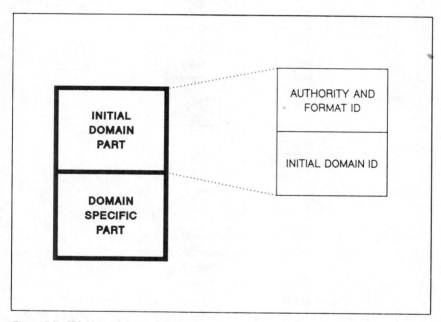

Figure 5.3 ISO Network Layer Addressing.

The specific format in use is determined by a two-step process. The Authority and Format Identifier (AFI) specifies the source of the Initial Domain Identifier. For X.121 addressing, the AFI is set to 37 hexadecimal to indicate binary encoding of X.121 addresses, and the Initial Domain Identifier is the X.121 address assigned to the locataion. Owner-defined network identifiers use an AFI of 49 to indicate locally defined binary encoding. The network identifier is then included in the Domain Specific Part (DSP) and there is no Initial Domain Identifier. The Network Identifier is either a single octet of 0s for the single location definition or a nonzero first octet and four additional octets specifying the specific set of interconnected local area networks. MAP

2.1 network implementations are only required to recognize the local AFI with five-octet network identifier; the other two forms are defined but optional.

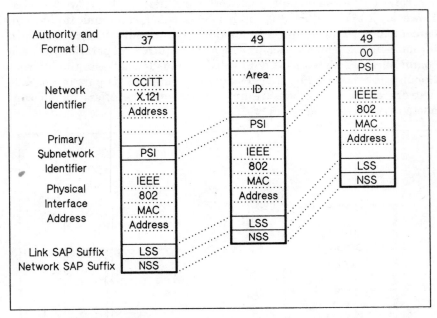

Figure 5.4   MAP NSAP address format.

The remaining nine octets making up the domain-specific part of a MAP/TOP NSAP address contain four fields, each of which takes the packet one step closer to the destination NSAP. The first octet of the nine is the primary subnet identifier. This primitive address is assigned by the local facility manager responsible for all LANs associated with the network identifier. It is used by any routers to get the packet to the appropriate subnetwork. Any network identifier can identify at most 256 interconnected LANs. If a single location supports more than the 256-LAN limit, multiple network identifiers must be used. The second through seventh octets (48 bits total) is the physical interface address of the destination. This identifies the IEEE 802.4 interface which should receive the packet on the subnet specified by the primary subnet identifier. The last two octets of the NSAP address guide the packet through the link and network layers once the first seven have gotten it to the correct machine. Octet eight, the data link SAP suffix, uniquely identifies which data link service user (network layer entity) is to get the packet. Octet nine, the network SAP suffix, similarly defines which network service user (transport entity) gets the packet.

Putting them all together, the MAP/TOP NSAP address not only specifies what machine to deliver the packet to, it specifies at each step of the way where to go next to get there.

MAP 2.1 network directory service

The above example of MAP/TOP NSAP addressing also illustrates most clearly the need for providing "user friendly" names for applications to use rather than forcing them to use the actual machine-oriented addresses. An application with MAP/TOP NSAPs hard coded in it violates commonsense software engineering. Imagine having to go out on the factory floor to reprogram hundreds of NC machines just because maintenance had to replace the IEEE 802.4 card on a host!

It is the function of the network directory service to provide the required mapping of meaningful names to computer-usable addresses. The MAP 2.1 network directory service is built upon a network directory database containing all available unique program names. Associated with each program (or service) name is the set of service access points used to communicate with it. In operation, the MAP 2.1 network directory service responds to any query in the syntax of the inquirer. If an ASCII name request is received, character strings in the response are also in ASCII. Similarly, a MMFS encoded query elicits a MMFS encoded response. For requests that cannot be fulfilled, the response "name not found" is returned.

Although not required, the MAP 2.1 specification recommends that each system also maintain a local directory (cache) of commonly used names and addresses. This provides several benefits. The biggest is relieving the network of the overhead traffic and delays associated with consulting the master database with every connection established. Even if the entries required cannot be predicted in advance, caching satisfied requests would minimize repetitive inquiries for the same information. A local directory also allows provision of private or "unlisted" services, known only to privileged users and not commonly available to general users. (Be aware, however, that an unlisted service is not a replacement for security provisions in sensitive applications; rather it is a means of reducing the inconvenience to casual or innocent users of invalid connection attempts.)

The MAP 2.1 directory service specification, like most practical directory services, also has a number of restrictions that users need to be aware of. There is no provision for dynamically determining the address of directory service, so the directory service must reside at a well-known address which can be hard coded into each accessing machine. Applications must be prepared for failure of the directory service to provide a usable address in response to a name request. The probability of this occurring in MAP 2.1 is increased by the lack of any provision for automatic or remote updating of the directory database. The only service specified for use over the network is read-only inquiry messages. Facilities for setting up and maintaining the directory database are all proprietary and locally administered.

MAP/TOP 3.0 directory service

MAP/TOP 3.0 network directory service will be a subset of ISO directory services. The changes to the protocols required to implement it should not be visible to the user; the improved flexibility and responsiveness because of the addition of remote update capability will be. While the ISO work is still in draft proposal stage, changes in the ISO definition as it progresses to international standard status should have minimal impact on MAP/TOP capabilities. Most likely are compatible upgrades toward the final standard in subsequent MAP/TOP releases. At worst it may be necessary to run two directory services in parallel to support both 3.0 and final releases.

Network Management

Network management shares many characteristics with network directory service. Neither is absolutely required to get a network up and running, but both are vital to keeping any network functioning long term. Both also share the dubious distinction of being the last of the indispensable protocols to be standardized. The only network management related standard available during MAP/TOP 3.0 development was ISO's architectural framework for network management. Capabilities useful for the actual management of a network were just reaching draft proposal stage. The IEEE 802.1 committee work on network management standards for the physical and data link layers covered by IEEE 802 protocols was also not stable enough for inclusion. Both can be expected in later MAP/TOP versions as the intent of MAP/TOP network management is to migrate toward the ISO standards as they evolve and stabilize.

MAP/TOP management goals

The MAP 2.1 specification gives some design criteria for the network management facility of a MAP/TOP network. First, network management control is to be distributed. The network management function is to assist the local systems with their own management rather than controlling the local systems as is the case in some proprietary network architectures.

Key to making this style of network management possible is the expectation that network management activities will be infrequent. The design philosophy is one of management by exception, the network management function is an error-correction tool. In keeping with this philosophy, the functionality of the network management should be unaffected by isolated failures in the network. After all, one of network management's primary functions is aiding recovery from those isolated failures in the network it is unable to prevent.

The network management should also be designed in recognition that the level of network management support will vary from node to node about the network. Different nodes will have different needs and purposes (consider, for example, a host, a router, and an NC machine) as well as variances in the available processing power, memory capacity, and local system management capability.

Given the status of standards at the time of MAP 2.1 development (there were none), the MAP task force was forced to invent their own. They deliberately chose to keep the definition of MAP/TOP network management very narrow, making it possible for vendors to implement at least minimal capabilities in the MAP 2.1 time frame. The intent was to make it expandable as standards developed, while minimizing the "waste" involved in moving from the temporary standard to ISO long term. Since most networking vendors already provided management tools for their IEEE 802.4 network components, the MAP/TOP network management specification only applies to layers three through seven.

Similarly, MAP/TOP network management is only defined in the context of MAP local area network segments. Wide area network management (again normally provided, to the extent required, by the network vendor) is specifically excluded. If a MAP network is interconnected to non-MAP LAN segments, all MAP management stops at the gateway or internet router connecting the MAP network to the non-MAP network.

The network management envisioned is best described by the MAP 2.1 standard itself:

> Network Management is responsible for gathering information on the usage of the network media by the network devices, ensuring the correct operation of the network and providing reports. The information that is collected is processed for the various types of users to affect planning, operations, or maintenance.
>
> Maintenance data is used by technicians to perform functions such as problem detection and diagnosis, installation and checkout, and preventative maintenance. Operations data is used by planners and operators in

performing performance monitoring, configuration management, and network access management. Lastly, planning data is used by managers in network design, modeling, and simulations.

MAP 2.1/TOP 1.0 specifics

MAP 2.1 specifies an application layer module implementation of network management. All functions are defined in terms of only 10 message types which utilize a layer seven protocol. (Exceptions are limited to failure management and initial program loading.)

Four primary functions are provided. Configuration management allows determination and control of the state of the network. This applies to the physical configuration of systems as well as the logical. Other parameters might be software version numbers, physical location of a node, type or manufacturer of a node, protocol sets supported, applications available, etc.

The performance management function is defined as a monitoring function. Any changes to be made to adjust performance would be a function of the configuration management function. Performance management collects the system statistics, starting, stopping, and adjusting that collection as required, stores the statistics collected, and presents them in a suitable fashion.

The event-processing function is the primary source of real-time information for the other three functions. An event is considered any occurrence that changes the state of the network. Changes can be either normal or abnormal. Normal changes are typically performance-related events, that is, changes in throughput, delay, buffer or connection utilization, etc. Abnormal state changes are usually associated with errors. They can be protocol violations, hosts going down, unsupported destination addresses, thresholds exceeded, etc.

The fourth and final function is fault management. The only fault management function provided in the MAP 2.1 context is loop-back testing. Three modes of loop back are defined, one at the application level and two at the transport level. Any provision for link level loop back is outside the MAP/TOP specification and must be supplied by the IEEE 802 network vendor.

MAP/TOP 3.0 directions

MAP/TOP 3.0 will expand on the network management functionality available in MAP 2.1/TOP 1.0 to provide the ability to manage all types of systems found in a MAP/TOP 3.0 network. This includes not only full seven-layer systems but also routers, bridges, MAP/EPA nodes, and

MiniMAP nodes. Many of the changes are incremental. More parameters are kept by individual nodes for reporting to network management. Fault isolation and recovery capabilities are improved. Performance monitoring and control are expanded and configuration management facilities enhanced. New capabilities include initialization and termination control and node enrollment and deenrollment procedures.

Basic Class Virtual Terminal

The ISO standard for NVT is basic class virtual terminal (VT). Even though not available as a standard until TOP 3.0, the equivalent functionality was one of the key features of the Kaiser Aluminum MAP 2.0 pilot in Erie, Pennsylvania, in 1985. VT resolves the differences between various terminals and hosts by defining a virtual terminal capability the same way FTAM defines a virtual file store. Each end of the virtual terminal session then translates between the local expectations of terminal capability to those defined by the network virtual representation.

ISO VT

The ISO standard specifies the operations available on the virtual terminal and any associated characteristics. Characteristics include such details as the number of characters per line, the number of lines on the screen, the colors available for display, and any emphasis modes available such as underline, bold, or inverse video. Operations may be character, line, or page oriented and can include items such as protected fields, light pens, and mouse inputs. The particular characteristics and operations to be used during any session are negotiated at the start of the VT session.

The VT service is based on the model illustrated in Figure 5.5. The local mapping function is an addition to the host operating system that breaks the normal data path between the user's terminal and the user's program and allows the data path to be redirected. On the local system, the local mapping connects the user's terminal to the virtual terminal protocol. Similarly, on the remote system, the local mapping allows the VT protocol to control the user's program as if it were a local terminal. Inside the application layer the VT protocol uses the Association Control Service Elements to set up the required association between the user terminal machine and the user program machine. ACSE then communicates through the presentation layer and on through the network.

The basic class virtual terminal protocol defines three service capability levels: VT-A, VT-B, and VT-C. VT-A is the simplest subset. It provides the ability to establish and terminate associations, transfer data, control delivery of information, and manage the dialogue (recover from errors). Delivery control provides the ability to buffer transferred data at the destination and deliver it to the receiver when commanded by the sender. VT-B extends the VT-A definition by adding the ability to negotiate profile switches. This allows negotiating use of more powerful terminal features (such as cursor addressing) if supported by both end systems. VT-C adds the ability to negotiate multiple interactions over the same association. This would allow a user to control multiple independent programs from a single terminal.

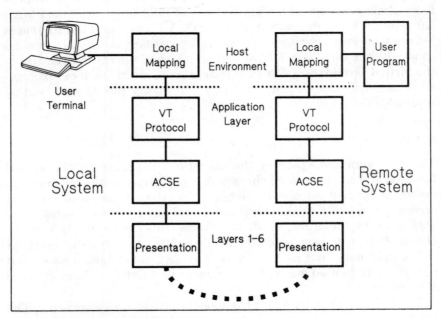

Figure 5.5 ISO virtural terminal architecture.

Two modes of operation are defined for the VT protocol. All the protocol subsets can operate in either asynchronous mode or synchronous mode. In asynchronous mode, the two directions of data flow, terminal to program and program to terminal, are independent. Synchronous mode coordinates the two data flows. For example, a program could allow keyboard entry only when input was expected.

The VT standard itself is quite flexible. Work is underway to extend the definition to include a forms-oriented virtual terminal, a graphics virtual terminal, and a mixed-mode (text, graphics, voice, image, and who knows what else) virtual terminal.

TOP 3.0 VT

TOP 3.0 VT is ISO Basic Class Virtual Terminal subset VT-B. The specification provides a connection-based service supporting interactive, full-duplex process-to-terminal communication. Only the asynchronous mode of operation is supported. Future TOP specifications will expand the definition of VT to include synchronous mode operation, addition of some of the features and functions of the extended facility set, and definition of a forms-oriented virtual terminal profile.

TOP 3.0 defines five different virtual terminal profiles to select from. Simplest is the ISO 9041 asynchronous mode default profile. This profile is also the default for TOP 3.0 and will be used if a profile is not explicitly negotiated. The TOP TELNET profile adds the ability to control local echoing. It models a simple scrolling terminal that cannot modify lines once they have been written. The TOP Paging/Scrolling profile allows direct cursor addressing, providing the ability to modify any location on the screen. It also provides support for an optional attached printer in addition to a keyboard and CRT display unit. X.25 network users will appreciate the profile supporting CCITT X.3 PAD operations. This profile allows a user with only a terminal to access TOP hosts via the PAD services available on most X.25 public data networks. Finally, a transparent profile is defined which allows exchange of data with no interpretation or translation by the virtual terminal facility. Matching of terminal capabilities with remote host expectations is up to the user. This allows compatible hosts and users to exercise all terminal features available to a local user without waiting for the required feature set to be defined as part of the standard.

Message Handling Systems (MHS)

The international standard for message handling systems is definedby the CCITT X.400 series of protocols. X.400 provides a worldwide standard for electronic mail as an extension of existing PTT public data network offerings. It defines the syntax, fields, and formats for messages to be transferred as well as the services and protocols for handling, transferring, and forwarding messages. Unfortunately, it pre-dates availability of ISO standards for the upper layers and uses neither CASE/ACSE nor presentation services. The ISO standard for MHS is Message-Oriented Text Interchange Standard (MOTIS). MOTIS deviates from X.400 in order to provide a better fit into systems based on ISO protocol stacks. Work is underway to harmonize the CCITT and ISO definitions and will result in revisions to the TOP specification after the initial MAP/TOP 3.0 release.

CCITT X.400 MHS

X.400 provides the means for a user on one machine to exchange a message with a user on a second machine without either machine being able to communicate directly with one another. In many ways, X.400 provides the same capability as FTAM file transfer. Both allow a user at one machine to move data in the form of a message or file to a user at a second machine. The key is that FTAM requires both ends of the transfer to be available and connected for the entire duration of the transaction. X.400, on the other hand, can use a series of independent connections in lieu of a single end-to-end association.

How this works is illustrated in Figure 5.6. The originator of the message interacts with the User Agent (UA) service on the local machine to prepare the message for transmission. The originator can be a person or a user application process. The message can be electronic mail or any other sort of data. When ready to send the message, the user agent connects to the local Message Transfer Agent (MTA) and hands the message over for delivery. Once this "local" transaction is completed, the originator and user agent are no longer required to maintain contact with the serving message transfer agent. The message transfer agent can wait, if desired, until lower-cost transport facilities (typically late night rates) are available and then communicate peer to peer with other message

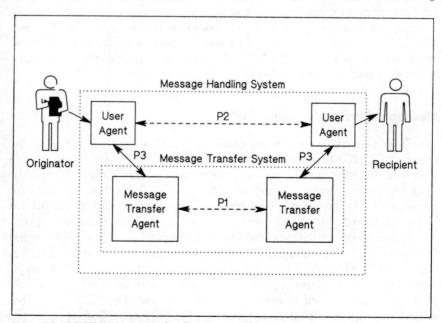

Figure 5.6 CCITT X.400 message-handling system architecture.

transfer agents to get the message to the message transfer agent serving the recipient's user agent. Once at the recipient's message transfer agent, the message is stored until the recipient's user agent accesses the message transfer agent and picks up the message with another "local" transaction.

The protocols used to perform all these transfers are given names like P1, P2, and P3. P1 and P2 are the best defined because they are required for a PTT to successfully offer X.400 service. P1, the protocol between message transfer agents, allows multiple X.400 systems to relay messages from one X.400 domain (e.g., France) to another (e.g., Italy). Message transfer agents may utilize intermediate message transfer agents if a direct connection from originator MTA to recipient MTA is not available. The user agents have their own end-to-end protocol called P2. P2 defines the syntax and semantics of the contents of the message so that both end users can understand the contents. It includes such items as the subject, to list, and from list. The interface between user and user agent is not defined. How the user accesses X.400 services is left to the implementor.

Other "P" protocols contained in X.400 are less stable. The P3 protocol defines the communications between the user agent and its message transfer agent when the two agents are not on the same machine and must be connected via a network. The European Computer Manufacturers Association, looking for a functionality split more suitable for local area networks, has developed the P7 protocol for distributed user agents (Figure 5.7). P3+ (P3 plus) provides another split between UA and MTA. P_C (P sub C) protocols are being developed to define syntax and semantics of message contents beyond the interpersonal messaging provided by P2.

TOP 3.0 MHS

The TOP 3.0 specification calls for a minimal but useful implementation of MHS based on CCITT X.400. The implementation specified has been deliberately restricted to minimize the disruption as ISO and CCITT MHS converge and protocols are added or modified. Plans are to update the TOP specification once the ISO/CCITT harmonization has yielded stable standards. The need for harmonization is shown in Figure 5.8, where the ISO and CCITT standards are compared, along with the TOP 3.0 selections from the CCITT standards. The ISO standards are more suitable for corporate-style networks, whereas the CCITT standards are oriented toward the needs of public systems. TOP 3.0 had to select the CCITT versions regardless because the ISO standards were not finalized in the TOP 3.0 time frame.

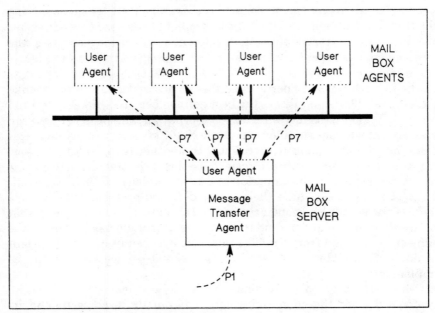

Figure 5.7   Distributed user agent in CCITT X.400.

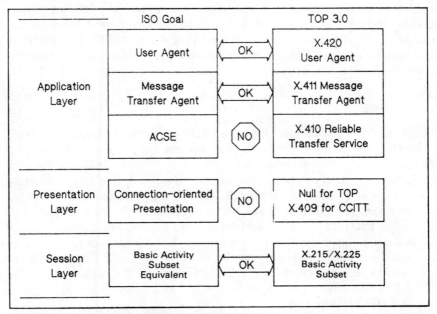

Figure 5.8   ISO, TOP 3.0, and CCITT protocol alignments.

TOP 3.0 only specifies the P1 and P2 protocols. While this means that multivendor communications are well defined, multivendor management of the mail system is not. Administration of the message-handling system within a Private Management Domain (PRMD) will initially be proprietary. The definition of Multivendor PRMD will only be available after TOP 3.0. Except for the restriction of user agents to a message transfer agent within the same PRMD, the lack of multivendor PRMDs may or may not be noticeable by the user. It will depend upon how the user's local PRMD has been set up to handle names and addresses, particularly those outside the PRMD. Standard directory service implementation is still under development. Multivendor PRMD will also be welcomed by the network manager, who will no longer be required to maintain independent routing databases using a different management tool for each PRMD.

Multivendor PRMD is not the only protocol under development for inclusion in subsequent releases of TOP 3.X. For example, there are specifications to allow interoperability with Administrative Management Domains (ADMD), those provided by public carriers in full conformance with CCITT X.400. A P7-like protocol that allows effective distribution of user agent functionality among personal computers and workstations is vital in many TOP environments. The user should be able to access mail on whichever MTA is most convenient or available.

TOP 3.0 does include one extension to the CCITT message-handling system standard. This extension is an interim method for transferring office document architecture, computer graphic metafile, and initial graphics exchange specification documents (see the following sections) through the mail system. Otherwise, the only contents required to be supported under the NBS Implementation Agreements is IA5 (ASCII) text.

Office Document Architecture and Interchange Format

One of the first discoveries that most computer users make is that getting a document from one machine to another, whether with FTAM or X.400, is insufficient. The incompatibility of word processors and text handlers makes it virtually impossible to revise any formatted document on any machine other than the one that created it. This is the challenge being attacked by the ISO Office Document Architecture (ODA) and Office Document Interchange Format (ODIF) protocols. Only ISO is not restricting itself to formatted text. The goal is to be able to create and transmit documents of any kind (word processing, spread sheets, graphics, facsimile, even typesetting) across a network and be able to reproduce, revise, and otherwise work on them at the other end.

Architectural concepts

Figure 5.9 is a conceptual model of the document generation process. It shows the three primary activities which must be performed in order to create a document. These are the editing process, the layout process, and the imaging process.

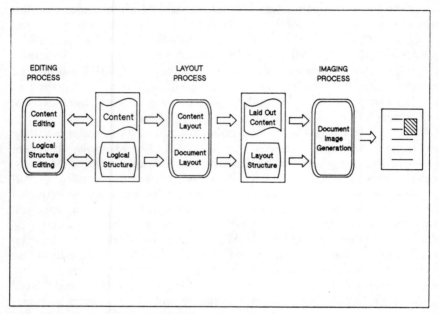

Figure 5.9   A document processing model.

The document editing process is split between the content editing and the logical structure editing. In a textual document, the content would be the words making up the document, while the logical structure would be the organization of the words into paragraphs, headings, footnotes, and chapters. For example, the logical structure for a letter might be a sender, a date, addressees, a main body, and attachments. In a compound document, the logical structure would include what contents are text, which are illustrations, and so on. The output of the editing phase is a document that can either proceed on to the layout phase or return to the editing phase for modification.

The output of the editing phase is not yet suitable for generating a human-usable document. That is the task of the layout process. Like the editing process, the layout process also consists of two interacting processes, the content layout and the document layout. Since the content layout must fit within the document layout, let us look at document layout first.

Document layout allocates the presentation medium being used to the various components making up the logical structure of the document. For example, a display screen may have areas reserved for menus, command entry, help annotation, and data display. A business letter may have specific areas on the page allocated for the sender's name, the date, the subject, and so on. Pages in this book have been laid out with specific margins surrounding the main text and illustrations fit inside the area normally used for text. Within the areas determined by the layout structure, the contents are formatted to fit. This may require sizing and scaling of graphic elements or breaking paragraphs of text into individual lines.

Once the document's contents and appearance are fully defined, the document is ready for the final step. The imaging process takes the document layout structure and the individually laid out contents within that structure and generates a physical document usable by humans. The output of the imaging process may be a display screen, printed paper, film, or whatever is appropriate to the document that is being produced.

The ISO Office Document Architecture is based on the document generation model in Figure 5.10. It is not intended to represent an actual implementation nor to restrict the processing which may be applied to an ODA document. The model defines three different forms of standard document interchange: processible form, formatted form, and formatted processible form.

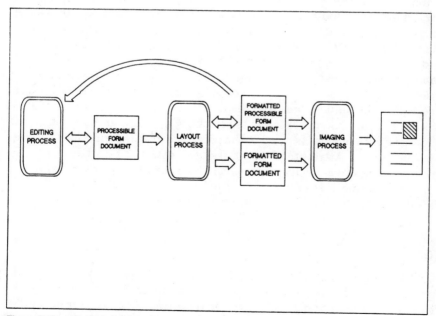

Figure 5.10 ISO ODA document types.

Processible form is the output of the editing process and may be either edited further or laid out. Formatted form and formatted processible form are the interchange outputs from the layout process. Formatted form is suitable only for input to the imaging process. No further editing or layout changes are possible as the information used to create the current layout is not retained with the document. Formatted processible form can be used as input to any of the three document generation processes. Formatted processible form contains not only the layout structure and laid-out content required to image the document but also the original content and logical structure it was derived from.

Computer Graphics Metafile (CGM)

The Computer Graphics Metafile standard is the ISO approach to moving graphics data from machine to machine. CGM specifies the format for storing graphics data in a file. It is graphics system independent as well as device independent. Once the picture description is encoded in a file, other tools such as X.400 or FTAM can be used for moving the data about the network. The key to CGM is the way it defines graphics in terms of the image content rather than as vectors or raster pixels.

CGM files are composed of metafile elements. There are three standards defined for encoding the metafile elements: clear text encoding, character encoding, and binary encoding. Each element consists of an element identifier and parameters. There are eight classes of elements. Delimiter elements provide functions such as begin metafile and end picture. Descriptor elements provide general-purpose description of capabilities assumed, such as numeric precision of arguments, number of colors available, and character sets used for textual information. Picture descriptor elements range from display scale factors to how line widths will be selected. Control elements set clipping limits and scale factors, while graphical elements provide the primitive drawing functions such as line and point. Attribute elements set the attributes to be used with graphical primitives such as line width and color or character orientation and size. Escape elements and external elements provide the ability to define functionality not provided in the standard.

TOP 3.0 ODA

TOP 3.0 specifies all three forms of document interchange, formatted, processible, and processible formatted. Content architectures are specified to allow interchange of character data (text), raster graphics data (facsimile), and geometric graphics data (using computer graphics metafile with binary encoding). Character content includes specification of details such as justification, fonts, character orientation, line spacing, and character spacing. Raster and geometric graphics contents provide similar flexibility.

Defined as part of the TOP 3.0 are two document "SUPER" classes. These define the logical structure for two generic types of documents; a memo or letter type document and a report type document. Using the SUPER class document profiles allows much more efficient transmission of data, as the information required to define the logical structure is known a priori and need not be included with the document transmitted.

Product Data Exchange

The need to transfer product data among users and applications is addressed by several standards. Product definition data, the subset of product data required to analyze, design, manufacture, and test a product, is addressed by the Initial Graphics Exchange Specification (IGES). Total product data, which includes data such as assembly instructions, process specifications, financial data, quality assurance, and testing data is addressed by two standards efforts. The IGES committee of the National Bureau of Standards is developing the Product Data Exchange Standard (PDES). PDES, in turn, is the basis for the ISO Standard for the Exchange of Product Model Data (STEP). The ultimate goal is for a single standard covering all product data needs over the entire product life cycle.

Initial Graphics Exchange Specification (IGES)

The Initial Graphics Exchange Specification provides high-level exchange of design information between CAD/CAM workstations. It provides indirect translation of data between the proprietary data formats in use on individual machines by translating the sending system's data into an intermediate neutral standard format that the receiving system can translate back into its native proprietary format. The IGES standard only specifies the translations. The transfer of translated data is provided by any convenient file transfer mechanism, for example, FTAM or X.400 in the TOP 3.0 world.

In many respects, IGES is similar to Computer Graphics Metafile. Both provide a commonly understood standard format for graphics data. However, the information content is vastly different. A CGM file is generated by an application from graphics data at the graphics device driver level. It is composed of lines, dots, characters, and fill patterns. It is like transmitting a raster image of a page of text. Although it is possible to reproduce the image, adding a line of text in the middle is very difficult, as the meaning and structure of the original data are not included. IGES, on the other hand, includes the generating data rather than the final image. For example, dimension lines retain their meaning as denoting dimensions. If a design change is made, the dimensions can change along with it. Rather than transferring the plotter output, IGES transfers the design database.

The composition of an IGES file gives the best indication of its orientation. The product definition data is divided into five sections. The start section is a text message for easy identification of the file contents. It does not require any translation to be read by a user. The start section is followed by the global section, which contains product-oriented information such as the name of the product, the responsible engineer, the company, and so on. The directory section describes the product data to follow while the parameter section contains the actual design information. A terminate section provides error checks on the contents.

MAP/TOP 3.0 specifics

In the absence of an existing standard for complete product data exchange, MAP/TOP 3.0 specifies version 3.0 of the Initial Graphics Exchange Specification. IGES version 3.0 provides for the exchange of data for drafting, curve modeling, surface modeling, finite element modeling, parametric design modeling, and electrical and electronic design. Version 4 of IGES, under development, adds solids modeling, plant design, manufacturing technology, architecture, engineering, and construction data interchange. Future versions of IGES, including version 4, will be considered for inclusion in MAP/TOP when they become available. The key to their inclusion would be the demand of users for the additional functionality. The same is true for the more efficient forms of IGES version 3 using binary and compressed ASCII file formats. Today these are not as widely implemented as the standard ASCII format chosen for MAP/TOP 3.0.

The TOP task force for product data exchange also intends to extend the product data exchange capability provided by MAP/TOP to include the Product Data Exchange Specification/Standard for Exchange of Product Model Data (PDES/STEP) when it becomes available. The addition of PDES/STEP will not replace the use of IGES in MAP/TOP 3.0. Rather it will provide an additional capability for future systems while IGES continues to serve the data exchange needs of current CAD/CAM systems.

Graphical Kernel System

The desire for a portable programming environment for graphics is met by the Graphical Kernel System (GKS). While technically not a networking standard, it has been included in MAP/TOP 3.0 for the same reason standard application interfaces are being specified for MMS, FTAM, and ACSE. The multivendor communications environment provided by MAP/TOP is severely diminished in effectiveness if applications remain tied to proprietary interfaces and languages and cannot cross vendor boundaries.

GKS provides a full complement of procedure calls for use in several programming languages. The two-dimensional version for simple images in document drawings and simple graphics on terminals has been an international standard since 1985. A three-dimensional version is under development but is not expected to reach standard status until at least 1988. MAP/TOP 3.0 specifies a subset of the two-dimensional version.

MAP/TOP 3.0 specifies GKS language bindings for Fortran-77, Fortran-77 subset, and C. Although not required by MAP/TOP 3.0, standard language bindings for GKS are also defined for Pascal, Ada, and BASIC. Subsetting of the available primitives is primarily in the nature of defining "private use" parameter values to simplify common programming needs in the MAP/TOP environment. For example, several public domain text fonts are defined for use, as are some extensions taken from the three-dimensional version for providing extended area fill capability.

Recap of Key Issues

The application services available to the MAP 2.1 or 2.2 user are limited. Those available as part of TOP 1.0 are even more so (FTAM file transfer only)! The rich array of services that make up MAP/TOP 3.0 will generate strong pressure on all MAP 2.X/TOP 1.0 implementations to upgrade, as well as causing many potential users to hold off until MAP/TOP 3.0 becomes commercially available in 1988. However, the power of MAP 2.X/TOP 1.0 should not be underestimated. The capabilities are very real and powerful, and they are available today for implementation of CIM solutions that are far superior to any available without MAP/TOP. Even those who plan to wait for 3.0 before full implementation can benefit from the experience of bringing up a MAP 2.X/TOP 1.0 pilot. It will provide a better understanding of what MAP/TOP networking technology really is and can do. Just remember to plan ahead for the conversion from MAP 2.X/TOP 1.0 to MAP/TOP 3.0, especially with any applications utilizing MMFS that will need to be revised for RS-511.

Applicable ISO Standards

ISO 7492 Computer Graphics Functional Specification of the Graphical Kernel System (2-D)

ISO 8571 File Transfer, Access, and Management (FTAM)

ISO 8613 Office Document Architecture (ODA) and Interchange Format

ISO 8632 Computer Graphics Metafile for the Storage and Transfer of Picture Description Information

ISO 8649 Service Definition for Common Application Service Elements (CASE)[1]

ISO 8650 Protocol Specification for Common Application Service Elements

ISO 8805 Graphical Kernel System (three dimensional)

ISO 8831 Job Transfer and Manipulation Concepts and Services

ISO 8832 Specification of the Basic Class Protocol for Job Transfer and Manipulation

ISO 8879 Standard Generalized Markup Language (SGML)

ISO 9040 Virtual Terminal Service

ISO 9041 Virtual Terminal Protocol

ISO 9066 Message Oriented Text Interchange Service—Reliable Transfer

ISO 9072 Message Oriented Text Interchange Service—Remote Operations

ISO 9506 Manufacturing Messaging Service (ISO version of RS-511)

---

[1]As this book went to press, the ISO subcommittee responsible for this standard was considering eliminating the distinction between SASE and CASE. This could result in ISO 8649/8650 being revised to include the Association Control Service Elements only, with Commitment, Concurrency, and Recovery being moved to their own standard designation number.

ISO 9594 Directory Services

ISO 9595 Common Management Information Service Definition

ISO 9596 Common Management Information Protocol Specification

Applicable CCITT Standards

X.400 Message Handling Systems: System Model—Service Elements

X.401 Message Handling Systems: Basic Service Elements and Optional User Facilities

X.408 Message Handling Systems: Encoded Information Type Conversion Rules

X.409 Message Handling Systems: Presentation Transfer Syntax and Notation

X.410 Message Handling Systems: Remote Operations and Reliable Transfer Server

X.411 Message Handling Systems: Message Transfer Layer

X.420 Message Handling Systems: Interpersonal Messaging User Agent Layer

X.430 Message Handling Systems: Access Protocol for Teletex Terminals

X.215 Session Service Definition for Open Systems Interconnection for CCITT Applications

X.225 Session Protocol Specification for Open Systems Interconnection for CCITT Applications

6

Common Protocol Layers

Once we move below the application services layer, MAP and TOP share common protocol specifications all the way down the OSI protocol stack through the link layer. In this chapter, we look at those common layers one by one. At each layer, we will examine the protocols specified and what they do, how they work, and their limitations. In the following two chapters, we will look at the physical layer needs of MAP and TOP respectively.

You can successfully build and run a MAP/TOP network without knowing any of the information in this chapter. Everything is provided by the network vendor. Except for network management, there is no way any user code can access these layers except through services such as those discussed in the previous chapter. You do not even get to pick and choose what you want, as these layers are all fully specified by the MAP/TOP specifications. The only area in which the options offer a significant choice is at the network layer, and that choice is simply whether you ever expect to have multiple LAN segments or if you are willing to forever be restricted to a single cable segment.

However, these layers do determine just what capabilities are available in the different MAP/TOP versions. They are the primary reason that MAP 2.X/TOP 1.0 cannot communicate with MAP/TOP 3.0. A knowledge of the intermediate layers makes it much easier to manage the network and keep it running once it is installed. Finally, vendors and others will assume you are familiar with the concepts whenever you are "talking networking."

Presentation Layer

The ISO OSI model delineates the application layer from the presentation layer on the basis of semantics versus syntax. The application layer is responsible for what the data means, while the presentation layer ensures that the representation of that data is understandable to the application protocols on both sides of the communication.

Another way to consider this division is in terms of abstract versus concrete encodings. The data handed to the presentation layer by the application layer for transfer to the remote application layer is in abstract form. For example, the data may be expressed as "the integer value of 241 decimal" or "a 14.5-mm-diameter hole 17 cm left of the line connecting points alpha and beta and 6 cm from the point named gamma." The data passed across the net from serving presentation to remote peer presentation is encoded in concrete terms. For example, "the integer 241" might be encoded as a single octet with value F1 hexadecimal or as the string of octets with values 30 hex, 32 hex, 34 hex, 31 hex (the ASCII string "0241"). One abstract representation of data used between application and presentation layers is ISO Abstract Syntax Notation 1 (ASN.1). The corresponding concrete syntax for presentation to presentation across the net is defined by ISO Basic Encoding Rules for ASN.1. The presentation layers can also negotiate other transfer syntaxes.

ISO connection-oriented presentation

The formal specifications for the ISO presentation layer are ISO 8822, Connection-Oriented Presentation Service Definition, and ISO 8823, Connection-Oriented Presentation Protocol Specification. ASN.1 is defined by ISO 8824, Specification for Abstract Syntax Notation 1, while the ASN.1 encoding rules are given by ISO 8825, Basic Encoding Rules for Abstract Syntax Notation 1. Before we look at ASN.1 and its encoding in the next section, let us first see how the presentation layer handles the encoding task.

At the time an association is being set up, and anytime thereafter, the presentation layer user can identify the data types it wants supported by the presentation layer. The presentation layer then selects and applies a set of encoding rules to use for the transfer syntax. The actual transfer syntax must be selected from a registered (and therefore unambiguous) set of named transfer syntaxes. The two peer presentation layer entities then exchange the selected name so that each knows precisely what transfer syntax is being used and knows that the other knows how to use it. These agreements on the transfer syntaxes to use are called presentation contexts and are key to the presentation layer's ability to provide communications independent of any syntax discrepancies between the two application layer entities being connected.

More than one transfer syntax can be negotiated into existence at any time. The presentation protocol includes as part of its Protocol Control Information (PCI) an indicator of the presentation context for each piece of data being transferred. The set of all agreed transfer syntaxes for the association is called the Defined Context Set (DCS). Maintaining consistent Defined Context Sets at each end of the association is the primary challenge faced by the presentation layer.

Defined context maintenance is performed using a confirmed protocol exchange whenever the DCS is changed. Typical of most protocols, most of the effort goes into the need to guard against Murphy's Law. For example, the presentation layer could be in the middle of such an exchange when it receives an Activity Interrupt and Discard packet from the session layer, leaving the local presentation layer in doubt as to whether its request for a new DCS got killed or the acceptance of that request got killed on its way back from the remote presentation layer.

Loss of DCS synchronization can result in one of the presentation entities receiving data in an unknown context. This event is seen by the user of that presentation entity as unreadable data received. To avoid this, the presentation user can negotiate the availability of Presentation DCS Restoration service. This service allows the presentation user to revert to the DCS active at a major synchronization point, a minor synchronization point, or an activity interrupt point.

Abstract Syntax Notation 1

One of the syntaxes used between application layer and presentation layer is ISO Abstract Syntax Notation 1 (ASN.1). ASN.1 is based upon the CCITT X.409 standard encoding syntax and is upward compatible with it. The structure of X.409, as implemented in ASN.1, has been modified to allow the addition of more data types. The most important change was the addition of the object identifier. The object identifier is a hierarchical notation used to identify and select a concrete syntax for any abstract one. This extension was critical in the more general environment of ASN.1 usage. Remember that CCITT X.409 was originally defined solely in the context of X.400 messaging. General usage in all environments requires a larger selection of concrete syntaxes of varying complexity.

ASN.1 is the syntax specified for many application protocols. It is part of ACSE (Association Control Service Elements), FTAM (File Transfer, Access and Management), MMS (Manufacturing Messaging Service), and Virtual Terminal. It is also used by both directory services and network management. However, ASN.1 is more than just an abstract syntax for communications between application and presentation layers. As a logically complete, well-defined syntax for describing complex abstract concepts, it is the preferred form for defining protocol data units in all current ISO and CCITT communications standards.

The fundamental concept of ASN.1 is the data element. A data element is any unit of information that can be named or identified. Each data element is composed of the data type and the data value. The data type specifies the type of information making up the data element, while the data value is the value of the information making up that data element. Any data element can be described in one of two ways. A data element can be described abstractly by its standard notation, a means of expressing the type or value without reference to any encoding detail, or concretely by its standard representation, which provides the rules for encoding values of a given data type.

Standard representation of data elements

The standard representation of data elements shows just how concrete the syntax must be for successful communication. Even the numbering of octets and individual bits in a data element must be defined. Figure 6.1 shows the convention used by ISO ASN.1 standard representation.

Start of packet	Octet n-1	Octet n	Octet n+1	End of packet
	X X X X X X X X	X X X X X X X X	X X X X X X X X	
	8 7 6 5 4 3 2 1	8 7 6 5 4 3 2 1	8 7 6 5 4 3 2 1	

Figure 6.1 Numbering of octets and bits.

The representation of each data element is composed of three components: the identifier tells what the type of the data is, the length specifies the size of the representation of the contents, and the contents of the data element is the value of the data. These three components are often referred to as the TLV (Type-Length-Value) of a data element.

The identifier uniquely identifies the data type by class, form, and class number. Bits 8 and 7 of the first octet are the class bits. If both are 0, the class is defined by ASN.1 (and X.409) and is called a universal class. The other three classes are application specific (class bits 01), defined by standards other than ASN.1; context specific (class bits 10); and private use (class bits 11), outside the scope of ASN.1 and X.409. Bit 6, the form bit, can be either 0, signifying a primitive form containing a simple value, or 1, signifying a constructed form composed of multiple values. The remaining five bits of the first octet are either the class number (or class ID) or a multioctet identifier indicating that the class number follows in one or more identifier octets. The number of octets making up a multioctet identifier is determined dynamically. Bit 8 of each subsequent identifier octet is checked. If the value is 1, bits 7 through 1 are part of the identifier and there is at least one more octet making up the identifier. If the value is 0, bits 7 through 1 are the last bits of the multioctet identifier.

The length component specifies the length in octets of the contents. This component can have three different forms. The short form is one octet long and is identified by bit 8 having a value of 0. Bits 7 through 1 then specify the length of the contents in octets. If the length of the contents is greater than 127 octets, the long form of the length component can be used. The long form is indicated by bit 8 being a 1. The remaining seven bits then indicate the length of the length field in octets. The impossible long form value of length-of-length of 0 is used to specify the indefinite form, where the length of the contents must be determined from the content itself (such as a string of ASCII printable characters terminated by an octet of 0s).

Finally, the contents field contains the actual information to be communicated. This must be interpreted in accordance with the identifier and may be simple or constructed. Constructions may be nested without restriction, although finite machine resources may result in the imposition of implementation limits.

The universal class single octet identifiers are called the built-in types. These are all defined by ASN.1 and X.409 to handle data types of general usefulness. Both the notation and the representation are part of the standard. Standard keywords have been assigned for each and will frequently be seen referenced in various standards without reference to their being defined by ASN.1 and X.409. Table 6.1 lists all the built-in types and their keywords.

TABLE 6.1 ASN.1 Built-In Types

Class number	Data type
0	Reserved
1	Boolean
2	Integer
3	Bit string
4	Octet string
5	Null
6–15	Unassigned
16	Sequence (or sequence of)
17	Set (or set of)
18	Numeric string
19	Printable string
20	Teletex string (or S61 string)
21	Videotex string (or S100 string)
22	ISO646 string (or IA5 string)
23	UTC time
24	Generalized time
25	Graphic string
26–31	Unassigned
31	Reserved (multioctet identifier)

MAP/TOP specifics

MAP 2.1/TOP 1.0 does not use the presentation layer. As a result, conversion of data representation is not available for applications layer use. MMFS provides its own representation standard and is not affected. User applications based on MAP 2.1 CASE must handle all their own data representation. Any requirements to match syntax or encodings are the responsibility of the user application. MAP 2.1/TOP 1.0 FTAM is similarly restricted to either a MAP 2.1 CASE-like stream of binary octets or the simple common mode of text file transfer. The representation burden has been shifted out of the nonexistant presentation layer and put into the local FTAM implementation. While adequate for usage in the United States, the restriction on text files to only the 7-bit ASCII character set forces other nationalities to communicate with incomplete alphabets.

MAP/TOP 3.0 includes ISO kernel presentation layer capability. This allows support of the international standard versions of MMS, ACSE, FTAM, VT, and other application layer protocols. The specifics will be determined by the NBS OSI Implementation Workshops as experience is gained building the first MAP/TOP 3.0 products.

Session Layer

The ISO session layer standard is defined by ISO 8326, Connection-Oriented Session Service, and ISO 8327, Connection-Oriented Session Protocol. The lowest layer to recognize the existence of users, these have been approved international standards since 1984. The fact that it preceded the standardization of the layers above it (such as Presentation, ACSE, FTAM, and Virtual Terminal) has created some challenges. Now that the upper layers have been defined well enough to determine what services they really need from the session layer, secondary and tertiary side effects of session layer definitions are being discovered. As a result, there were minor changes both proposed and occurring at the session layer at the same time MAP/TOP 3.0 was being finalized. Such "surprises" are one of the key reasons why you should utilize standard protocols rather than develop your own whenever possible. The standards review process will resolve more problems than most users will ever experience, but you certainly do not want your first indication of an oversight to be a halted production line or an aborted process.

The ISO session layer provides a wide variety of support functions desirable in a connection-oriented user protocol exchange. It provides for establishment and termination of a communications session. It maps the user association onto an appropriate transport connection capable of providing the services requested by the user. And it can provide low-level capabilities such as data synchronization, independent activities over a single association, and control over who gets to "talk" when and for how long.

Flexibility in implementing the session layer is provided by dividing the various capabilities into "functional units." Then, depending on the applications being supported, only the functional units required need be supplied. The functional units defined are kernel, half-duplex, duplex, negotiated release, typed data, major synchronize, minor synchronize, resynchronize, capability data exchange, exceptions, and activity management.

The ISO connection-oriented session was derived from CCITT connection-oriented session. CCITT defines four standard subsets of the 11 functional units: the Session Kernel, the Basic Combined Subset (BCS), the Basic Synchronized Subset (BSS), and the Basic Activity Subset (BAS). The relationship of the functional units to the CCITT subsets is shown in Figure 6.2.

Although not part of the ISO standard, the subset terminology is often seen in discussions of session level capabilities.

	Session Kernel	Basic Combined Subset	Basic Synchronized Subset	Basic Activity Subset
kernel	☆	☆	☆	☆
half-duplex		☆	☆	☆
duplex		☆	☆	
negotiated release			☆	
typed data			☆	☆
major synchronize			☆	
minor synchronize			☆	☆
resynchronize			☆	
capability data exchange				☆
exceptions				☆
activity management				☆

Figure 6.2 CCITT session subset capabilities.

Session functional units

The kernel functional unit provides the bare minimum session layer services. The only services provided are connect, disconnect, and transfer data. Some services, such as segmentation and reassembly, are optional. There are three unique disconnect services, each serving a different need. Orderly disconnect provides for dismantling of the underlying connection with no loss of data. User-initiated abort allows a using entity to unilaterally terminate the association. Network-initiated abort occurs when the underlying connection is lost and the session layer is unable to replace it and maintain the user-to-user association.

Two-way communication over a session association requires either the duplex or the half-duplex functional unit. Duplex allows either end of the association to transmit data to the other end at any time, including while receiving data. Half-duplex provides a token exchange which determines which end of the association is permitted to transmit at any particular moment. The half-duplex functional unit permits efficient utilization of the half-duplex data communications links which are common in long distance point-to-point dial-up and leased line telephone communications environments.

The typed data functional unit provides independent verification that the sending and receiving session entities are properly synchronized. For example, this capability is used when multiple activities are being served over the same association. Typing the data transmitted ensures that data is delivered to the correct activity when it arrives. Typed data is also used when the backup and resynchronize after a failure capabilities are in use. In this case, it serves to ensure that both sender and receiver are truly back into synchronization.

More sophisticated applications working with distributed interdependent transactions or large data streams (such as an FTAM with resynchronization and crash recovery) require the services provided by major synchronize, minor synchronize, and resynchronize functional units. These functional units provide the ability to checkpoint work in progress and back up to a checkpoint for restarting in the event of failure. The two key capabilities are major synchronization and minor synchronization. The difference is in the guarantees and overhead involved. Major synchronization checkpoints are negotiated whenever they occur so that both ends of the connection know that they can back up to the last agreed major synchronization point if required. Minor synchronization checkpoints have less overhead and are not negotiated. Resynchronization to a minor checkpoint is on a best-efforts basis. There are no guarantees. You can imagine a large file transfer interrupted by a system crash trying to get restarted. Each end would start with the latest minor synchronization point known to it and work back until both recognized a common one. If none could be found that were more recent than the last major synchronization point, the major synchronization point would be used.

The negotiated release functional unit is usually considered a part of the synchronizing functional units as it serves a similar function when terminating a session. Continuing our FTAM example, it is not sufficient for all the data in the file to have been transmitted to the remote system and its receipt acknowledged. The file transfer is not complete until all data is written to the disk drive and the remote copy of the file closed. Negotiated release allows both ends of the transaction to be assured that all functions associated with the current association are completed before releasing the association.

The last three functional units (capability data exchange, exceptions, and activity management) combine to accurately and easily handle multiple activities. Multiple activities allow an application to independently operate, suspend, and resume different activities with different requirements over a single session association. These functional units are required by message-handling systems based on CCITT X.400.

The choice of which functional units to implement is an important one. Different applications require different functional units. Two-way communications require at least the kernel and either duplex or half-duplex functional units. Few applications can function on any less.

MAP/TOP specifics

MAP/TOP has been based on the ISO session definition since MAP 2.0. Since there were no applications available at the time that required any of the extended services associated with the synchronization or activity functional units, the implementation was kept minimal. MAP 2.1/TOP 1.0 specifies only the kernel and the duplex functional units.

MAP 3.0 and TOP 3.0 diverge in their session-level specifications because of the support of message-handling systems by TOP 3.0. The MAP 3.0 session is the same requirement as MAP 2.1. The kernel functional unit provides session connection, data transfer, orderly release, provider abort, and user abort services. The duplex functional unit makes the services bidirectional. TOP 3.0 adds to the MAP 3.0 functional units the minimum requirements for CCITT X.400 message handling. The exceptions are activity management, half-duplex, and minor synchronize functional units. The specific session services required from these functional units are specified in the NBS OSI Implementation Agreements.

Transport Layer

The transport layer is assigned the responsibility of providing reliable, transparent data flow across the network between end users. In the process, ISO defines three different types of networks the transport may be required to work over: type A, type B, and type C. A type A network is one which already provides a reliable enough connection from the point of view of the user. To be classified type A, a network must meet two criteria. First, the number of communication errors which are not detected and corrected by the network, the undetected or residual error rate, must be low enough to meet the needs of the application without any additional service on the part of the transport. Second, the number of communication errors which are detected but not corrected by the network, the rate of signaled failures, must also be acceptable. These are errors for which the network informs the transport that a failure has occurred but leaves any recovery action up to the upper layers. In other words, a type A network requires neither error detection nor error recovery capability from the transport layer in order to provide adequate service to the user.

Type B networks are similar to type A networks in safely detecting error of concern to the user but differ in having too many unrecoverable (by the network layer) errors to meet the user's needs. With a type B network, the transport can still depend on the network to detect errors but now must provide services to recover from those errors detected by the network.

A type C network is inadequate for the user application both in terms of the number of errors which occur that are not reported and in terms of the number of errors which occur that are reported. Provision of useful service to the user requires the transport service to both detect and recover from errors. Note that the definition of adequacy of network service is up to the user. A type A network for one application may very well be considered a type C network by another application.

Classes of transport

The ISO standard for transport protocols defines different classes of transport protocol service to meet the varying user needs for operation over different types of networks. They also add in a second class distinction, multiplexing. Figure 6.3 shows the mapping of different network types and multiplexing capability to the five defined classes of ISO transport.

Class 0 transport, also known as simple class or TP0, provides the simplest kind of transport connection. This class of transport does little more than map session requests to the transport layer directly to the network layer. It was originally developed by CCITT for use with Teletex.

	Type A Network	Type B Network	Type C Network
One–to–one	Class 0 Simple Class	Class 1 Basic Error Recovery Class	none defined
Multiplexed	Class 2 Multiplexing Class	Class 3 Error Recovery Class	Class 4 Error Detection and Recovery Class

Figure 6.3 ISO transport classes.

One step up from simple class is basic error recovery class (class 1 transport or TP1). This protocol specification takes the basic TP0 functionality and adds the ability to recover from errors detected by the network. This protocol was also originally developed by CCITT, this time for use over X.25 networks. It too is intended as a low-end protocol for use on low-cost, minimal function hardware.

A different first step up from simple class is multiplexing class (class 2 or TP2). Class 2 takes the minimal capabilities provided by class 0 and adds the ability to multiplex multiple transport connections over the same type A network connection. This allows the user to make cost versus throughput trade-offs in the usage of network resources while still taking advantage of the quality of service provided by the network.

Class 3 is the error recovery class or TP3. It combines the error recovery capabilities of TP1 with the multiplexing capabilities of TP2. It is used to provide the same cost versus throughput trade-offs available under TP2 along with the ability to recover from lost connections and other failures such as might occur over a period of time.

Class 4, the error-detection and recovery class or TP4, is the most complex protocol definition. It not only provides all the functions available in the other four classes but also adds the ability to detect errors which were not detected by the network service. This makes it the only transport definition capable of providing connection-oriented reliable data transfer over a connectionless network.

Services provided

All classes of ISO transport provide the same two basic services to the transport user. These are connection service and data transfer service. Connection service enables the transport user to establish a transport connection and to terminate an existing transport connection. The disconnect service is not required to guard against loss of data, as that function is provided in the session layer protocol according to the ISO OSI model.

Data transfer service is also divided into two separate categories. Normal data transfer service provides a reliable data stream connection between transport users on two different machines, including segmentation and flow control as required by the underlying network and receiving transport user. Expedited data transfer service, on the other hand, allows the transfer of a limited amount of data (a single packet) outside the normal data stream. The expedited packet is not subjected to the flow control applied to the normal data stream.

MAP/TOP specifics

MAP/TOP networks are built atop a connectionless network facility— ISO connectionless internet over IEEE 802.2 type 1. The only ISO transport capable of providing adequate service is class 4. The MAP 2.1 specification calls for the complete ISO TP4 protocol, including expedited data and segmentation capabilities. It also called for the ability to negotiate down to TP2 from TP4; however that requirement was removed in the MAP 2.1 errata, where it was made optional and rejectable.

While the full protocol is required by MAP 2.2, many aspects are not fully defined. For example, connection setup parameters such as security, acknowledgment time, throughput, transit delay, priority, and residual error are ignored when a connection is set up. At least some of these will probably be defined for MAP/TOP 3.0. A network management interface for specifying parameters such as timeout values, counters, preferred negotiation bids, and addresses is strongly recommended; but no guidance is provided on how to implement it in a standard way. TSAP and SSAP value assignments are left up to the local implementation as well. However, it is required that the combination of NSAP, TSAP, and SSAP be sufficient to uniquely identify the application entity involved in the communication.

Aside from further clarification, the only significant changes probable in MAP/TOP 3.0 are the reinstatement of the requirement to negotiate down to TP2. This will be part of the movement to allow MAP/TOP to take advantage of the connection-oriented network services provided by X.25 that did not get settled in time to make it into MAP 2.2.

Network Layer

The network layer tends to be the most confusing conceptually because of the recursive nature of networking networks. The confusion is not helped by inconsistency between the models used to describe the network layer. The ISO standard governing the network layer, "Internal Organization of the Network Layer," and the IEEE 802.1 LAN architecture standard both divide the network layer into four sublayers. However, each divides the functionality up differently and uses different names for the sublayers. The MAP 2.1 and 2.2 standards add to the confusion by defining their architecture in terms of the IEEE model, then specifying protocols defined in terms of the ISO version. TOP 1.0 is more consistent and restricts itself to just the ISO structure.

IEEE network layer internal structure

We will discuss the IEEE model of the network layer first, as it provides a more intuitive view of the various functional requirements inside the network layer. While the overall structure (Figure 6.4) consists of four sublayers, it can be thought of as two layers, each made up of two sublayers. Each pair of sublayers, 3.1 plus 3.2 and 3.3 plus 3.4, functions similarly. The lower two sublayers provide the ability to communicate with any other node on the same network, selecting the proper link to use to send the data toward the ultimate destination. The upper two sublayers do the same, except they work on the scale where each network is a link, and the choice to be made is which network to send the packet out on to get it to its ultimate destination. The upper, internetwork routing sublayer is not concerned with the routing required within any particular network. That is the responsibility of the lower, intranetwork routing sublayer.

Within the upper two or lower two sublayers, the functionality split is along a different dimension. Sublayers 3.2 and 3.4 are both concerned with network routing (the former within the specific subnetwork attached, the latter in the global, internetwork sense). Similarly, sublayers 3.1 and 3.3 are both concerned with matching the needs of the routing sublayer to the actual services provided by the next layer down (the data link layer in the case of 3.1, the intranetwork routing sublayer in the case of 3.3).

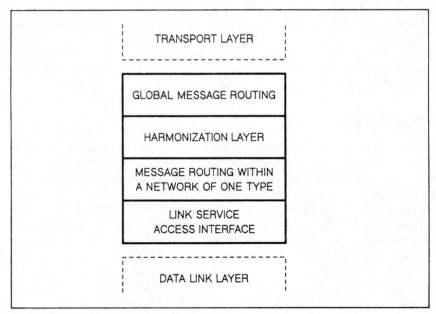

Figure 6.4   IEEE organization of the network layer.

The goal is to keep the individual sublayers as simple as possible, while allowing mixing and matching of various protocols. The internetwork routing sublayer can perform its tasks without regard to the addressing needs of the intranetwork routing sublayer. That translation is handled by the harmonization sublayer. The glue sublayers (3.1 and 3.3) can even provide such services as matching a connection-oriented link or network to a connectionless network or internet, implementing a complete protocol to set up and tear down connections as required and are completely transparent to the using sublayer. Conversely, any of the sublayers could be null if their services were not required by the particular protocols above and below them.

ISO network layer internal structure

The ISO structure, while it appears similar, is derived from a very different set of objectives and as a consequence divides the required functions differently. It is important to note, however, that there are two critical commonalities between the ISO and IEEE structures. First, both are only models. Neither dictates how the network layer must actually be implemented (the same as with the ISO OSI reference model). Second, they both include the same functionality, only the split-up is different.

The IEEE version was motivated by the need to show how a network layer could be built atop the IEEE 802 LAN standards, which defined

the physical and data link layers. Beyond that, they just wanted to keep
it as simple as possible for maximum understanding. This they succeeded in doing quite well. Their structure emphasizes how little impact
any differences between the services provided by the IEEE 802.2 link
protocols and those services required by any other network protocol need
have on the total network layer. All the glue can be provided in the access
sublayer, with no changes required in the network protocol.

ISO, on the other hand, needed a framework for developing the
protocol standards which would make up the network layer. They opted
for the split of functionality shown in Figure 6.5 to facilitate standards
development. In effect, what they have done is the same as the IEEE
structure, but they have split out the routing and relaying function from
the internetwork protocol in the top sublayer and merged the access
layer (as defined by IEEE) into the intranetwork sublayer. Routing and
relaying were split out because they recognized that while a common
internetwork protocol was vital to provide open systems, the routing and
relaying function is unique to intermediate systems and the needs are
much too diverse to allow the same commonality. The lower layers were
merged because they recognized that cost-effective networks are
matched to their underlying data link layer. The split between the two
lowest layers of the IEEE model, while convenient for consistency within
the model, would never be specified in isolation and could be combined
into one sublayer.

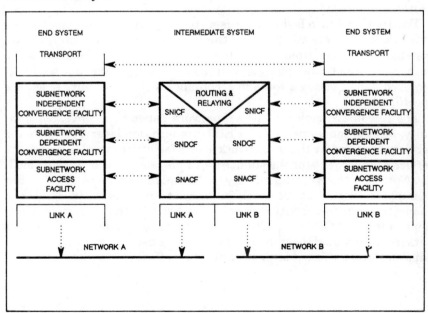

Figure 6.5 ISO organization of the network layer.

The specific functional split of the ISO network structural model is straightforward. The lowest layer, the Subnetwork Access Facility (SNACF) provides the network layer functions of the particular subnetwork attached. For example, a node attached to an X.25 network would require the X.25 network layer protocols to be provided by this layer. On an IEEE 802 LAN, on the other hand, there are no network layer requirements specific to 802, so the layer would be null.

At the other extreme, the highest layer is the Subnetwork Independent Convergence Facility (SNICF). This layer is the internet protocol that the using transport sees. Because it is independent of the specifics of the particular underlying subnetwork, it allows a common open systems interface for all transport users. Thus, the using transport on an X.25 node would see the same network capability as the using transport on an 802.4 network and could communicate successfully without consideration of the specific subnetwork in use by either end of the connection or any others that might be used in providing the connection. The specific services that are provided to the transport user will, of course, reflect the assumptions made about the network capabilities utilized, such as the expected network topology, the technical and economic trade-offs associated with assuming any particular underlying service rather than another, the difficulty of constructing the required services from those provided by the underlying network or link protocols, and just the degree of complexity acceptable in the implementation protocol.

The routing and relaying layer is a special provision for constructing networks of networks. It provides the relaying function in intermediate systems to connect from end system to end system. It determines the path over which the packets will travel, interpreting addresses as required and selecting a route in accordance with any quality of service specifications.

The remaining sublayer, the subnetwork dependent convergence facility, has the same role as the IEEE harmonization layer. It adjusts the services provided by the subnetwork access facility protocol to match the service requirements of the subnetwork independent convergence facility. Note that this adjustment may be "negative" as well as positive. For example, using a connectionless internet protocol SNICF over a connection-oriented SNACF requires an SNDCF that sets up connections in the SNACF as required but uses those connections solely to pass datagrams. Again, depending on the already existing services at the two adjacent levels, this sublayer may also be null.

ISO connectionless internet protocol

One protocol designed to take advantage of the ISO network layer organizational structure is ISO connectionless internet protocol. It provides data and control information exchange in a connectionless environment and can also function, albeit with less than optimum efficiency, when the underlying service is connection oriented. When used as the subnetwork independent convergence facility, the only service it requires from the subnetwork dependent convergence facility is the ability to deliver a protocol data unit by specifying only the source address, the destination address, and the quality of service required.

The ISO connectionless internet protocol provides all other functions required to deliver a connectionless network service to the using transport. This includes a wide variety of functions. It must put together protocol data units and properly remove the protocol control information upon receipt. It must analyze the header of each PDU to determine whether it should be delivered to the transport layer, forwarded to an end user on its own subnetwork, forwarded to another intermediate system gateway, or discarded as undeliverable.

All the steps required are illustrated in Figure 6.6. Protocol data units come in either from the using transport or up from the network. Service data units received from the using transport must be built into protocol data units. Packets coming in from the network must be reassembled if segmented, then checked for header errors. Any errors, including timeouts caused by an inability to process in a timely manner, will cause the packet to be discarded, which may then generate an error report PDU.

Regardless of source, all valid PDUs eventually get to the PDU processing section. There they are first subjected to header format analysis to determine where they should go next. Those that pass the optional security tests are either decomposed for delivery to the local transport layer or checked by lifetime control before handing control over to outbound processing. The lifetime control consists of decrementing a counter in the header of the packet each time the packet passes through the internet protocol on a system and discarding the packet if the counter reaches 0 before it reaches its final destination. The lifetime counter may be decremented by more than 1 if processing is particularly slow.

Outbound processing is hierarchical. The first step is determining which subnetwork to send the PDU out on, which may depend on the quality of service required as well as the ultimate destination. Once the network is picked, the particular destination on that network must be chosen (either the end-user system or the next gateway on the route to the end-user system). If at either point the routing or forwarding process fails to determine a valid, usable route, the PDU is discarded. If a valid route is available and route recording is turned on, the decision is recorded in the packet header. Finally, with all changes to the header completed, the checksum for the header can be calculated. Note that the protocol uses a checksum over just the header information and not the entire packet. As a connectionless protocol, it needs to be sure its header

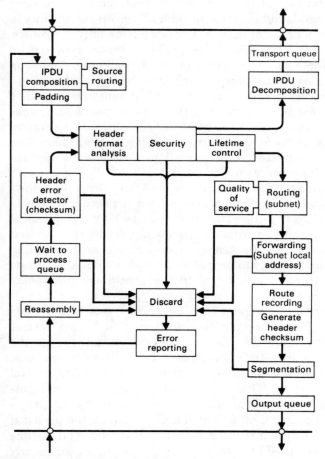

Figure 6.6 ISO connectionless network protocol. *(By Permission of General Motors. Reproduced from GM's* Manufacturing Automation Protocol—A Communication Network Protocol for Open Systems Interconnection Version 2.2, *August 1, 1986.)*

information is correct. However, it is not responsible for delivering error-free data, so it does not assume the burden of protecting all user data in addition to its own. The final step before delivering the protocol data unit to the subnetwork for transmission to the next destination is to perform any segmentation required by the selected subnetwork. If the packet requiring segmentation has the "do not segment" flag set, it is an error, and the packet is discarded.

ISO connection-oriented network protocol

The ISO standard for connection-oriented networks is X.25 Packet Level Protocol for Data Terminal Equipment, often abbreviated as X.25 PLP. This protocol is based on CCITT recommendation X.25, which is the dominant wide area network standard offered by PTTs and their equivalents worldwide.

CCITT X.25 is an interesting recommendation for a number of reasons. Historically, it has numerous parallels with the MAP/TOP movement. First approved in 1976, it was rushed through the standardization process to meet the demands of PTTs for a common packet switching protocol standard. Like MAP/TOP, it specifies a whole series of protocol standards aimed at providing vendor-independent wide area networking. And, like MAP/TOP, it has become a tremendous success. The challenge for the MAP/TOP task force is to avoid falling into the same traps that snared X.25 during its development. In the rush to make the standard, ambiguities and errors got into the specification and were not found until widespread implementation had occurred. This resulted in incompatible connection requirements which persist to this day. A computer vendor wishing to offer CCITT X.25 networking must certify its offering with each individual X.25 service provider because of implementation differences between providers. At the same time, each service provider must have its own certification test suite, as there is no common standard defining conformance to the X.25 standard. This is equivalent to each MAP/TOP user (such as GM, McDonnell Douglas, or *you*) having to develop their own qualification test suite and subject each vendor to it before purchasing their equipment. Clearly, this is not the goal of MAP/TOP and any delays in MAP/TOP 3.0 availability required to avoid similar problems are well worthwhile.

Technically, CCITT X.25 is composed of a series of protocols spanning the services normally provided by the physical, link, network, and even transport layers of the ISO OSI reference model. (Remember, the ISO work on the OSI reference model started in 1977, the year after CCITT approved X.25; therefore CCITT cannot be blamed for ignoring it.) Since X.25 was a service being offered to computer-user customers, it also includes specification of the interface protocol into the network services as well as the peer-to-peer protocols providing the service.

The ISO version strips away the data link and physical layer parts of CCITT X.25 and concentrates on the connection-oriented network layer capabilities (the fact that some services, such as providing multiple connections between the same two end users, are normally provided by the transport layer is ignored). The result is a protocol specification which allows access to worldwide X.25 network service from architectures, such as MAP/TOP, based on the ISO OSI reference model.

ISO X.25 PLP can be used as the subnetwork independent convergence facility, providing a connection-oriented networking capability suitable for use with simpler transport protocols such as ISO TP2. Development work is under way to extend this facility to transparently include networks based on LAN as well as on WAN connections. ISO X.25 PLP can also be used as a subnetwork access facility, providing worldwide communications to networks based on other subnetwork independent convergence protocols, in particular ISO connectionless network protocol. While not as efficient, the connection-oriented service provided by the X.25 protocol is thrown away by the connectionless internet and must be duplicated by transport to provide connection-oriented service to the application; it does work well.

MAP/TOP specifics

MAP 2.X and TOP 1.0 specify the ISO connectionless internetwork service. This protocol provides a perfect fit on top of IEEE 802 networks. As the subnetwork independent convergence protocol, it does not need a subnetwork dependent convergence facility or subnetwork access facility between it and the 802.2 link layer. For wide area networking, the ISO X.25 PLP (or whatever equivalent is required by the local PTT providing X.25 service) can be installed as a subnetwork access facility, and the subnetwork dependent convergence protocol specified by the NBS OSI implementation agreements can be used to match it up to the connectionless internet sublayer. Since the routing and relaying algorithm is undefined in the ISO connectionless network protocol, one defined by GM for the MAP 2.1 standard is used.

Two versions of the ISO connectionless network protocol are allowed, the inactive subset and the full protocol. The inactive subset may be used only if no internetting is required and no segmentation is required. That is, all destinations can be reached directly using 802.2 link level addresses. All destinations are on the same subnetwork or one connected by repeaters or bridges. The transport must also have already segmented all packets down to the size required by the link level. If all of these conditions are not met, the full ISO connectionless protocol is required. PDU composition, PDU decomposition, header format analysis, PDU lifetime control, routing, forwarding, segmenting, reassembly, discarding, header error detection, and error reporting must all be supported. All other functions, which are padding, security, complete source routing, partial source routing, priority, route recording, and quality of service maintenance, are optional and may or may not be provided by the implementor. The only requirement is that if any of the optional functions are requested in a packet and not available in the implementation, the packet will be processed as if the function had not been requested rather than treating it as an error and discarding the packet. The only exceptions are the security and complete source routing functions. Unsupportable requests for these must cause the packet to be discarded and an error report generated.

The NBS OSI implementation agreements specify how the subnetwork dependent convergence facility will be used to provide service for the connectionless internet over X.25 virtual circuits. Most of the agreements are aimed at keeping the implementation as simple as possible rather than optimizing cost or performance. Connections will be opened upon demand (permanent virtual circuits will not be used) and only closed by administrative request or timeout. The same virtual circuit will be used for all outbound packets to any given intermediate system or end user system on the X.25 network. There will be at most two switched virtual circuits at any time between any pair of systems. The default throughput class must be used, and the delivery confirmation and transparent data (D-bit and Q-bit) facilities must not be used. Window and packet size negotiation must be supported, but only the default sizes must be accepted. About the only X.25 facility taken advantage of is the M-bit (more flag), which is used to simulate support of up to 1000-byte packets if the actual packet size negotiated is not at least that large.

The actual provision of X.25 service is considered outside the scope of the MAP/TOP specification. Since it is being used strictly to provide a point-to-point connection for the internet protocol, it could even be considered an alternate link level protocol. As long as it meets the needs of the NBS implementation agreements, implementation details are up to the local system.

MAP/TOP 3.0 plans for the network layer all include the MAP 2.1 protocols and capabilities. Work is under way to define a connection-oriented network layer as well to avoid wasting the connection-oriented capabilities inherent in X.25. This work was originally planned to be included in MAP 2.2 but was incomplete when MAP 2.2 was finalized. Since there is much sentiment in the MAP/TOP community in favor of connectionless internetting, the inclusion of an efficient connection-oriented network layer is not certain even in MAP/TOP 3.0.

Link Layer

Like the application layer, there is a profusion of accepted standards available at the link layer. The only two which count for MAP/TOP purposes are IEEE 802.2 (required for IEEE 802 local area networks) and Link Access Protocol, Balanced (LAPB, required for CCITT X.25 connection). The specifications for LAPB are set by the provider of the X.25 public data network service, right down to required and forbidden options. Since they have no impact on MAP/TOP network operation, we will not consider them further.

IEEE 802.2 logical link control

The IEEE 802.2 standard defines a multipoint peer-to-peer protocol optimized for use over local area networks such as those defined by the other IEEE 802 standards. The standard itself specifies three totally different types of link level service. Type 1 and type 2 services are the basic connectionless and connection-oriented services, respectively. Type 1 allows the exchange of data without the overhead of setting up or maintaining a connection. No message sequencing, acknowledgment, flow control, or error recovery are provided. Conversely, type 2 does establish a connection before providing service, and it provides message sequencing, flow control, and error recovery. Type 3 service provides reliable connectionless service using limited frame acknowledgment, limited flow control, and retransmission on a single-frame basis. All three types use 32-bit cyclic redundancy check codes to ensure that any packets delivered are free of random bit errors.

There are three classes of IEEE 802.2 protocol implementation defined. Class 1 provides type 1 connectionless service only. Class 2 provides both type 1 connectionless and type 2 connection-oriented services. Class 3 also includes type 1 connectionless service but adds type 3 single-frame service rather than type 2 as class 2 did.

Type 1 connectionless service

The type 1 service provides a single-access service. That means that no overhead is required to set up communications. The first time it is accessed, it can communicate. Since it is connectionless, no context is maintained by the link level, and each access must include all the information required for successful delivery. This per-packet overhead includes addresses, quality of service selections, and any options desired. In return for the extra overhead on each packet, no call setup time or overhead is required nor are there any resources to be released when communications are completed.

Since there is no call setup, all those parameters normally negotiated during call setup must be agreed to a priori. Both users must agree in advance on all options, including class of service and maximum data unit size. Not only must both users agree, but each user must have compatible agreements with the link layer service provider at its end. Since it is up to the user to detect duplicated, missing, or out of order packets, the link layer is under no obligation to notify the user of invalid service requests. Any such notification is a local implementation decision, governed by network management needs.

Type 3 confirmed service

Type 3 confirmed service, also called single-frame service or acknowledged connectionless service, is in many ways similar to type 1 service. Like type 1, each access request must include addresses, quality of service, and any option requests. There is no context maintained by the link layer and no call setup time or traffic. The three-way a priori agreements between users and between each user and its serving link on class of service, options, and data unit size must also be supplied. The big difference is that single-frame service certifies delivery of each packet and automatically retransmits any which are not acknowledged.

Type 3 service frees the link layer user from concern over delivery of each packet. This is done by detecting and correcting for missing or duplicated protocol data units and notifying the requesting user of any errors or invalid requests. The price paid for this service is a stiff one. The requesting user cannot present a second packet to the link layer for delivery until the previous one is either successfully delivered or determined to be undeliverable. Transfers of data streams can be handled far more efficiently by using a connection-oriented protocol which does not have to stop and wait for each packet, either in the form of type 2 link layer service or a full-powered transport protocol over type 1 link service. Making up for this restriction is the ability to send small amounts of data reliably, without the delays inherent in setting up a connection.

There are actually two varieties of single-frame transfer defined as part of type 3 service. They are Send Data with Immediate Acknowledge (SDA) and Request Data with Immediate Reply (RDR).

Send Data with Immediate Acknowledge lets the sender know immediately whether or not the data was received. The link layer will keep sending the data packet until it is either acknowledged or the retry limit is exceeded. As long as both sender and receiver are on the same subnetwork (that is, they are both on the same physical cable or at most separated only by repeaters), the transport layer will see a type A network rather than the type C network normally associated with connectionless service.

Indeed, the whole intent of type 3 link service is to eliminate the need for the transport layer and the session and network layers as well. Type

3 link service is the foundation of the Enhanced Performance Architecture. It is targeted at work-cell and process control communications which require real-time response to small messages. It can also help meet the need for simpler, less costly local communications by reducing the memory and processor requirements needed to support the full MAP/TOP protocol stack. However, the cost savings can easily be consumed by the need for gateways to communicate outside the local cell or subnetwork.

Request Data with Immediate Reply is aimed strictly at cost savings. Using this link service, a master station can poll simple stations for any available data. The only requirement is that the simple station must have the data ready and waiting, usually in response to a preceding SDA from the master. The key benefit of RDR is the ability to support large numbers of low-cost devices on a single network. Since the RDR allows the controller to receive as well as send, it is unnecessary for the slave devices to handle the token. This permits large numbers of devices to be controlled on a single LAN without slowing down the token cycle time. At the same time, it does require all the devices to reside on the same physical LAN segment (again, ignoring repeaters).

MAP/TOP specifics

All MAP/TOP networks, beginning with MAP 2.0 and TOP 1.0, use IEEE 802.2 logical link control with type 1 connectionless service. Each station is required to have a unique link address, so the optional 48-bit address field length is used rather than the 16-bit default. Except for the provision of point-to-point and X.25 link protocols, which are considered local implementation issues and not subject to MAP/TOP specification, no other link level protocols are specified for TOP 3.0.

Starting with MAP 2.2, the Enhanced Performance Architecture for MAP will also require IEEE 802.2 type 3 single-frame service. (Note that the MAP/TOP specifications reference the IEEE standard rather than its ISO equivalent ISO 8802/2.) MiniMAP uses type 3 exclusively since usage of type 1 requires a transport protocol for reliable data service. MAP 3.0 has the same link level requirements as MAP 2.2.

Recap of Key Issues

A great deal of complexity is hidden inside a network to make it work smoothly and effectively. The sign of successful implementation is for that complexity to be invisible to the user. This can be seen in MAP/TOP, where interoperability and ease of use have been emphasized even at the expense of efficiency. This is the correct trade-off, as the cost of CPU cycles, memory space, and bits per second of bandwidth is diminishing with time, while the cost of custom software solutions continues to increase.

MAP/TOP 3.0, with its complete definition of all the supporting layers, physical through presentation, will be able to provide the underlying capabilities required by most applications well into the future. The trauma which has accompanied the incompatible growth of MAP 2.X/TOP 1.0 into MAP/TOP 3.0 will soon be in the past and forgotten. Future work on MAP/TOP can concentrate on compatible extensions and expansions of capabilities.

Applicable ISO Standards

Presentation layer specifications

ISO 8822 Connection-Oriented Presentation Service Definition

ISO 8823 Connection-Oriented Presentation Protocol Specification

ISO 8824 Specification for Abstract Syntax Notation 1

ISO 8825 Basic Encoding Rules for Abstract Syntax Notation 1

Session layer specifications

ISO 8326 Connection-Mode Session Service Definition

ISO 8326 Addendum to the Session Service Definition Covering Symmetric Synchronization for the Session Service

ISO 8327 Connection-Mode Session Protocol Specification

ISO 8327 Addendum to ISO 8327 Covering Session Symmetric Synchronization for the Session Protocol

Transport

ISO 8072 Transport Service Definition

ISO 8072 Addendum to the Transport Service Definition Covering Connectionless-Mode Transmission

ISO 8073 Connection-Oriented Transport Protocol Specification

ISO 8073 Addendum to ISO 8073 to Include a Network Connection Management Sub-protocol

IS8 O602 Protocol for Providing the Connectionless-Mode Transport Service Using the Connectionless-Mode Network Service or the Connection-Oriented Network Service

Network layer specifications

ISO 8473 Connectionless-Mode Network Protocol Specification/Service Definition

ISO 8473 Addendum to ISO 8473 Covering Provision of the Connectionless-Mode Subnetwork Service

ISO 8348 Addendum to the Network Service Definition Covering Connectionless-Mode Transmission

ISO 8208 X.25 Packet Level Protocol for Data Terminal Equipment

ISO 8648 Internal Organization of the Network Layer

Link layer specifications

ISO 8802 Local Area Networks Part 2: Logical Link Control

MAP Physical Layer Specifics

The physical layer is where MAP and TOP again differ. The communications and environmental needs on the factory floor are quite different from those in offices and engineering. The result is the specification of different local area network technologies for the two environments. Each has its advantages and disadvantages; indeed some users have chosen TOP technology for their factory floor network wiring, while others are using MAP technology in their offices. Nor are MAP's IEEE 802.4 and TOP's IEEE 802.3 and 802.5 the only choices available.

This chapter explores the technology chosen by MAP for the factory floor, the IEEE 802.4 token-passing bus media access protocol running over broadband or carrierband wiring. We will start with token-passing theory and see how it is implemented in IEEE 802.4. Then we will explore the characteristics of broadband and carrierband media, how they are specified in IEEE 802.4, and what options were selected for MAP.

Token-Passing Theory and Practice

Communications by multiple users over a shared communications channel have always had the problem of determining who should transmit and when. Consider the situation shown in Figure 7.1 in which station A and station B are both trying to transmit data to station C. As long as both avoid transmitting at the same time, communications can proceed with no problems. However, as soon as there is any overlap, the message received by C contains both transmissions, and neither can get through.

The question is how to regulate access to the shared communications medium so that overlap does not interfere with communications.

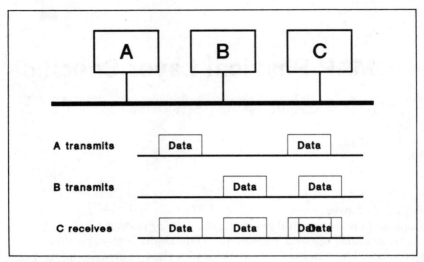

Figure 7.1   The need for media access control.

Many techniques have been developed to regulate access to shared communications media. Long before the term local area network was invented, radio operators were communicating over shared radio channels and computers were operating with remote peripherals over multidrop telephone lines (the data communications euphemism for a party line). The most common technique used to control access was simple polling. The base station (in the case of a radio communications net) or the host computer (on a multidrop line) would be master over all communications. No other stations could transmit unless explicitly told to by the master. Once given permission, a slave station could use the shared communications channel for a limited time period before being required to release it back to the master station.

Polling works well for radio communications and computers, but it does have limitations. The most significant one is a philosophical one. Polling depends on one station being a master while the others are all subservient. It is incompatible with a network of peers in which each is required to be autonomous, capable of functioning even though others on the network may not be. The advent of local area networking between minicomputers and workstations, in which the hierarchical structure of host-oriented networks no longer fit, led to the search for alternate, more egalitarian, media-sharing controls.

Two basic approaches to peer-oriented media sharing have evolved. One lets the individual stations fight it out for access and strives to minimize the probability of two or more stations overlapping their transmissions, the losses when they do overlap, or both. This development path led to the media access control used by TOP and discussed in the next chapter. The other evolutionary path takes the principle of polling but distributes the function of master to all active stations. This eliminates the need for a specific master station to be designated and eliminates the master station as a single point of failure capable of total disruption of all communications on the shared media.

Token-passing bus

The polling function can be fully distributed by making only two changes to traditional polling. First, the station which has been polled is allowed to communicate with any other station and is not restricted to replying only to the master station which polled it. In other words, the poll is treated as blanket permission to access the media rather than strictly as a request for information. The second change has the station polled assume the role of master and poll the next station once it has utilized its quota of media access. The poll is passed like a baton from station to station so that each gets a chance to access the media without interference and to accomplish its communications objectives. The baton is called a token in computer science parlance, so the access technique is called token passing.

The normal operation of the token-passing bus consists of two distinct phases. One is the data transfer phase, in which the current holder of the token exercises the access rights granted by the token to actually communicate with another station over the shared medium. The other is the token-passing phase, in which the current holder of the token passes the token on to the next station in line to receive it. Although any station on the bus can directly communicate with all other stations on the bus, the token passing itself is sequential. A logical ring is formed with each station passing the token on to the next in the ring until the last passes the token on to the first for yet another cycle through the ring. This logical ring is independent of the actual physical ordering of stations on the bus. Nor do all stations need to be included. Any station can respond to a query from the token holder whether it is part of the logical token-passing ring or not. Figure 7.2 shows just one such configuration.

Each station must also be prepared to handle abnormal operations as well as the normal data transfer and token transfer phases. Ring maintenance requires stations to provide functions such as ring initialization so a logical ring can be formed to begin with, lost token recovery in case the packet containing the token is lost or the station holding it dies, addition of new stations to the existing logical ring, and repair of the logical ring if any members drop out. As is typical of most networking protocols, these "abnormal" functions contribute the vast majority of complexity to development and implementation.

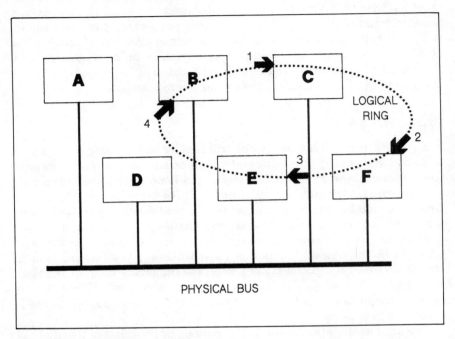

Figure 7.2 A logical ring on a physical bus.

Benefits

Token passing as an access control mechanism for a bus-oriented communications medium offers a wide range of benefits. Some are capabilities taken for granted in a bus-oriented network such as coordinating the transmissions of each station to minimize and control interference with other stations, not requiring any station to use its full allocated share of the medium's capacity, and efficient utilization of the available capacity of the medium when the aggregate demand of all stations far exceeds that available capacity (i.e., when overloaded, the network does not crash). I mention these as a reminder that while they are commonly desired features in a bus-oriented local area network, they are not requirements. Special purpose networks may trade them off against "uncommon" user needs, such as the ability to function efficiently over error-prone communications media or absolute minimum per station cost in a network in which usage never exceeds a very low percentage of media capacity.

The token-passing user sees a number of benefits. Not only is the communications medium used efficiently under high loading, but also each station is guaranteed its allocated share of the medium's capacity regardless of load. Multiple priorities of users can be supported so that different users can be allocated different shares of the medium's capacity. Most important in many industrial environments, the maximum delay seen by any station waiting for the token can be guaranteed, at least to the extent that failures in the user stations and medium do not occur. In the absence of noise on the medium or other system failures which can cause loss of the token (for example, a station in the ring loses power while it is holding the token), the longest possible time required for the token to circulate around the logical ring is computable and deterministic. There are no probabilistic dependencies involved. The calculations remain deterministic as long as the number of system failures (including noise incidents) remains finite.

The challenge in designing a token-passing bus protocol is recovering from loss of the token. Token recovery can only occur after the loss of the token is discovered. Because of the disastrous consequences if a new token is created while the original still survives, token recovery will normally impose significant additional delays and may even require reconfiguration of the logical ring.

The other major advantage of token passing for the user is the minimal number of constraints placed on how the station holding the token uses its share of the medium's capacity. The station can communicate using open loop (no response by the receiver) or closed loop (immediate response or acknowledgment by the receiver) data transfers. Communications may be with any station connected to the medium and are not restricted to just those taking part in the token-passing activity. This allows the presence of large numbers of low-cost, reduced-function stations on the medium which function only as slaves, responding as required to whatever master currently holds the token.

Another benefit which shows up in the cost of the network is the lack of additional requirements on the media or modems over those necessary for transmission and reception of data packets. The token is passed between stations the same as data. It does not require a special communications channel of its own nor any special detection capabilities.

The network manager responsible for keeping the network functioning also sees benefits. Since the token-passing protocol prevents two stations from transmitting at the same time, the only interference on the medium will be that caused by exterior noise except during that part of the token-passing cycle reserved for new stations to contend for admission to the logical ring. Since the allowed interference zone is predictable and distinguishable from normal operation, it is possible to make reliable system noise-level measurements while the system is in operation and without degrading network performance.

Trade-offs

The long list of benefits just cited may make you wonder why anyone would ever consider using a media access method other than token passing. Indeed that very attitude was expressed by many during the 1970s and on into the early 1980s. Today most of the rhetoric has died down, as proponents of various networking schemes have come to recognize that users are too smart to believe that one networking scheme will fit everyone's needs. This can be seen just in the IEEE local area network standards, in which three totally different media access methods are standardized, each with multiple options for the actual media to be used. Although many applications could use any of the IEEE standards successfully, there are also many which are particularly sensitive to the individual strengths and weaknesses of each.

There are four primary weaknesses associated with the token-passing bus access method. The first is the sheer complexity of the protocol required to properly manage the token. While the actual passing of the token is a simple process, detection of its loss and recovering from that event is not. The penalty incurred if two tokens happen to be in existence concurrently is too high to allow the use of probabilistic methods for its recovery. The station creating the replacement token must be certain that the missing token is truly gone and not just delayed somewhere because another station's clock is running slow. That station must also be certain that it is the only station recovering the token, as two stations recreating the missing token is as bad as recreating a missing token which is not missing. The challenge to the protocol designer is handling all these concerns while subject to the imperfections of the real world— clocks in different stations which are not exactly synchronized, propagation delays on the communications medium, varying computation speeds between stations, even the situation in which the station which should be recreating the token is the one which caused the loss by failing in the first place. Added to this is the desire to add and delete stations in the logical ring while it is operating. Fortunately, the availability of IEEE 802.4 media access control on a single VLSI chip has greatly reduced what used to be a substantial implementation burden.

More important to the user, and not subject to fixing with hardware, are two critical performance limitations in token-passing busses. Both are direct consequences of the benefits of fair sharing and predictable access time. The same as a finite, computable upper bound limits the maximum time a station will have to wait between possessions of the token, a substantial lower bound is imposed on the minimum length of time any particular station is guaranteed to have to wait between token possessions as the token must be processed by all other stations in the ring before it comes back to the same station. This will be seen as a significant average delay time for access, even on a totally idle network in which no other stations have data to transfer, but all others must pass the token. Because the delay is proportional to the number of active stations in the logical ring, the impact is usually not noticed in pilot networks. However, when the pilot is scaled up to include hundreds of stations, a few extra milliseconds of token-holding time at each station can add up to seconds of delay.

Total throughput, as well as delay, is affected by fair sharing. Even when no other stations have need of communications services, each must be given a turn at the available capacity. The station holding the token can only transmit a limited amount of data before its token-holding time expires and the token must be passed on. Then the station must wait for the token to work its way around the logical ring before it gets a chance to send more data. This cannot be easily fixed by increasing the token-holding time, as that increases the full-load maximum delay seen by all stations. Users on a token bus must recognize that their total throughput is constrained to some maximum percentage of the total available capacity even when no other stations are competing for it. Again, the impact is linearly proportional to the total number of stations that are participating in the logical ring, getting worse as the network gets larger.

Finally, token passing is sensitive to system noise. Token passing does not make a communications medium more sensitive to noise; rather the impact of noise sufficient to disrupt communications may be further exacerbated by the delay incurred in recovering the token if it is lost because of the noise. Like the first trade-off mentioned, protocol complexity, this too is generally considered a nonissue. The physical media specified for use with token-passing busses take this sensitivity into account and, as a result, tend to be more immune to noise than most other alternatives.

IEEE 802.4 Media Access Control

The token-passing bus media access control implementation selected for MAP networks is that specified by the IEEE 802.4 standard. It provides sequential access to the communications medium by passing the token from station to station to form a logical ring. The standard determines when a station has the right to use the medium (by possessing the token) and how long it can retain that right each time it receives the token. The standard does not specify how a station must use the communications medium while it is holding the token. The token-holding station can transmit data, broadcast packets, ask the receiver of a data packet to immediately respond or acknowledge it, or even grant another station permission to communicate with yet a third station (provided the token holder is certain they will be done before it is time to pass on the token).

In addition to the token-passing rules, the standard also specifies all the procedures required to detect and recover from loss of the token, as well as those needed to build, patch, and drop out of the logical ring.

Media access control sublayer functions

The IEEE standard specifies a number of media access control functions. The lost token timer is used to detect loss of the token. All stations monitor the bus, and if no bus activity is detected for longer than a timeout value, the first station to notice it will issue a claim-token frame. Contention between token claimers is resolved by a scheme based on timing relative to their physical addresses. A token-holding timer provides four classes of service based on how long a station can utilize the communications medium each time it receives the token. Each class of service has associated with it a maximum ring circulation time. When a station receives the token, it transmits its top priority traffic first. Traffic in a lower priority class may be sent as long as time remains in that class's token circulation timer. Other token-passing functions are valid token recognition (so the station knows it has the token) and token preparation (for passing it on to the next station in the logical ring).

Ring management functions other then ring initialization and lost-token recovery are performed by the current token holder. Ring additions are made by issuing a "solicit-successor" frame while holding the token, a function all stations must perform periodically. This allows stations with addresses between the token holder's and that of the next station in the ring to request admission to the ring. If the token holder gets no response, the token gets passed to the next station on the ring. A single response will add the new station to the ring. Multiple responses are sorted out by the token holder. Dropping out of the ring is easier. The station wishing to drop waits until it has the token, then informs its predecessor to pass the token to its successor. If a station fails before it can splice the ring, its failure to respond to the token pass (by not immediately issuing either a data frame or token pass) will be detected by its predecessor, and the predecessor will try to find the new successor or, failing that, reinitialize the ring. The token holder also continuously listens to the bus for evidence that some other station is holding a token. If such a frame is detected, the token holder immediately drops its token and returns to listening mode.

Also included in the media access layer are several functions not specific to token passing. There is limited data buffering to allow validation of information before passing it up to the next layer. There is node address recognition to filter out packets not addressed to the particular station (including individual, multicast, and broadcast addresses). The frames to be transmitted are put together in this sublayer and the frame check sequences generated. Similarly, the frame check sequences of received packets are checked before proceeding with any processing.

Media access control sublayer architecture

The IEEE 802.4 standard for token passing is defined as a combination of four finite state machines, as shown in Figure 7.3. A fifth finite state machine, called the regenerative repeater machine, is defined for use in physical layer repeaters and head end remodulators. The sublayer itself interfaces to the logical link layer (normally IEEE 802.2), the physical layer modem below, and with network management (called station management by IEEE 802.1).

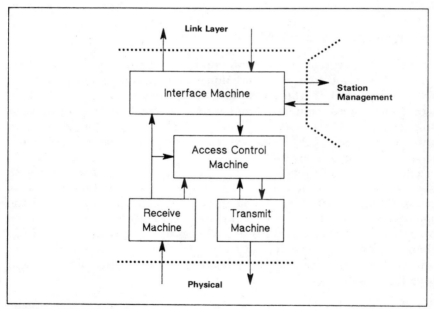

Figure 7.3   IEEE 802.4 media access control architecture.

The four state machines do just what their name implies. The receive machine watches all data on the communications medium, verifying that each has a proper frame check sequence and selecting only those packets that have locally enabled individual and multicast addresses and broadcast addresses. It is also constantly watching for the token.

The transmit machine provides the outgoing packaging function, putting together packets and calculating their frame check sequences whenever the access control machine gives it permission to put packets out on the network. Among the packets it must assemble and transmit is the token itself.

The interface machine provides the common interface to the IEEE 802.2 link layer, relieving it of any concerns over the particular media access method or media in use.

The most complex of the state machines is the access control machine. Here all the handling of the token and management of network changes occurs. It waits to receive the token from the receiving machine. As soon as the token is received, it gives packets to the transmit machine until the token timer expires and then gives the transmit machine the token to pass on to the next station in the logical ring. The complexity, of course, comes from all the subsidiary token management functions: restoring lost tokens, patching breaks in the logical ring, getting into the logical ring, initializing the ring, and so forth.

Broadband Theory and Practice

Broadband networks are a natural outgrowth of the cable TV industry. Cable TV evolved from the community antenna television distribution systems designed in the early days of television to bring television reception to those communities outside the normal broadcasting range of "big city" television stations. The original acronym for community antenna television, CATV, has evolved to refer to cable TV in general, regardless of program source.

The evolution of broadband networking can be seen if we start with the simplified view of a cable TV system shown in Figure 7.4a. A "simple" change of viewpoint on the source of programming from the community antenna to the users themselves (Figure 7.4b) and we have a broadband network. The multitude of ways used to provide that reverse channel from the user back up to the head end for retransmission to other users is what creates the variety of (and incompatibility between) broadband networks.

Types of broadband networks

There are two basic ways to get signals from the user back up to the head end (Figure 7.5). The simplest to implement is what is called dual-cable broadband. One cable is used for signals going from the head end out to the user, the second cable is used for the other direction. This allows the use of standard components originally designed for CATV systems and is easiest to design.

Since many users did not like the expense and inconvenience of having two cables, an alternative was developed: single-cable broadband. In single-cable systems, part of the capacity of the cable is used to send signals up to the head end while other channels are used by the head end to send to the users. This is done by dividing the capacity of the cable by frequency, with signals on lower frequencies being sent from the user to the head end, while higher frequencies are used by the head end to transmit to the users.

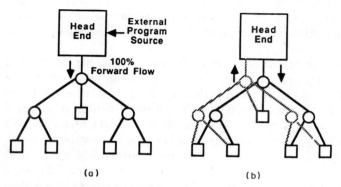

Figure 7.4 Programming sources and signal flows. (*a*) Cable TV and (*b*) broadband network.

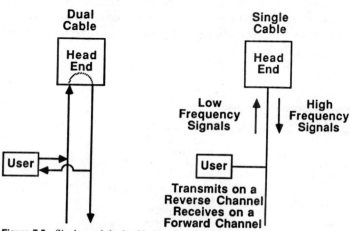

Figure 7.5 Single- and dual-cable broadband systems.

Single-cable systems have two main drawbacks. First, the components used to assemble them are more complex. For example, rather than using a single broadband amplifier to restore signal levels, two amplifiers must be used, one for each direction. The signal fed to each amplifier must be limited strictly to those going in the correct direction. This requires frequency sensitive splitters that pass only the appropriate signals on to each amplifier and completely block the others on the cable. The second drawback is a direct result of this need for frequency splitters. Since filters are not perfect in their response, it is necessary to avoid using frequencies between their cutoff points. So a single-cable system must split up the cable capacity three ways rather than two. In addition to the forward and reverse frequency bands, capacity must be allocated to the unusable guard band between the two directions. This guard band can consume up to 18 percent of the total capacity of the cable system, depending on the total bandwidth of the cable and the specific split frequency chosen.

There are three standard splits defined for single-cable broadband systems (Table 7.1). Subsplit is the normal path taken when upgrading an existing CATV system. It ensures that the forward channel includes all broadcast TV channels standard in the United States (channel 2 starts at 54 MHz). As a result, however, only 25 MHz of bandwidth (enough for four U.S. TV channels) are available for the reverse channel. The introduction of broadband systems designed primarily for computer communications created a demand for far more reverse channel capacity than that provided by CATV upgrade. This led to midsplit single cable, which divided up the 300 MHz of standard CATV systems almost equally in the forward and reverse directions. Improvements in radio frequency technology have also allowed the extension of the total capacity of the broadband medium from the 300 MHz used in CATV systems to over 400 MHz. As 400-MHz systems became cost competitive, high split was introduced to provide equal forward and reverse capacity on a 400-MHz cable system.

TABLE 7.1 **Standard Broadband Channel Assignments**

Cable split	Reverse channel, MHz	Forward channel, MHz
High	5–174	232–400
Mid	5–116	168–300 or 400
Sub	5–30	54–300
None (dual cable)	5–300 or 400	5–300 or 400

Standard splits are not used by all vendors. There are many networks on the market based on nonstandard splits. If you are planning to use an existing broadband installation, check first to avoid any unpleasant surprises.

In the MAP world, IEEE 802.4 is defined so it can be implemented on either midsplit or high-split networks. The IEEE recommends using high split for new broadband installations to take advantage of the increased bandwidth on 400-MHz broadband. The MAP 2.1 specification recommended midsplit; however, that was amended in MAP 2.2 to simply state that many midsplit systems are already installed, but high-split and redundant media (either midsplit or high split) also meet the intent of the MAP specification.

Broadband communications capabilities

The lure of broadband is the sheer number of services that can be provided on a single cable. Just about any communications signal can be connected from one point on the broadband network to any other point. Even limiting consideration to only television signals provides a plethora of applications. Video conferencing, commercial programming distribution, security monitoring, and training come to mind immediately. Any kind of video or audio signal from either internal or external sources is reasonable; even public address systems can use the broadband network to avoid dedicated cable runs between outlying areas.

The addition of data communications to the basic broadband repertoire did not take long. Point-to-point modems have been in use over broadband networks since before the term local area network was invented. Over 100 asynchronous or synchronous connections at any standard data rate from 110 bps through 19.2 Kbps can be provided in a pair of 6-MHz cable TV channels. These can be used for applications ranging from terminal-to-computer hookups to fire alarm monitoring and environmental controls. Standard telephone T1 connections (1.544 Mbps) can be used to interconnect digital branch exchanges for both voice and data communications. IEEE 802.3, IEEE 802.4, and proprietary (including Ethernet compatible) local area networking are just additional options in the broadband service selection menu.

Broadband components

Another attraction of broadband for networking is that most of the components are readily available from the CATV industry. These components and their manufacturers have a long track record of ruggedness and reliability: ruggedness to allow exposed installation on power poles in the salt air, heat, and humidity of Florida as well as in the frigid winters of the Canadian Northwest Territories; reliability to meet the customer service demands of a regulated common carrier environment, with mean times between failures measured in years and with off-the-shelf redundant components.

A typical broadband communications systems requires substantially more than just some coaxial cable. Figure 7.6 shows how the more common components are interconnected in a typical cable layout. The head end, commonly referenced as if it were a single component, is usually a collection of components performing a single conceptual function. In a standard CATV system, the head end is the source of all programming on the cable. In a broadband communications system, the head end is where all forward channels originate and all reverse channels terminate. Various components may be required to turn around communications channels from reverse to forward. Although not required to have any other function, it is also usually the central control point for the cable plant. The head end may include cable plant and signal monitoring and control equipment and power supplies for equipment located elsewhere but powered from the cable.

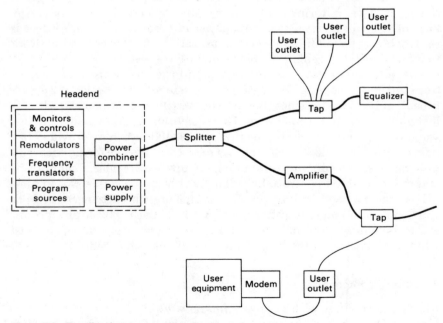

Figure 7.6 Broadband system components.

Sources of forward channel transmissions are varied. Some will come from outside the broadband system, perhaps from a satellite or other program source. Others will come from reverse channel traffic into the head end from sources out on the cable. Filters may be required to split the reverse channel signals up and to route individual signals or clusters of channels to the appropriate components to convert them to forward channel data. For most signals, such as video channels and point-to-point broadband modems, this requires amplifying the inbound signals and translating them up to the proper frequency. If any of the services being translated use a nonstandard split frequency, this can present a problem. It may mean some services will not be usable because of frequency conflicts.

IEEE 802.4 high-performance broadband modems are specified to be independent of split frequency. The regenerative repeater machine in the 802.4 media access control architecture defines the 802.4 remodulation function. Remodulators at the head end receive the reverse channel data stream and retransmit it on the forward channel. In effect, the head end contains a receive modem at the reverse channel frequency tied through a timing restoration module to a transmit modem at the forward channel frequency.

Some network designs will include telemetry and remote control of amplifiers, power supplies, and other critical components throughout the network. Monitors for the inbound data and controllers for those components remotely controllable will usually be located at the head end as well. Locating them anywhere else in the network may be more convenient, but it doubles the consumption of cable capacity with no corresponding increase in functionality.

Cable plants which are extensive in size will require amplifiers to restore signal losses in the cable. High-performance local area networks typically need amplification every few hundred meters to maintain proper tolerances on signal levels. Power for amplifiers is often provided over the cable itself as 30- or 60-V ac. This allows using high-reliability power sources (often located at the head end, which also requires continuous power) to power the amplifiers remotely and keep communications functional even during localized power failures. Uninterruptible power supplies may be used to ensure communications availability under adverse conditions. The power supplies are connected to the trunk cable using power combiners so that the RF signals on the cable do not get diverted into the power supply. Some power supplies have the power combiner function built in.

Higher-performance networks face a second challenge with signal losses on the cable. The higher frequencies on the cable are attenuated more than the lower frequencies. This can require the use of equalizers in the network even when the losses are not enough to require an amplifier. Most amplifiers will have equalizers built in to minimize total component count in the network.

The treelike branching in broadband cable layouts is provided by splitters and taps. The splitters allow a trunk cable to be split into two or more trunk cables for broader coverage. Taps provide the means of connecting drop cables to a trunk cable. While the trunk cable is usually heavy, rigid or semirigid, high-performance, low-loss cable, the drop cables are flexible and relatively lightweight (usually about 6 to 8 mm in diameter compared to trunk cables at around 2 cm). The drop cables need to be terminated at some sort of user interface, usually a wall outlet or the equivalent for the particular environment. The challenge for all these passive components (splitters, taps, and wall outlets) is minimizing the mismatch at each juncture so that signal quality is maintained. For example, wall outlets are available which automatically terminate the drop cable at the wall outlet until a user cable is plugged in, when it is assumed the user will properly terminate the connection. Which wall outlets must be terminated and which ones do not need to be is one of the many design decisions which go into broadband cable plant design.

Modems provide the interface from digital data into the radio frequency world of broadband. They come in a wide range of capabilities, from 110-bps Teletype connections up through 10-Mbps IEEE 802.4 local area networking. Careful attention must be paid to all frequencies used by each capability on the network to avoid conflicts. These can occur long before the network is filled to capacity.

One last category of component is the test and monitoring equipment required to verify that the broadband is functioning as designed. The tools required to maintain the network are often forgotten until failure occurs. This includes not just the remote device monitoring and control already mentioned, but also devices such as channel monitors to verify that all the various signal sources on the network are putting out the signal they are supposed to, LAN analyzers to track down incompatibility and configuration problems, and spectrum analyzers to identify and track down sources of interference.

Broadband installation

The lure of broadband, with its incredible range of communications support capabilities, can seem irresistible. However, all this power is not free. Broadband cable plants are not known for their low cost and ease of installation. Nor is support for all the wide-ranging services automatic. Many companies, General Motors included, are discovering that some of the broadband systems installed in the 1970s in anticipation of computer networking needs are not capable of meeting the performance demanded by state-of-the-art networks such as IEEE 802.4 MAP.

Broadband cable plant design for high-performance computer networking is not a "do-it-yourself" project. Poor system design cannot be compensated for after installation is complete. In many of the cases alluded to in the previous paragraph, the lowest-cost upgrade to the existing broadband cable plant was to discard it and start all over with a new design and installation. While the IEEE 802.7 advisory committee is dedicated to generating meaningful guidelines for broadband installation and usage, there are still many loose ends for the system designer to resolve. Unless you expect to design enough systems to pay for the investment in learning, rely on an experienced, reputable system designer to insure integrity in your broadband cable plant system design.

Once the cable plant is designed, almost anyone can do the physical installation. The key is to base the installation on an adequate design and demand documented, physically measured conformance to the system design. Spot checks are inadequate. At a minimum, performance in accordance with the design must be verified at the head end and at each tap housing, across all frequencies planned for use. Nor is it adequate to test once and forget it. Plan to verify conformance on an ongoing basis, which will require adequate test equipment and operator training.

In general, unless you have major doubts about going with a broadband cable plant, it is more cost effective to cover the whole plant with the initial installation rather than designing and installing the cable plant piecemeal. This includes installing all taps planned for future use. While the installation cost savings may or may not balance out the time value of the money involved, do not forget the cost of disrupting current users when the time comes to add more users. Along the same lines, seek a design which provides uniform signal levels at all locations over all frequency bands. Again, you do not want to have to redesign the cable plant if manufacturing decides to move a process from one end of the building to the other.

Carrierband Theory and Practice

Broadband systems have many advantages, but they are not perfect for all applications. Not everyone needs to blanket their entire facility with video, voice, point-to-point data communications, and multiple local area networks. Broadband systems are a major capital investment, requiring extensive planning and long-term commitment to ongoing maintenance. When used for computer communications and local area networking, the modems required are a significant expense, and there does not appear to be the opportunity for cost reduction that is seen in other areas of computer networking. Radio frequency modems are still beyond the state of the art in integrated circuit technology.

What was needed was something more cost effective for small industrial networks such as work cells and local process control, a network medium that was cheap and easy to install and hook up to, yet rugged enough for the plant floor environment. Rather than a pipe dream, the answer turned out to be relatively simple, a marriage of broadband and baseband technology called carrierband.

Carrierband takes the philosophy of baseband, putting the signal on the cable and transmitting it omnidirectionally to all other users, and combines it with the easy part of the broadband cable plant, the cable, splitters, and taps. All the expensive parts of broadband, the head end, amplifiers, RF modems, and complex design, are eliminated. Replacing them are straightforward restrictions on size (maximum distance between users and total number of users) and performance (only one communications channel on the entire cable). Note that carrierband is not a replacement for broadband. Rather it is a way to keep broadband where it belongs, as the backbone communications medium connecting all parts of the plant, and not trying to force fit it where it does not belong, handling localized traffic for a work cell. It allows the use of a separate carrierband network for each work cell and leaves the broadband network capacity available for those tasks that can only be handled by the backbone network, such as communications between work cells.

Trade-offs

Carrierband has many advantages for the factory floor network. A purely passive cable plant requirement not only reduces costs by eliminating expensive radio frequency components but also greatly simplifies cable plant design. No special skills are required. Carrierband modems are already available in VLSI integrated circuits, reducing the price of carrierband modems to less than half the cost of their broadband equivalents. As integration continues, carrierband modems will become small enough and cheap enough to be built into low-cost stations.

Life-cycle cost is similarly enhanced. A communications medium containing only passive components means only minimal maintenance is required. There is not even a power supply required for the cable. The much lower frequencies involved also reduce the need to periodically sweep the cable for spurious emissions that can cause interference.

The simplicity and low cost which make carrierband the preferred solution for many applications do have an impact. Carrierband is limited in many ways to make the simplicity possible. It is designed for small networks such as work-cell control subnetworks, small factories, and process control. The cable plant is totally dedicated to running the single carrierband network. Capacity and range are also limited. Carrierband networks can only handle a few tens of nodes within a range of a few hundred meters. Most support only a 1 Mbps or 5 Mbps data rate as well. Since the primary impact of data rate in most applications is on the number of users who can receive adequate services rather than the performance seen by individual users, this is normally not a consideration.

In larger networks of networks, some of the modem savings may disappear due to the added cost of gateways onto the main backbone broadband from each individual carrierband segments.

IEEE 802.4 Physical Layer

The IEEE 802.4 physical layer standard provides a number of options for the physical media and signaling method. The three main categories are called phase continuous carrierband, phase coherent carrierband, and broadband. All three are based on CATV 75-ohm coaxial media, but beyond that they are widely different.

Phase continuous carrierband

The lowest performance option is phase continuous carrierband. It uses CATV cable and taps to provide a simple omnidirectional bus. The cable layout is required to be a single, unbranched truck cable with short (less than or equal to 36 cm) drop cables to reach individual stations. If stations are scattered throughout an area, it is necessary to snake the trunk cable around the area to keep stations within range of the short drops.

The signalling method used on the cable is frequency shift keying (FSK), where a high level is represented by a frequency of 6.25 MHz and a low by 3.75 MHz. The actual ones and zeros of the data being transmitted are encoded using a technique called Manchester encoding. Manchester encoding has the benefit that all timing information required to reconstruct the original data is supplied as part of the signal. This is achieved by modualting the signal on the cable at twice the data rate. This limits phase continuous carrierband to a data rate of 1 Mbps.

Phase coherent carrierband

The other carrierband alternative is called phase coherent carrierband. It provides many advantages over the phase continuous version. The cable plant is less constrained, allowing branching and splitting the trunk cable to provide broader coverage. Longer, flexible drop cables are permitted, very much as in a standard broadband setup. The data rate is also higher, with a choice of 5 Mbps and 10 Mbps. This higher performance is achieved by directly encoding the digital signal into the modulation scheme.

Phase coherent modulation encodes each zero bit in the data stream as a single cycle at the bit rate. Each one bit in the data is encoded as two cycles at twice the bit rate. If the data rate is 5 Mbps, then each zero bit consists of one cycle of a 5-MHz carrier and each one bit contains two cycles of a 10-MHz carrier locked onto the 5-MHz one. This not only minimizes the bandwidth requirements in the sender and receiver for a given data rate, it also provides simple clock recovery for the receiver directly from the received signal.

Due to the lack of redundant information in the direct encoding, care must be taken in cable plant design to ensure that any electrical noise in the environment is kept out of the cable. This should not be a problem, and many claim that this modulation technique is not particularly more sensitive to noise than any other available.

Broadband

Until 1986, broadband was the only medium specified by the IEEE 802.4 standard. There is still just the one broadband standard, which you may see referred to as Multilevel Duobinary AM/PSK (Amplitude Modulation with Phase Shift Keying). This is the highest performance media option available under the standard, and the most expensive. It is targeted at full capability broadband systems, limited in size and number of stations connected only by the budget of the user and the delays from the media access control acceptable to the application.

The term multilevel duobinary AM/PSK refers to the modulation technique defined for use in the broadband modems. Data rates of 1 Mbps, 5 Mbps, and 10 Mbps are specified, consuming 1.5 MHz, 6 MHz, and 12 MHz respectively. In other words, one broadband channel pair (a 6-MHz channel to and from the head end) can support four 1- Mbps or one 5-Mbps networks. The maximum data rate of 10 Mbps requires two channel pairs. In real life, the consumption of channel pairs is greater, as the IEEE channel pairs do not align with the standard U.S. CATV broadcast channel frequency assignments (Figure 7.7). Not only do the channel pairs overlap multiple TV channels, they also overlap other broadband local area network definitions, such as Decom Ethernet and IEEE 802.3. The problems are only compounded in countries where the CATV standards differ from those in the United States. For example, European video channels are 8 MHz wide.

Frequency allocation is not the only challenge faced by IEEE 802.4. The definition of the specification preceded the ability of state-of-the-art modem manufacturers to produce 10-Mbps RF modems. It turned out that the specification was not tight enough to ensure that modems from one vendor could communicate with those of another. The only sure solution for those who could not wait, and one endorsed by the MAP 2.1 specification as an interim measure, was to either buy all 10-Mbps modems from one manufacturer (which is exactly the situation MAP/TOP is driven to eliminate) or back off on performance and use 5-Mbps modems, which have no interoperability problems. This is another of those "little" problems which the MAP/TOP movement is forcing to be resolved.

CATV and IEEE 802

We have already seen that the channel assignments (Figure 7.7) for IEEE 802.3 and 802.4 conflict with each other and with standard video channel assignments on CATV. The main cause of this is a simple one. The video channel assignments on CATV were originally determined by the broadcast industry in each country, where television broadcast of video signals had only part of the radio spectrum. The result in the United States is odd-sized channels in the midst of the video assignments, such as the FM band from 88 MHz to 108 MHz, and the gap between channels four and five set aside for other radio services too small for a video channel.

There are no standards for using channels on broadband. CATV specifications are designed around broadcast TV signals, but modem signals do not behave like video signals. There are no standards for measuring how adjacent channels carrying nonvideo signals do or should interact. Engineers are still just discovering what they are sensitive to. This lack of standards extends to the user service outlet. IEEE 802.7 has the charter to determine where users are considered to have tapped into the network. Some argue that the-user-to-network boundary is where the drop cable comes out of the wall, others declare the boundary is where the cable plugs into the modem. Some even argue the boundary is at the tap on the trunk cable. The difference determines what the user has control over and what the system designer controls. Only after we define what the connecting point is can we start to define what the user can and cannot modify concerning that connecting point.

More technical problems are also being examined. System designers and managers need to know what constitutes acceptable levels of impulse and ingress noise, and limits on the sensitivity of modems to signal propagation characteristics such as group delay and phase differential.

MAP specifics

The MAP 2.1 specification for physical media requires IEEE 802.4 running over broadband. The particular broadband recommendation was for full capability midsplit rather than the IEEE recommendation

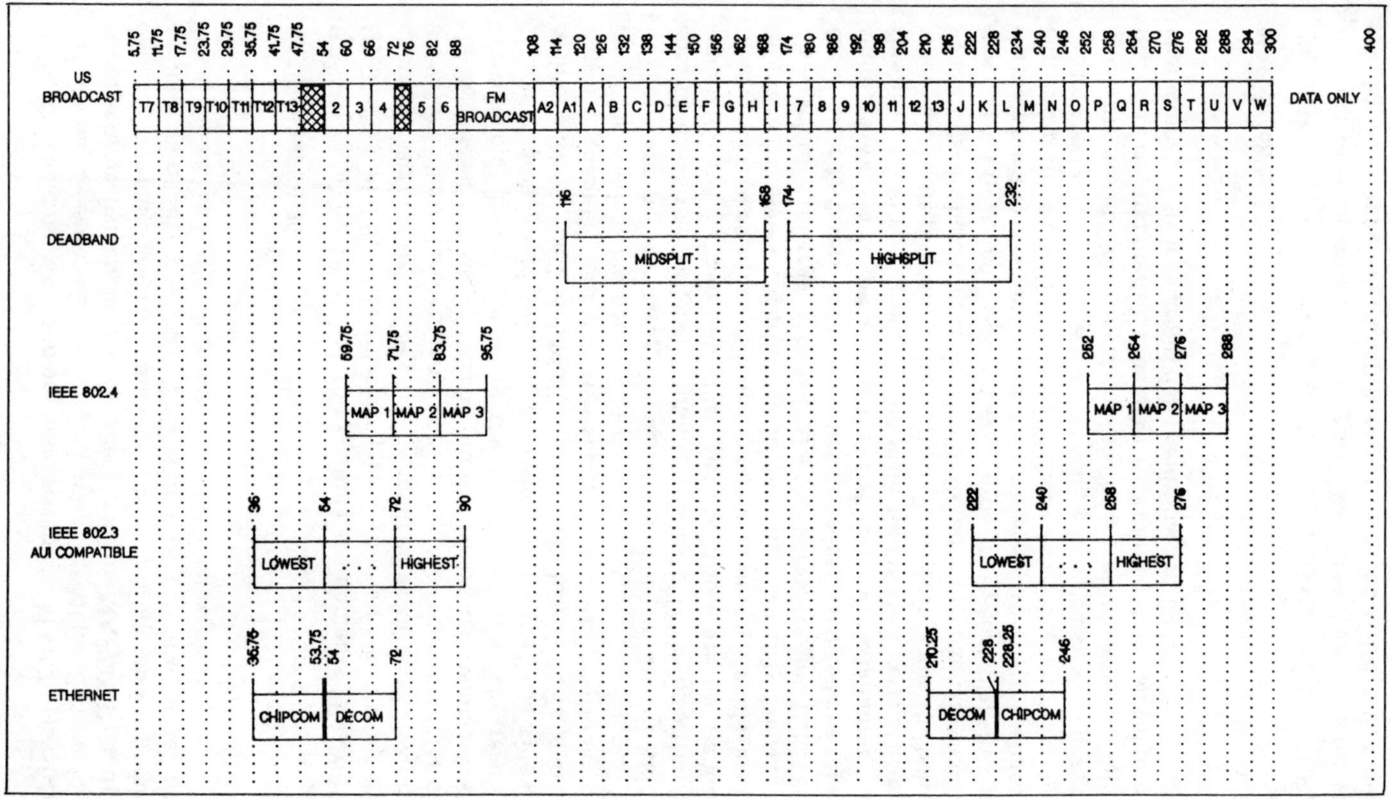

Figure 7.7 Broadband channel assignments and IEEE 802.4.

for new installations of 400-MHz high split. MAP 2.2 expanded the options by stating that high split and other options would also satisfactorily meet the intent of the specification, which is to be media independent. All require the two-channel, 10-Mbps broadband communications. The early MAP implementations using 5-Mbps modems were only an interim measure until interoperable 10-Mbps modems became available.

MAP 2.2 also introduced the option of carrierband for subnetworks and small facilities. The 5-Mbps phase coherent version was selected testing showed it to be no more noise sensitive than the much lower-performance 1-Mbps phase continuous version.

Network topology itself is left flexible in order to meet individual plant requirements. The expectation is that the backbone network would be broadband, but carrierband may be used for workcells, other localized communications, and where minimum propagation delay is required for real time response.

Recap of Key Issues

Token bus makes sense on the factory floor. It allows the distances required to connect large facilities with broadband networks and provides the guaranteed response times required for control applications. Carrierband provides an effective, low cost alternative for small IEEE 802.4 networks and has some performance advantages in real-time applications. Broadband provides the flexilibity needed to meet more than just the computer networking needs of factory facilities, including video for security and communications, and replacement of point-to-point wiring. Broadband network cable plant has design issues not seen in standard CATV installations, which can be expensive to correct after installation. Most users will agree that broadband makes sense, and many will install it whether they install MAP or not.

TOP Physical Layer Specifics

Our discussion of token passing in the previous chapter concluded that while token passing is an excellent protocol for the factory floor, it is not perfect. In this chapter, we will look at the standard alternative for token passing on bus-oriented local area networks, Carrier Sense Multiple Access with Collision Detection, CSMA/CD. The strengths and weaknesses of CSMA/CD complement those of token passing and match up well with the needs and usage patterns of office and engineering workstation users. This is the technique chosen for TOP 1.0 networks, and as we explore its advantages and shortcomings, we will see why the TOP program decided the incompatibility was worthwhile.

Contention-Based Access Control

The history of CSMA/CD also starts with a radio network, but in this case it was a computer access network developed by the University of Hawaii. They had the challenge of connecting remote terminals on the outer islands to the central computer host at the main campus. Their communications environment was very similar to many radio networks because the base station on the main campus could communicate with all the remote locations, but remote locations could only communicate with the base station. Remote locations were unable to hear the transmissions of other remote locations. While they could have used polling to keep the remote stations from interfering with one another, they decided to explore a different approach.

The remote locations were primarily time-sharing terminals with the radio link substituting for full duplex hard-wired links. If polling were to be used, the delay time for each user to see a keystroke echoed would be excessive. However, since the transmission required to send a single keystroke was very short and individual keystrokes occurred relatively infrequently, they tried an experiment. Rather than polling, they just let any user station transmit whenever it had any data. If it happened to collide with another user, they could both try again. Given the total percentage of time actually consumed by user transmissions, the likelihood of collisions was low. Much to some people's surprise, the resulting network worked quite well and the university was saving money on utility bills by not transmitting polls and negative responses to polls. The impact of their research was sufficient for the name of the project, Aloha, to be given to the mode of access.

Carrier Sense Multiple Access

The next step to improve the efficiency of an Aloha type network was a simple one. In a local area network in which all stations are on the same bus, there is no problem detecting if another station is transmitting. Rather than transmit whenever data was available, a station would "listen before talking." By sensing the activity of others, stations were much less likely to interfere with one another. Numerous techniques were developed to minimize the probability that two stations waiting for a third to finish would both start to transmit at the same time, colliding with each other. The general technique is called Carrier Sense Multiple Access (CSMA), and the waiting strategies go by names like persistent CSMA, nonpersistent CSMA, and p-persistent CSMA.

Carrier Sense Multiple Access was good, but it was not good enough. When collisions did occur, the performance impact was huge. Since the physical layer had no way of detecting loss of data, it was up to higher-level protocols to time out and retransmit the data. Two paths were pursued to reduce the losses caused by collisions. One path, called Carrier Sense Multiple Access with Collision Avoidance (CSMA/CA), took the approach of investing in some overhead to minimize the probability of a collision occurring. In one version, for example, before sending a data packet, the station wanting to transmit would send a short "reservation" packet first, then listen to see if any other station had transmitted a reservation packet as well. If none was detected, the station was guaranteed a clear channel to start transmitting the actual data packet. If some other station had started transmitting a reservation burst before the local station's had arrived, then one or the other or both would detect the other, and back off before trying again. CSMA/CA could work very well; the only disadvantages were the engineering challenge of rapidly switching between receiving for carrier sensing and transmitting and the overhead time spent avoiding collisions, even though collisions are rare under most loading conditions.

Carrier Sense Multiple Access with Collision Detection

The alternative to CSMA/CA is to run at full speed and figure out a way to minimize the damage when the occasional collision does occur rather than invest the overhead in preventing an infrequent event. The best way to minimize the effect of a collision is to recognize that one has occurred, abort the transmission in progress, and recover and retry at the physical level. This approach is called Carrier Sense Multiple Access with Collision Detection, or CSMA/CD for short. The challenge of detecting another station's signal while transmitting your signal on the same medium is not trivial. Engineers at the Xerox Palo Alto Research Center (Xerox PARC) invented a way, and Ethernet was born in 1975.

The resulting network is elegant in its simplicity. Any station wishing to transmit can do so as long as another station is not in the middle of a packet. There is no delay waiting for a token to come around, not even any overhead to reserve cable capacity. If the medium is not in use, the station needing it just takes it and starts sending packets on their way. Whenever the next packet is ready to send, the scene repeats itself. If the cable is not in use, the packet goes immediately. If the cable is in use, it goes as soon as the current user finishes sending its packet. As demand goes up and we reach the situation in which more than one station is waiting to transmit after the current packet is done, we get a collision. However, unlike simple CSMA, CSMA/CD detects that a collision has occurred and aborts the current packet transmission. To ensure that all parties transmitting realize that a collision has occurred, the Ethernet specification includes a requirement that any station transmitting that detects a collision must abort its transmission by transmitting a short jam sequence, ensuring that all parties on the network realize that their current transmission was in a collision.

Subsequent collisions are minimized by each party involved in the collision backing off a random amount of time before retransmitting the packet. If the same packet collides again, the back-off time is doubled each time, until the packet finally gets through. This keeps utilization of the network efficient under heavy loading but only at the cost of unpredictable delays for random packets. It is statistically possible, albeit unlikely, for a packet to take hours to be delivered. This lack of deterministic delay under load is the price paid in a CSMA/CD network for its high efficiency under light load. On the factory floor, where

productivity and sometimes even safety are dependent upon predictable
response times, token passing is the clear choice. In the office, where user
needs are much more sporadic in nature (such as the engineer who once
or twice an hour needs to transfer a 10-Mbyte graphics design), the
choice is equally clear for CSMA/CD. Granted, an occasional operation
could be aborted by network congestion; in the meantime the average
access time has more than made up for the delay.

IEEE 802.3

The IEEE 802.3 standard is intended to be "a comprehensive standard
for Local Area Networks employing CSMA/CD as the access method."[1]
It was the first local area network standard developed by IEEE, and it is
an interesting case study in the politics of standardization. Based on the
Ethernet standard promulgated by DEC, Intel, and Xerox (the DIX
Ethernet standard), ratification of the standard was blocked for over a
year by minor points. The crux of the problem was not really technical,
however; it was economic. DEC, Intel, Xerox, and other Ethernet
supporters had too much invested in Ethernet to discard it for an
incompatible standard. At the same time, other vendors who had not
jumped on the Ethernet bandwagon could ill afford to concede the head
start in the marketplace that ratification of an Ethernet compatible
standard would give the Ethernet consortium.

The committee was deadlocked, and users were giving up hope of a
unified LAN standard when the European Computer Manufacturers
Association came to the rescue. They decided not to wait for IEEE and
ratified their own version of Ethernet, called ECMA-80. Their action
broke the deadlock in the IEEE 802.3 committee. The ECMA standard
showed that a compromise was possible which would prevent Ethernet
from being directly competitive with a standard LAN, yet would be close
enough that those with major investments in Ethernet would not lose
their investment. The IEEE committee soon reached a similar compromise and the first IEEE local area network standard was approved and
published.

Today the IEEE 802.3 committee charter is to provide standards for
CSMA/CD networking at signal rates ranging from 1 to 20 Mbps. Light
industrial and commercial applications are targeted. The needs of heavy
industry or home use are not considered in the standards. Media types
supported range from twisted pair to broadband coaxial cable. The
Ethernet equivalent, 10-Mbps IEEE 802.3 running on high-performance
baseband coaxial cable, has been ratified as an ISO standard as well.

---

[1]IEEE 802.3 Standard.

Media Access Control sublayer functions

The Media Access Control (MAC) functions defined by IEEE 802.3 look a lot like Ethernet, as you would expect given its history. The MAC accepts data to be transmitted from the link layer; constructs a frame from it with headers, frame check sequences, and appropriate flags; and generates the bit-serial data required by the physical sublayer. [Note that literature, including the standard itself, which predates the movement of the MAC sublayer from the link layer to the physical layer, refers to the logical link control (LLC) sublayer and the physical layer rather than the other way around.] The sequence is reversed when receiving; the MAC accepts the bit-serial data stream from the physical layer, verifies the frame check sequence, and delivers any broadcast or directly addressed frames to the link layer.

CSMA/CD implementation requires a number of functions. The MAC must defer transmission whenever the physical medium is busy. Once the medium is free, it continues to defer transmitting for a short period of time (9.6 μs for high-performance 10-Mbps media) called the interframe gap time. This delay is to allow the receiver of the previous frame time to deliver it out of the MAC sublayer up to the link layer and to be ready to receive the next frame if that frame is also addressed to it.

Detection of a collision halts the transmission, either immediately or after transmission of a jam signal if required by the media to ensure detection of the collision by all stations in the process of transmitting. The MAC will schedule retransmission after a collision using a random back-off algorithm with increasing delays on each retry attempt (the same as described earlier for Ethernet) until retry limits are reached.

Media options

IEEE 802.3 has set standards on four different physical media and associated signaling methods for CSMA/CD networks so far. The different versions are identified by the nomenclature defined in Figure 8.1. The basic format is number-name-number as in 10base5. The first number is the data rate used in megabits per second, in this case the Ethernet 10-Mbps data rate. The name in the middle specifies the signaling method used. Base, for baseband, means that the encoded 1s and 0s are directly impressed on the medium rather than indirectly using a modem to convert the digital data to an analog signal. Baseband allows cost-effective, high-speed communications with simplified detection of collisions, but it does require the medium to be dedicated to the network channel. In the case of 10base5, the data is Manchester encoded with high level being no signal on the cable and low level driving the cable to − 2.05 V. Collisions are detected by noticing that the voltage on the cable has not returned to 0 when the transmitter is not driving it negative, i.e., another transmitter is driving the cable at the same time. (In Manchester encoding, the center of each bit cell has a level transition from low to high if the data value for that bit cell is a 1 and a transition from high to low if it is a 0. Transitions will occur as required between bit cells to allow the proper transition to occur in the center of each bit cell. See Figure 8.2.) The final number gives the maximum length of a single cable segment in hundreds of meters. Further distances require either the use of repeaters or a different 802.3 physical layer option.

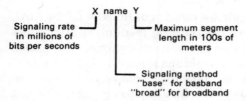

Figure 8.1   IEEE 802.3 media specification nomenclature.

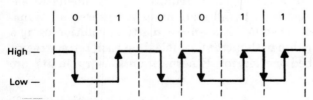

Figure 8.2   Manchester encoding.

10base5.   The original 802.3 specification is 10base5. This is the high-performance Ethernet equivalent network built on the famous thick (slightly over 1-cm diameter) yellow-jacketed coaxial cable. Maximum performance in terms of number of connected stations (100 per segment) and distance between repeaters [500 meters (m)] required very tight specification on such cable characteristics as impedance and propagation speed. The resulting cable is not only heavy but can be permanently, yet invisibly, damaged by bending it too sharply. The transceivers used to put the signal on the cable must be physically attached directly to the main cable. The remainder of the 802.3 interface is in the user station and connects to its MAU by a cable which may not exceed 50 m in length. This cable and the connectors at each end and the signals carried (power, transmit, receive, and collision presence) are all defined as part of the standard.

The high performance of a 10base5 network is not low cost, nor with the two repeater maximum limitation is it able to cover large facilities. Media options have been defined to handle both these concerns and are described next. Today, 10base5 has two primary application areas: as a migration path to international standards from existing Ethernets and as a backbone CSMA/CD network interconnecting, via repeaters and bridges, multiple 10base2 and 1base5 subnets providing lower-cost, more flexible connections for PCs and workstations in offices and engineering.

10broad36. The broadband version of 802.3 is 10broad36. It extends the range limitations of 10base5 from the baseband maximum of 1500 m (10base5 is limited to a maximum of two repeaters between any two communicating stations) to a more respectable 3.6 Km. The improvement is even better than the two-to-one ratio of the numbers implies, as the broadband network can branch as much as required to provide area coverage as long as the distance from station to head end to other station does not exceed the limit.

There are two main drawbacks, however, both of which we covered in the previous chapter on broadband. First, broadband modems are even more expensive than baseband transceivers, so there is significant cost involved in attaining the extra distance. If the broadband cable plant is not already available and it is necessary to install one, the cost differential is even greater. Second, the frequency spectrum assigned (10broad36 requires the equivalent of three channel pairs) overlaps that specified by 802.4. This can lead to conflict if extensive MAP or other 802.4 networking is also planned for the cable.

On the positive side, 10broad36 is AUI compatible with 10base5. AUI is an acronym for access unit interface, and AUI compatible means that no change is required to the interface in the user station. Switching from 10base5 to 10broad36 or back is as easy as unplugging the transceiver cable from the 10base5 MAU and plugging it into the broadband modem.

10base2 and 1base5. The quest for lower cost has led to the most recent two alternatives in 802.3, Cheapernet and Starlan. Cheapernet, also known as Thinlan, goes by the official designator 10base2. Originally a low-cost alternative to Ethernet, it reduces cost by integrating the 10base5 transceiver function right onto the user station interface card. The elimination of isolated dc-dc power supplies, access cable drivers and receivers, and case parts reduces the incremental cost by an order of magnitude from that of a separate MAU and access cable. The other big cost savings comes from replacing the heavy, inflexible Ethernet cable with lightweight, flexible RG-59 coaxial cable, the 50-ohm equivalent of the RG-58 coaxial cable used for home TV connections. The net result is that rather than expensive ties from individual stations to a centrally located 10base5 cable, Cheapernet brings the network to the individual station.

The low cost and ease of installation of Cheapernet are not free, of course. The maximum segment length is reduced to 175 m, while the maximum number on nodes on a single segment is 30. It is amazing how quickly the full length allowed for a Cheapernet segment is used up in a typical office as the cable goes from the repeater on the 10base5 backbone, down the hall, and in and out of every office. Planning and discipline are required to achieve the full cost savings available.

Starlan, on the other hand, takes a different approach to cost savings. Originally developed by AT&T, Starlan uses twisted pair as the communications medium rather than coaxial cable. This allows many facilities to utilize some of those extra phone wires going to each desk that phone companies have been recommending for over a decade. The trade-off made this time is capacity. The lower speed of 1 Mbps is inadequate for many graphics-oriented engineering applications but perfectly suitable for most clerical offices. By the time the office workers get to the point at which they need the kinds of bandwidth the engineers currently demand, twisted pair signaling technology will probably have grown to match, or there will be other technologies.

TOP specifics

The TOP 1.0 specification calls for IEEE 802.3 on 10base5. CSMA/CD was chosen for its proven capability in business and engineering applications. The needs of applications driven by human inputs tend to be characterized by long periods of inactivity randomly punctuated by occasional bursts of heavy activity. The inefficiency of token ring under unbalanced loading, when only one or a few stations require any network capacity, makes it inappropriate for the environment; so the TOP developers really had little choice.

The selection of 10base5 media was made to provide compatibility with existing Ethernet local area networks. Ethernet version 2.0 and IEEE 802.3 10base5 can coexist on the same backbone cable, although they cannot communicate with one another. Users can use Ethernet-based services, such as those available on Unix engineering workstations; they do not have to put in a whole new network cable plant to utilize TOP.

Ethernet and 10base5 use the same coaxial cable, the same signaling on the cable, and identical media access control. The differences between the two standards are much more subtle and have no impact on the ability to run both networks simultaneously on the same cable. Where they differ is on points like the packet format used. Ethernet packets have fields not available in 802.3 and vice versa. The connectors on the transceiver cable, although the same physically and using the same signals on the access cable, are wired differently. Other differences are even less drastic; often one specification is slightly more restrictive than the other. The two specifications are close enough that vendors can use the same hardware for both protocols. The main requirement is for the software at the link level to be "smart" enough to identify which protocol is being used, react accordingly, and route the data up the correct protocol stack.

Long term, there is no intent to keep TOP restricted to IEEE 802.3 10base5. Ethernet/10base5 is not the universal choice by all engineering and office network planners. In some cases, the performance is more than required. There are many text-oriented applications for which a 64-Kbps link through the PBX is more than adequate. There are also applications for which even a 10-Mbps link is not fast enough. Nor is 10base5 inexpensive, even on a cost-per-connection basis. Popular usage of TOP, even just as an access mode to MAP, requires the flexibility to match the network media to the environment and users.

TOP 3.0 expands the available media selection in two dimensions. In one dimension, additional 802.3 media, such as 10base2 Cheapernet, 1base5 Starlan, and 10broad36 AUI compatible, are under consideration. The second dimension is expansion into other 802 media access methods and their associated media. IEEE 802.5 token-passing ring is being added for compatibility with wiring installed for the IBM token ring, the same as 802.3 10base5 was required for Ethernet. From the user's viewpoint, the issue is moot. The choice of cable plant, as long as it is one of the IEEE 802 standards, will be invisible to the software from the link layer on up. The challenge for MAP/TOP is to specify the options in such a way that the user gets the advantage of a range of media to choose from without either forcing vendors out of the MAP/TOP market because they cannot justify offering all the choices or putting users in the position of having to choose a network other than MAP/TOP because of the physical layer desired.

Recap of Key Issues

Carrier Sense Multiple Access with Collision Detection (CSMA/CD) provides real advantages over token ring in the office and engineering environments. TOP provides a solid baseband network specification with a clear growth path from existing Ethernet networks. Lower-cost link standards will enhance the utility of TOP. But the real benefit of TOP is the user services provided by the upper-layer protocols introduced in MAP/TOP 3.0. Once MAP/TOP offers better services on more vendors than existing de facto standards such as ARPA/Berkeley and IBM SNA, its success will be assured, regardless of the media and access options available.

Chapter

9

Defining Network Requirements

Now that we have covered the technical aspects of networking, it is time to examine the management and planning side of the equation. For the next three chapters, we will look at the challenges in defining the needs for the network, developing a specification which meets those needs, selecting a network which meets the specification, and finally, installing and managing that network. We will start in this chapter with a look specifically at the challenge of understanding the user requirements for the network and translating them into network requirements. Understanding user needs is critical to the entire process. Like a ship at sea, if you do not know where you are and where you are trying to get to, the chances of success are very small.

The Need for Automation and
Computer-Integrated Manufacturing

Before we can discuss the specific networking needs of users, we first need to find out why we are considering networking at all. It is not cost effective to implement a multivendor MAP/TOP network if there is no benefit to be gained from networking. Although the official answer to the question "Why network?" will almost always be "productivity" or "cost improvement," there are usually many other reasons which are not as clearly stated but have a major impact on the choices made.

Competition is a frequent factor. Whether Ford Motor Company thinks MAP/TOP is optimum or not, they certainly feel the competitive pressure from General Motors. Can they risk missing out on the benefits of computer-integrated manufacturing if it has even a fraction of the expected payoff?

Prestige can also be a factor. However, prestige is a positive factor only if there are other payoffs to go along with it. The same cautions apply to the justification of testing the frontiers of technology. Somewhere down the line there has to be a payoff, even if it is concluding that there is no payoff in pushing on that frontier.

In some cases, automation is just a necessary cost of doing business, and the only real choice is in how to implement it. For example, design engineers in many product areas would consider lack of computer-aided design and engineering tools the equivalent of asking a mechanic to tune a race car with a penknife. Similarly, word processors for typists and calculators for accountants are no more optional than a desk, chair, and telephone.

Computer-integrated manufacturing may be the only way to attain the quality and flexibility of product that is being demanded by the market. The Japanese domination of the electronics industries was made possible by their realization that quality pays rather than costs if it is designed into the process rather than inspected out of the product. Of course, quality does not automatically result from automation and communications. Quality is a management function, and the various aspects of computer-integrated manufacturing are merely tools that can support the implementation of that function.

The same applies to the objective of superior information-handling capability. The desire to implement ready-made solutions to nagging management and organizational problems creates a dangerous trap for the unwary. Fix the problem first, then automate. Automating a counterproductive process only makes it a more efficient counterproductive process.

Reasons for reluctance

There are many valid reasons for being reluctant to implement a factory floor network or any other one. MAP/TOP attacks one of the biggest, lack of compatibility, but there are others it does not. Many continue to doubt the cost effectiveness of MAP/TOP. Not all users are convinced that full interoperability in a multivendor environment is worth a premium price or a sacrifice in functionality or performance. Although the intent of MAP/TOP is to get prices to come down and turn computer networking into a commodity market, that status remains in the unknown future. The size and complexity of the ISO protocol stack and application services in MAP/TOP 3.0 leads to concern over what performance levels will be ultimately attainable. The cost of MAP/TOP could be more than just the capital expense; the performance difference between a MAP/TOP and a special-purpose proprietary solution will always remain. The question is whether it will be significant.

Unfavorable early experiences can generate a great deal of reluctance to try again. This can be particularly troublesome if compounded with a lack of knowledge. Many companies do not have the resources to devote to learning the technology and are unable to design and install even a pilot project unaided. At the same time, they are reluctant to place their fate in the hands of vendors or even consultants. This is where industry users' groups, such as the MAP/TOP Users' Group, can provide major benefits. Learning from the successes and mistakes of others can help avoid surprises. This can greatly reduce the fear of errors which paralyzes many projects.

The biggest challenge facing MAP/TOP projects is the uncertainty about how far to commit now and how long to wait for future advances to be introduced. This is the classic dilemma of the computer industry, in which many vendors have discovered that by the time they can get the latest technology into a product, it is obsolete. In the MAP/TOP world, the normal level of uncertainty is compounded by the anticipation of MAP/TOP 3.0 and its availability from major vendors. This uncertainty affects more than users. Major vendors are reconsidering their development plans and commitments as the promise of the MAP/TOP market remains just that, a promise, and real sales remain elusive.

Remember that no automated system has ever been developed that could be inserted intact into a plant without a great deal of thought and planning. Computer-integrated manufacturing stands today where data processing did 20 years ago. Equipment is available, it is expensive, and the path to success is tough and unclear. But the need for change is compelling, and those who fail to find the way risk being left behind.

A path to success

There are three prerequisites to success, whether you are planning a massive effort to leapfrog your competition on the road to computer-integrated manufacturing or simply upgrading an existing factory floor network to MAP. First and foremost is the need to set reasonable expectations at all steps along the way. A 100 percent increase in productivity will be considered a dismal failure if the promise was for a 10 times improvement.

The second prerequisite to success is to make sure you are organized for success. It is hard to install any kind of a network in a large company without crossing departmental boundaries. Telecommunications will think it is their job because communications are involved. The data processing department will expect it because computers are involved. Plant management will also claim authority because they are responsible for the processes being implemented or modified in their plant. Engineering, marketing, finance, quality, and other departments affected will rightfully demand some say in what is happening to the operations in their departments. Make certain from the start that there is a person responsible for computer-integrated manufacturing who can handle all aspects of the job and work with data processing, telecommunications, management, and all other departments affected.

Finally, recognize that you will be altering the techniques and procedures used by individuals and departments to get their jobs done. People are used to the old way and are naturally reluctant to change, even when the benefits are clear. Depending on what is being automated, there may even be concern by individuals about whether they will continue to be employed. The feelings exhibited by those affected may or may not be justified, but they do exist and must be respected.

The role of a master plan

The role of computers and communications in your facility should be derived from your corporation's strategic plan. Computer-integrated manufacturing is a major undertaking and requires top management commitment for success. False starts will severely punish the poor planner who has not put together a plan which supports top management needs. Getting the comptroller involved early in the project can provide not only insight into how operational changes will change the bottom line but also a valuable ally when selling the plan to top management. Finally, do not expect fixed versus flexible automation to go away as an issue.

Develop the CIM master plan based on the goals of the corporate strategic plan. The master plan should state where you are today, where you want to be 3, 5, and 10 years into the future, and how to get there from here. Even if you cannot predict 10 years into the future, the plan is vital to hook together the various pieces so that they can be implemented one by one and still work together once in place. Like the corporate strategy it is based on, the master plan must be flexible enough to handle competitive changes and technological advances, yet solid enough to provide meaningful guidance to the implementation process.

Be sure to stress the unity of communications and computers. Many companies have already combined the data processing and telecommunications departments into a single department. This can be critical, as direct labor savings is usually one of the smallest gains seen from computer networking and computer-integrated manufacturing. The big gains come in the harder to measure areas such as material handling and information processing.

The master plan will also dictate the approach used to manage vendors. On the one hand, it is possible to depend on large vendors' development programs to keep current. While this approach has lower direct costs associated with it, it also prevents you from gaining an edge on your competition, as they can buy the same technology. The other extreme is to develop all your hardware and software internally. The benefit here is that nobody knows your operations as well as your own people, and you can develop capabilities unavailable to your competition. The disadvantage, of course, is the expense of internal development programs. This is both in terms of direct costs, such as staffing, and indirect costs, such as passing up the external solution which provides 80 percent of the needs while waiting for the in-house version.

When developing or working from the master plan, always be on the lookout for invalid assumptions. Many plans have failed because the production volumes required to make them profitable were unrealistic, market projections were based on wishful thinking rather than actual demand, or production costs assumed a learning curve where none applied. Challenge the assumptions rather than blindly accepting them. It all comes back to setting realistic expectations.

Establishing the Need for Computer-Integrated Manufacturing

The best way to approach the challenge of justifying computer-integrated manufacturing is through the process flow charted in Figure 9.1. While all the publicity that total quality control has been receiving in the 1980s might have you believe that the process is something new, it is really just common sense. The main contribution of the total quality control movement has been the reminder to proceed around the circle in the correct direction and choose the alternative to solve the problem rather than the more common approach of choosing the problem to justify the alternative.

The first step is to identify the problem which requires solving. This is not always as easy as it sounds because many different problems can often cause the same or similar symptoms. Poor productivity in a particular work cell may be caused by anything from peer pressure among workers afraid of a quota increase to faulty design of the part being produced. Automating the work cell will be a waste of money if the productivity problem is caused by faulty parts from a vendor.

Once the problem to be attacked is identified, the next step is to set the criteria for victory. That is, to set the objectives for measuring the success of the solution. While often overlooked, this step serves more than one useful purpose: It provides the team putting the solution together with a common goal, it provides criteria for evaluating the utility of implementing alternate solutions, and it even provides guidance when the time comes to evaluate whether another cycle through the process is warranted.

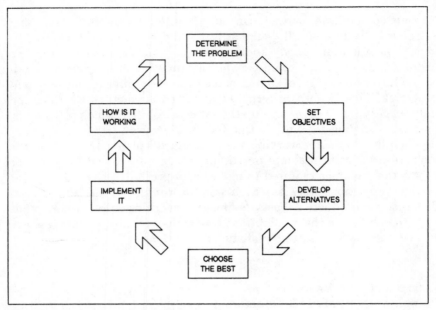

Figure 9.1 Total quality control process.

Only when you know where you are (the problem identified) and where you want to be (the objectives) does it make sense to start thinking about possible solutions. I divided this step up into two steps: develop alternatives and choose the best alternative. This emphasizes the need to keep looking after the first "obvious" answer comes to mind. This is all the more important if the first step, identification of the problem, is not certain. As you are working on any step, be aware that it may be desirable to back up to a previous step either to refine it or to start over again with fresh insight.

The next step is what too many people consider the last step. That is, implement the plan. Far from being the end of the process, it is just one stage in the cycle. It is vital to reach the next stage and measure the real success of the solution in action. And it is not sufficient to check once and be happy. The checking needs to be an ongoing process so that deviations from the objectives can be detected and acted upon while they are still minor. While this may seem like a great deal of work, constant checking and correcting is far less work in the long run than the open loop alternative, putting up with mounting minor problems until the process is out of control.

The nature of productivity

When the problem has been defined as "inadequate productivity," the challenge becomes defining productivity. The concept of productivity is deceptively simple. It is the ratio of output to input. While the equation is the same as that for efficiency, the concept is not. Producing an output which is not required in half the time does nothing for productivity while it doubles efficiency.

The question then becomes what are the inputs and what are the outputs. To measure productivity, we must include all the inputs and all the outputs so that gains in one area are compensated by any losses they cause in another. During the oil embargo of the 1970s, the U.S. automotive industry could have been producing large cars with twice the production line productivity of the small foreign car suppliers and they still would have done poorly. The market had shifted away from large cars and there was little demand for them at any price. The ultimate measure of corporate productivity is profit and loss. Unfortunately, the resolution provided is too crude to provide any useful data.

There is no single way to measure total productivity. But it is worth trying. After all, if you cannot measure productivity before networking, how can you prove your work made any difference?

Defining Network Service Requirements

The full specification of network requirements demands specification of six related but independent areas. They are the services required, the traffic characteristics, the physical environment, availability, maintenance, and growth. While the remainder of this chapter is devoted to discussing each of these six specifications, it is vital to remember that each must ultimately be traceable back to the needs of the users. The network designer must first understand the users' requirements so that the network meets the users' real needs, which may not be the solution the user is demanding after reading about the latest networking advance in some recent journal.

Development of the "service requirements document" is a three-step process consisting of collecting information, developing a service architecture, and writing the service requirements. Let us look at each in turn.

Collecting information

The information to be collected answers these three questions:
1. What is the network to be used for?
2. What devices are to use the network?
3. What services must the network provide?

The key question, of course, is the first. Once you know what the network will be used for, the answers to the second and third come easily. This is one place you cannot afford any shortcuts. The entire process of specifying, selecting, and implementing the network depends on having the right answer here at the first step. Time spent in this stage—gaining a true understanding of the users' needs—will pay off for the lifetime of the network. It will make each succeeding step easier and more productive.

The difficulty of this step should not be underestimated. The users who truly understand their own needs, let alone how they translate into networking requirements, are rare. Sometimes this step is impossible without experimenting with prototypes or pilot projects to see how they work. The prototype or pilot network is also a useful cure for paralysis of analysis, but it should always have solid goals and objectives. Otherwise, 2 years later you may find yourself with no more knowledge about user needs than you started with.

Look for the equivalent of a work study on the user processes considered for the network. If one has not been done, participating in it can be an excellent way to gain a better understanding of the users' needs and perspectives. The objective of the work study should be to learn all the functions of the plant, eliminate those which do not contribute to productivity, identify work flows, and determine what the current processes should be producing.

Within each discrete process, you want to identify the major activities involved, obtain volume counts of the minimum, maximum, and average content, and make a flowchart of how the different steps fit together. The goal is to ensure that each process is designed to meet the objectives of the organization and eliminate any unnecessary work. For example, at one stage in a work cell, parts may be removed from one station and dropped in a bin for transportation to the next. At the next workstation, the operator must spend time reaching into the bin and correctly aligning the part for additional tooling. Since the alignment information was available at the previous workstation but discarded when the part was dropped into the bin, it might pay to palletize the transfer so that alignment could be retained, perhaps even allowing the robot which unloads the second workstation to load it as well.

The work content is evaluated and the work time estimated with the objective of determining how much time each function should take under different conditions. Developing a model of the process, it is possible to simulate changes in work time, staffing levels, activities within the process, and so on. While this does not allow determination of whether the process is properly designed, it does provide a baseline for comparison and may provide preliminary indications of operations which lend themselves to automation or network communications.

The final step in the work study is to determine the causes of deviations measured in operation from the ideal determined in the previous step. The sources of deviations are legion and may range from inaccuracy of the analysis to inefficient work flows or methods. Other common causes include lack of control of inputs, inadequate management, poorly designed support systems, and improper sizing of the work force. The bottom line is that it makes no sense to automate inefficient or unnecessary processes. All that results is automated inefficiency and waste.

Developing a service architecture

Once we know what the network is to be used for, what devices will be connected, and what services will be utilized, the next step is to translate the user requirements into networking requirements. For example, a user requirement might be expressed as:

> Each bearing will be tested before packing to measure the total free play. Units out of specification will be set aside for evaluation by quality assurance, who will be notified whenever the reject carton is filled or when more than ten rejects are detected per thousand tests. Records of all measurements will be maintained on file for analysis by quality assurance for a minimum of 30 days.

Note that even this level of specification will take considerable work to obtain. The initial response when asking for the data probably read more like "Check each bearing and notify quality assurance when there are too many rejects." And we are still lacking such critical information as how many tests are performed, how frequently rejects are expected to occur, how often quality assurance needs to be notified (do they normally empty the bin once a year or five times a day?), or whether the 30-day storage requirement requires one sheet of paper or billions of bytes of disk storage.

The corresponding network service specification would be Network Interprocess Communication between test station counter and quality assurance dispatcher, and Remote Data Base Access (data entry only) from test station to QA database machine. Even at this stage we are remaining generic. Until we have all the requirements, we do not know whether we need a true RDBA capability or if a simple update application program using NIPC would do the job.

Expect to make several passes through this step, developing an overall structure for the applications identified by the user needs study, allocating the functionality required between user application programs and the services provided by the network, and checking the answers for feasibility. With each pass, measure the results against two criteria. First, are the services identified available from any network currently on the market which is compatible with all the devices requiring connection? Second, does the split of services between network and user devices make sense for the individual applications and devices? A prime goal of MAP/TOP is to answer these questions affirmatively even when devices from multiple vendors are involved.

The service requirements document

The final step is to document all the work done in the previous two steps. Start with a list of all network standards applicable to the services required. Normally this would be the current MAP or TOP specification unless the outcome of the service architecture development process was some other network. Include a high-level description of the basic applications that will use the network, as well as the hardware and software that will be attached to the network. Since the service requirements will normally be part of the procurement specification, this shifts some of the responsibility for fitness for use to the supplier. It also provides others with the background to understand the reasoning behind your particular service choices and enables them to contribute alternatives to the design.

The detailed part of the service requirements consists of a description of the actual services required from the network, a list of specific devices that are to be attached to the network, and any special requirements such as size, management, or control. Note that this may extend beyond the scope of the computer network requirements and include facilities such as closed circuit television, point-to-point data links, and environmental control facilities.

Establishing Network Traffic Characteristics

The second phase of network requirements definition is determining the network traffic requirements. The goal is to determine how much data (and other traffic) will be going over the network and under what conditions so that the network can be designed to carry the load. If the form of the network is predetermined, as in a MAP/TOP pilot network, the same study will tell at what point network performance will begin to degrade as more users are added or when it will need to be split up into multiple subnetworks. This phase can be divided into five steps: collection of basic information, determination of basic application characteristics, development of the transfer matrix, development of individual device statistics, and specification of aggregate network traffic.

Collection of basic information

This step should be the easiest. Two lists are required: one of all the user devices that will directly access the network and one of all the applications associated with each device that will be demanding network services. All this information should be in the service requirements. If it is not, you should go back and fix the service requirements before proceeding. One piece of information which may not be in the formal service requirements document but will be extremely useful as you proceed is the name of the person associated with each list entry to contact for more information.

Determination of basic application characteristics

The determination of basic application characteristics is really a precursor to the development of the transfer matrix. Many aspects of the communications requirements are common among multiple users of the same or similar application services. The goal of this step is to determine those common basic characteristics for each application which are independent of the particular user device they are running on.

In the world of MAP/TOP, the two basic characteristics that can be determined at this stage are the data unit sizes (how big is each packet sent?) and the class of traffic (stream or transaction). The scope of the term "application" can also be adjusted to minimize the effort required. For example, FTAM file transfer users may be divided into three application classes. First, there are those sending large files (say 50 Kbytes and up). With these users, the partial packets involved in setting up and completing the transfer are a small fraction of the total packets sent. It is reasonable to treat the application as a one-way stream of maximum-sized (approximately 1400 bytes in a MAP/TOP network) packets from source to destination and minimum-sized acknowledgment packets flowing in the reverse direction. The second obvious FTAM user class is the small file transfer, in which the actual data transfer phase is minimal compared with the overhead of the operation. With these users, whether the file size is 1 byte or a few thousand bytes, the demand on the network is almost identical. The third class is those users who are in between the large and small file transfer domains, in which both the overhead and the data transfer proper are significant and should be accounted for.

Services such as CASE and MMS are even more dependent on the user application, and will need to be clustered on that basis. For example, MMS user applications may be robot control, sensor monitoring, and program download. Understanding the users' needs is critical. More than likely, the original user request was for communications between cell

controller and three robots to provide coordination of activities. Using
the contact name in the list of applications, you were then able to track
down what was really required. Be extremely wary of making assumptions about user needs at this stage. Another set of users asking for
communications between cell controller and three robots to provide
coordination of activities may need real-time interlocks between the
actions preprogrammed into their robots, a totally different network
requirement.

When done, we should have a description of the network characteristics for each application class. At a minimum, it should provide such data
as typical data unit sizes (may be direction specific, as with file transfer),
stream or transaction orientation (that is, how do user requests get
mapped into data units, is there reverse traffic to piggyback acknowledgments onto, etc.), and key dependencies and assumptions that could
affect any of the numbers.

Development of the transfer matrix

Based on data characteristics of the various applications, we want to
develop a model of the typical traffic patterns between each pair of user
devices. This step needs to be approached systematically if the network
being developed is at all sizable. Computer-based tools such as a spreadsheet or simple database can ease the movement of the data developed in
this stage to the different forms required in the following stages.

The result we are seeking in this step can best be expressed in a data
flow diagram (Figure 9.2). Each node (circle in the figure) represents a
user device attached to the network. Each arrow between nodes represents the data flow for a particular application and is specified in terms
of the user application needs. At a minimum it should include the name
of the application, the frequency and size of transactions, and any special
requirements such as allowable delay or time to complete. You will
actually need two data flow diagrams, one for average conditions and one
for peak and worst-case requirements. Whether you decide to develop
data flow diagrams or not, the information required is the same.
Computer-based tools are available to automatically generate data flow
diagrams.

Start by listing the applications that require data exchange between
each pair of nodes. Since we will need to look at each direction
separately, the easiest approach is to define a master and a slave for each
application definition. Taking each node in turn, link it with every other
node in turn and list all the "master applications" the node supports
over that link. It does not matter if the applications are truly master-
slave or peer to peer. The key is to count every transaction and avoid any
double counting. While this process may sound like a combinatorial

nightmare, in practice you will find that the vast majority of pairings do not communicate. For example, a cell controller might only communicate with devices in its own cell, the plant host, and the network manager.

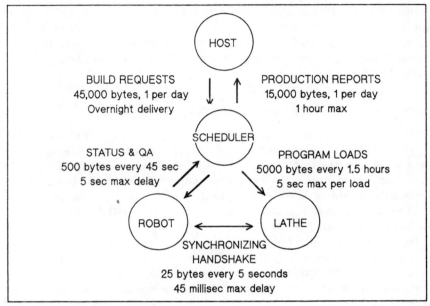

Figure 9.2 A simple data flow diagram.

Each application on each user device can then get an average and a peak number of activations per unit time associated with it, along with the data transfer requirements for each activation. An activation can be whatever action is convenient to count on the application, such as a file access with FTAM or a limit switch test with MMS. This is where the classification of applications and their properties comes into play with a consistent set of definitions and their translation into network traffic. Remember to determine both average and peak (or worst-case) numbers.

You also need to identify any performance requirements for each application between each pair of users. Delay is the most common need specified, usually in the context of time required to complete an activation. Costs can often be reduced by recognizing that needs themselves come in varying degrees. For example, there may be some applications, such as real-time process control, which cannot succeed if delay exceeds some value. These should be considered "musts." If the network service cannot be unconditionally guaranteed to meet the requirement, there is no sense implementing the network at all, at least from the viewpoint of that application. Other applications will have "want" delay requirements. They will perform better if delay is kept under a certain value but will degrade, rather than fail, as delay is increased. This is often the situation with user interactive applications. Some applications may have both "must" and "want" requirements, where the "want" is the delay value at which degradation starts and the "must" is that value at which the degradation becomes intolerable. Some applications may have multiple specifications, such as an occasional need for "priority" service. These can usually be handled using common sense, such as splitting the single application into two applications, one normal and one special.

Development of individual device statistics

This step takes the user-oriented application-level data that was developed in the previous step and converts it into the actual traffic each user device contributes to the network. All the user application data flows into and out of each device are converted to network traffic flows (including protocol overhead in each packet, connection setup and control, and acknowledgments), and the total calculated for each device. As before, we want both peak and average values.

Because of the nature of network protocols and their implementation, we actually need to specify the traffic two different ways. First of all, we need to know the traffic loading in terms of the quantity of data being transmitted through the network (the average and peak bytes-per-second load presented to the network). But equally important, we need to know the number of network accesses per second independent of how many bytes are actually transferred (the average and peak number of data units per second). Most network implementations are limited in the number of packets that can be handled per second as well as in the total number of bits. In MAP networks, for example, not only are there packet framing bits included with each packet, but there is also a wait for the token to make its way around the logical ring before a packet can be sent.

Another key factor in any network (such as MAP/TOP) which uses connection-oriented applications is the total number of concurrent connections required at each node. Again this should be two numbers, an average and a maximum. Even idle circuits consume network resources such as buffers, state tables, and connection assurance packet traffic (where the transports exchange "I am alive" packets in the absence of user traffic).

The output of this step is a table with ten entries for each device (Table 9.1). This is the key specification in the traffic requirements document. The preceding steps were preparatory work to allow its generation, and all that remains to be done is sum the results to determine if network partitioning is required.

TABLE 9.1 Sample Device Traffic Table Entries

Device Name	Packets/second		Bytes/second		Concurrent connections	
	Average	Peak	Average	Peak	Average	Peak
Bearing tester no. 47					2	2
Input	1	2	100	150		
Output	1	5	150	750		
QA Data Base Machine					25	72
Input	84	427	14,730	435,200		
Output	114	196	139,548	550,018		

Specification of aggregate network traffic

The final step is to sum up the average and peak loading of the network as a whole. The average is the simple sum of all the individual device averages (sum inputs and outputs separately; they should be equal). The peak will not exceed the sum of all peak values, but a lower peak design point is often safe to use to the extent that the device peaks are statistically independent. Reduction of the aggregate peak to as little as 50 percent of the simple sum may be possible but should be tempered by the number of devices and the criticality of the applications. If the peak aggregate traffic exceeds the capacity of the network, you will need to look at breaking the network up into linked subnets so that traffic may be isolated to individual partitions.

Keep in mind any delay requirements that may be affected by either the average or the peak loading. They may require network partitioning at a lower load than might otherwise be required. This is especially true in token-passing networks such as MAP in which the access delay waiting for the token can become unacceptable long before throughput is adversely affected. While the 802.4 priority levels can help keep priority response time acceptable under an increasing lower-priority load, the sheer number of token passers affects how quickly the token makes it around the logical ring even when no stations have data to transfer let alone when all have top priority data pending.

Physical Network Environment

The physical requirements for the network also need to be defined. These requirements extend beyond the specification of networking services to specification of the implementation constraints imposed on the provision of those services. They tend to fall into one of three categories. Environmental constraints cover aspects such as operating temperature range and media distance requirements. Supported equipment defines the user devices which must be able to connect to the network and where the dividing line is between network and user. For example, VMEbus network interfaces may be a requirement for the robot controller, while the cell controller may require Unibus. Finally, the information to be transmitted needs to be specified. What services need to coexist with the MAP 802.4 signals on the broadband network? These categories are all interrelated. For example, including terminal-to-host connections in the supported equipment list means that point-to-point asynchronous modem data needs to be transmitted through the network.

Environmental constraints

Determining environmental constraints tends to be the largest of the three definition tasks because it covers so many factors. The first question which needs to be answered is how flexible are the implementation options. A production line in operation which can tolerate no service interruptions is a very rigid environment in which to design a network. On the other hand, if the building is just being designed and the architect is asking if there are any special requirements for network installation, tremendous freedom is available to optimize the network installation. Reality usually falls somewhere in between.

The geography of the network may force numerous considerations. The number of buildings being networked and where they are located is a major consideration, as is the location of individual pieces of equipment within each building. In a geographically dispersed network, traffic requirements often identify opportunities for subnetworks. Be particularly cautious of requirements for high speeds over long distances. Even with satellite communications, megabit data rates over distances of more than a few kilometers are expensive. Keeping closely communicating equipment on the same subnetwork normally pays off, as does collocating network interfaces with user equipment.

Space requirements, while often not important, can be extremely expensive to overlook when the space is not available. This can cover a wide range of space needs. Floor space may be required for network hardware collocated with user equipment. Even if the network hardware is only a plug-in interface card, you need to be sure there is a slot available in the user's equipment capable of supporting it. If the network interfaces are stand-alone units, specify size and weight requirements commensurate with expected frequency of movement. Space requirements for the cable plant need to be considered as well as those of the interface units. What wall or floor space is available for taps, transceivers, or outlets? How much space is available inside the walls, ceilings, or floors for cabling, amplifiers, media access units, and such? Network control units and head end hardware require dedicated floor space, and do not forget to leave access clearance around it for maintenance technicians.

Finally, there is the climate and exposure of components to consider. There may be direct exposure of cable and amplifiers to exterior weather in runs between buildings. Climatic conditions inside a building can be even more extreme, especially in enclosed spaces. Consider both normal and abnormal exposure conditions to factors such as dust, humidity, temperature variations, electromagnetic interference, shock, and vibration. Remember nonoperating storage as well as normal operation. It does no good to keep a supply of spare interface cards on hand if they are all destroyed before use by storing them next to the main boiler. Nor is it enough to just consider how the components will survive the existing environment. It is also necessary to consider how components will affect that environment. The temperature rise because of the added power dissipated by active components may be as important as the availability of sufficient power of adequate quality to power the active components. And, while it may seem obvious, make sure it is possible to access components for maintenance, troubleshooting, and repair when required.

Supported equipment and interfaces

The second major environmental constraint is the equipment and applications which already exist and must be supported by the network. Supported equipment that we will be considering comes in two flavors; MAP/TOP and non-MAP/TOP. Let us consider non-MAP/TOP equipment first. From our viewpoint, this is any equipment which uses broadband services other than the IEEE 802.4 channel or channels supporting our MAP network. It is not safe to assume that just because you have broadband, you can put any service you want on it. As we discussed in Chapter 7, there is no consistent standard governing the usage of broadband frequencies by multiple services, and even the IEEE 802.3 and 802.4 standards overlap. If you want to provide remote video for security services over the broadband, it needs to be specified; the same with point-to-point modems to connect existing terminals to their respective hosts. If you want terminal users to be able to select which host they connect to, either frequency-agile modems or other switching support needs to be provided. Several vendors offer black boxes which attach terminals and hosts to a network and allow any terminal to talk to any host.

Nodes already in existence provide another set of constraints. For example, are compatible MAP/TOP version interfaces available on all machines requiring communications? Special gateway hardware may be required to get from the MAP/TOP world to the networking environment supported by the host.

The specifier on the leading edge of MAP/TOP will not have the luxury of standard interfaces and instead will need to specify both the hardware and software interfaces. For example, one device may require a VMEbus plug-in card while another requires MultiBUS. At the software level, you will need to specify what services are required and how they are accessed.

Transmitted data

The final environmental specification is that of the data requiring transmission. Like the supported equipment specification, transmitted data is also best defined by first splitting OSI data from non-OSI. Non-OSI data is simply the signal requirements of all applications not part of the MAP/TOP network. This may be digital data (similar to that carried by MAP/TOP), voice (either analog or digital), video (a natural fit for broadband when in analog form), imagery (including facsimile, raster graphics, and slow-scan video), or anything else supported on broadband cabling.

Inside the MAP/TOP world, we still have to worry about what data is being transmitted. Only now, the question is one of comprehensibility rather than transmissibility. We do not have to worry in a MAP/TOP network whether or not we can get the bits from one machine to another. But we do have to be concerned if the bits, once delivered, will be usable at the destination. Protocol standards for encoding graphics, product data, word processing documents, and such are being introduced starting with MAP/TOP 3.0. You need to worry whether the machines depending on the transfer of such information have those protocols implemented or if you will need (as is the case on any MAP 2.X network) to provide your own translations as part of the application.

Reliability and Availability

Specification of reliability requirements consists of reviewing the application service requirements, then specifying the network availability and service quality needs required to meet the application requirements. Our goal is to clearly define two independent aspects of network reliability. The first is the availability of network services, determined by the reliability of the network as a whole system as well as by the individual pieces making up the application. This aspect is usually dependent on traditional reliability measures such as mean time between failure and mean time to repair. The other aspect of network reliability is the quality of the services provided when they are available. Here we are measuring the degradation of services under heavy loading or other adverse conditions (such as a repair crew using the broadband coaxial cable for grounding their arc welder). Service quality may be measured by abnormal connection terminations, packet retransmission rate, token restoration delays, or any other factor which influences the ability of the network to provide timely or reliable service.

Applications review

The first step, as usual, is to gather all the required background information. The first question to answer for each application is how critical is that application to the productivity of the plant. For example, in the bearing tester example we used earlier, notification of the QA department to come and pick up rejects for analysis is just a convenience. Not until the bin starts to overflow and the bearings scattered about the floor create a safety hazard is the plant productivity liable to suffer. However, inability to notify the quality assurance department that the manufacturing process has gone out of control and 50 percent of all bearings tested are failing delays correction of the problem and may even result in damaged machinery from lack of timely maintenance. This function is clearly more critical than the previous one; just how critical would, of course, depend on the actual plant process and needs.

A key question to answer is whether or not the application can be accomplished in the face of periodic loss of the network. For example, full bin notification can clearly wait, while faulty process notification has a definite cost associated with delay. Some applications, such as real-time process control, cannot tolerate any outages. If possible, connect a monetary cost with network outage, as all users will declare their applications as critically sensitive to any loss of network services. Network reliability does cost money, and you want to be sure that money is properly invested.

A corollary to the question of application criticality is that of application flexibility. Many applications can be done on any of several devices (so all that is required is that at least one of them has adequate service) while others are limited to only one device (so that a failure which affects the device, but not the network, will still prevent successful accomplishment of the mission). Also determine the cost of recovering from network failure. A semiconductor fabrication line may lose all work in progress and require days to recover, while a machining cell may be able to restart after network service is restored as if nothing had happened.

Network availability requirements

Network reliability requirements are set by the most important application on the network, so start with the applications deemed most
critical in the previous analysis. All MAP/TOP networks share some
common critical elements regardless of the applications running. The
network address directory server and the head end are just two areas in
which a single failure can have major impact on all users. Determine the
mean time between failure and mean time to repair values for all critical
components required to meet the availability needs of the most critical
applications. Network components such as drop cables, modems, and
interface cards, which only affect the associated user, do not need to be
more reliable than the application devices they support. Be careful,
however, that the probability of any failure modes which would affect
overall network operation are compatible with the most critical applications.

The network as a whole should be more reliable than the individual
user devices connected to it if the user applications are dependent on the
network for successful operation. You may need to adjust the network
configuration (using redundant components, putting critical applications on their own subnetwork, and so on) to keep the required
component reliability within reach of available technology.

Service quality requirements

Like the availability requirements, the service quality requirements are
also specific to each application under consideration. Different services,
such as MMS and basic virtual terminal, will each require specific service
quality requirements, as may major subservices within each service, such
as FTAM file access and file transfer service.

Start by listing each application which uses each service. For each
application, determine its tolerance to degradations in the basic service
provided. For example, if FTAM fails to transfer a file, will the
application use other data or will it halt and wait for human intervention
to correct the problem? In a MAP/TOP network, in which the services
are provided at a high level with protocols like FTAM and MMS, the
network design considerations normally associated with service quality
requirements such as bit error rate and connection failure rate are totally
covered by the network architecture specification. However, it is still
vital to determine the service quality requirements at the service access
level to ensure that the needs of critical applications are met. MAP and
TOP are not perfect networks; they assume that a certain degree of
failure is permissible in order to keep costs reasonable. If one of your
applications requires the ability to complete transactions even across

network and user device failures, you may need to use a network with full commitment, concurrency, and recovery capability rather than MAP/ TOP. Only you can decide if the benefits of a standard network make up for the need to provide the extra capability in the application so it can handle its own recovery or if the number of applications requiring the service make it worthwhile to go with a different standard which better meets the needs.

Maintenance Requirements

Maintenance costs can easily dominate the total life-cycle cost of a network. Maintenance is vital to ensure that the network availability requirements just specified can be met long term over the life of the network. The challenge is to provide that maintenance within the financial and personnel resource limitations of the organization.

Hardware and software

Network maintenance has two sides, hardware and software. Hardware maintenance consists of both periodic preventive maintenance and recovery from failures. Software does not have a physical wear-out mechanism as hardware does, but it still requires maintenance in the form of enhancements and repair of defects that interfere with operations. Even standard, off-the-shelf software requires configuration management (so that compatible versions are running on all machines), network configuration management (so that addresses, timers, and other parameters can be set properly), and a means to get defects repaired. (Defect-free software remains a dream. The only question in today's software is whether the defect is critical or can be worked around.)

The biggest maintenance challenge on any reasonably sized network is troubleshooting network failures. The boundary between network hardware and network software is nebulous, and the maintenance of one in isolation from the other can lead to total frustration. It can be next to impossible to determine whether a network failure has been caused by hardware malfunction or a software defect. Because of the nature of layered protocols, each layer is designed to cover up any malfunctions in lower layers. Multiple independent defects may be required before a user-detectable network failure is generated. When the problems finally do become detectable, hardware defects may be reported as software failures and vice versa. Nor is the confusion necessarily the fault of poor design. There are many defects which can cause identical failure symptoms, and it takes real skill and experience to develop tests that can detect the difference.

Specification of maintenance requirements

Before you can specify the maintenance requirements, you need to estimate how complex the needs are and to what degree you want to meet them with in-house technical support. Providing your own maintenance in house has a number of potential advantages. Quick response to problems and total control over individual maintenance decisions are two of the biggest. In general, in-house technical support will result in enhanced technical control over all network functions. However, it also requires a technically competent staff and adequately documented hardware and software. The former can be costly to develop, if it is not already in place, both in terms of recruitment (skilled network technicians are rare, and their salaries reflect it) and training (not just courses but also degraded network performance while they learn their jobs). The latter may be too expensive or even nonexistent depending on the vendors.

Determining the complexity of the needs can also be a challenge. The protocols making up MAP/TOP are extremely complex, but they are also relatively well defined and testable. The same is true of broadband cable plants; the design requires an expert, but the ongoing maintenance is straightforward. The maintenance options are incredibly varied. Responsibility for hardware and software maintenance can range anywhere from the vendors providing everything to your staff doing it all. You can even purchase single-vendor support for a multivendor network. The cable plant vendor can be asked to provide suitable monitoring equipment for use by your staff. You need to determine if modifications are required to vendor-supplied software and who will do them. If your staff does it, can you require the vendor to supply source code? Who is responsible for development and maintenance of applications and interface software?

You may choose to leave maintenance to contractors (either the vendors or independents) but still do your own network monitoring so you know when to call them and whether or not they have done their job. Instruments are available to gather statistics on utilization and error rates by network channel and by node. Automatic failure detection is available for critical system components from head end remodulators to amplifiers and filters. Artificial traffic generators can be used to probe element status, exercise specific network functions, or verify remaining available capacity. Signal quality monitoring can help detect network degradation before it has an impact on quality of service. The choices are many.

Regardless of the choices you make, the maintenance requirements must depend on cost analysis as well as technical analysis.

Network Growth Requirements

Successful networks grow, evolve, and change as users' needs mature and new applications develop. The final aspect of specifying network requirements is allowing for that growth and evolution.

Types of network growth

Networks can grow in many ways. Additional processing capacity supporting existing applications, either in the form of expansion of existing nodes or the addition of new nodes, usually increases the total network traffic. Redistribution of centralized applications into a distributed processing environment may enhance the reliability and modularity of the application and could increase or decrease total network traffic. New applications can result in demand for more nodes, more use of current services, addition of new services, changed loading factors, and different availability, reliability, delay, throughput, and other performance requirements. They may even require the expansion into other broadband channels or the installation of totally new links.

Changing operations can also change traffic characteristics. Successful users tend to use more network services more often. Traffic volume and traffic generation statistics will evolve and may require modification or tuning of protocol parameters such as timeouts to keep performance optimal. A frequent need is the expansion of connectivity outside the current domain to other networks, both local and distant. This may be a result of expansion of the domain requiring communications, or it may be the only way to provide enough link capacity in the face of mounting usage. Even though internetting may not even have been thought of by the initial users, sooner or later it almost always becomes a necessity.

Physical flexibility is also desirable. It is often necessary to move equipment between offices, work cells, or buildings. Network characteristics which support flexibility are worth pursuing. This includes easy and inexpensive physical attachment to the cable plant as well as network control mechanisms that are independent of the physical location of particular nodes. It is vital to consider the likelihood of equipment relocations before it is too late. This is particularly true in MAP 2.X networks in which the network directory service does not include any standards for updates or maintenance.

Four steps to network growth requirements

Start by analyzing existing applications. For each application, look for additional traffic that might be generated by devices that already participate in the application. Consider new devices that may be added to the network in the future to participate in the application. Also consider other existing devices already on the network that might be brought into the application.

Second, list for each identified application the likelihood of growth of each type. List the probabilities of occurrence within specific time frames and the magnitudes anticipated and possible.

Third, identify any possible new applications. List all applications which might be added to the network and their probability of occurrence. List any new network services needed to support them. Consider the network services under development in the MAP, TOP, and ISO OSI communities. Go back and add to the original list the applications these brought to mind.

Finally, use these growth directions and probabilities to specify a total growth profile. Assign probabilities of occurrence to each type of growth and its magnitude. From these probabilities, estimate the number of new user-device attachments anticipated within 2, 3, and 5 years. Similarly, estimate the increase in aggregate traffic volume in bytes per second in the same time frame. Conclude with a description of new applications and new network services anticipated within 2, 3, and 5 years and congratulate yourself for chosing a MAP/TOP network so the evolution to the new services can be compatible with the existing network service architecture and available from a variety of vendors.

Recap of Key Issues

There are many aspects to specifying networking requirements, but they all depend on an understanding of the user needs. It is impossible to specify or obtain a useful network without understanding what it will be used for and how. Your biggest challenge will be translating the needs specified by users in terms of their applications into specification of the networking capabilities required to meet those needs. MAP/TOP provides a solid architecture for meeting real user needs in the manufacturing, office, and engineering worlds.

10

Network Design and Selection

The preceding chapter discussed how to develop the network requirements from the user application needs. Now it is time to translate those
network requirements into a specification for a network and see what
vendors have to offer. Since this is a book on MAP/TOP networking, you
are probably already leaning toward specifying MAP/TOP as the network architecture. The intent of this chapter is to provide tips on when
that decision may or may not be valid. It is well beyond the scope of an
introductory-level book like this one to explain all the possible considerations in selecting a network architecture, but I will try to cover some
of the more important ones.

General Guidelines

Clear objectives are vital to provide common understanding among all
concerned of the problems to be solved. Clear objectives focus the team
so it moves in a unified direction and can greatly enhance overall team
motivation. Good objectives can be recognized by several characteristics:
They are clear and understandable, realistic and attainable, and most
important, quantifiable and measurable. There can be no doubt when
they have been reached.

The urge for a quick fix is powerful. Vendors will bombard you with
packaged solutions for almost anything. However, you must keep your
sense of perspective and remember that solving the wrong problem is not
a solution. As I stated in the previous chapter, you must understand the
users' problems before you can successfully apply corrective action. If
you are working from a good set of objectives, they will be understand-

able to your users as well as to your staff, and all will agree that they are worth pursuing and do their best to make your network (and you) a success.

Traps on the road to CIM

As you pursue your vision of computer-integrated manufacturing tying the diverse areas in your plant together, there are some common misconceptions that must be avoided. First is the myth of the one-stop CIM supplier. CIM by its very nature is too multidisciplinary to be available from a single vendor. The closest you can get is to use an integrator who pulls the various vendors' pieces together for you. Beware of any supplier or consultant whose CIM models assume engineering is minor compared to manufacturing (or vice versa) or ignore marketing, sales, finance, or administration. Full solutions may cross both corporate and geographic boundaries, as well as departmental ones.

Second, while I have emphasized many times the importance of understanding user application needs, that alone is not sufficient. The decision to pursue CIM must be a strategic, top management one that is based on factors such as time to market, business growth, product mix, asset management, quality, and customer satisfaction. Isolated task automation does not automatically contribute to productivity. A new CAD system may give engineering 3 times the drafting productivity, but if the result is 3 times the amount of paper waiting for manual entry in the production system, there will be no impact on the bottom line. The factor which counts, time to market a new product, is unaffected.

Finally, many articles you read may imply that CIM is founded on a single, massive, shared database. In reality, centralization of data may not be desirable, let alone possible. You must recognize the heterogeneity in data management and applications intrinsic to today's islands of automation. Shared databases should be limited to functions which cooperate and communicate regularly and which need to access consistent data. The key to CIM is not the single database but rather the ability of any user who needs (and is authorized) access to data to be able to get that data in a usable form at a cost which does not exceed its value.

A rational approach

Implementing total CIM can be likened to eating an elephant. You are not going to be able to do it all at once and survive. However, you can do it the same way you eat anything else, one bite at a time. This is one of the hidden strengths of MAP/TOP networking. The overall solution can be implemented an application at a time with confidence that as the pieces come on line, they can all communicate with one another and build on each other's capabilities.

The implementation of CIM is the networking of networks of networks. You can think of layers of networks relating to the corporate hierarchy, tied together through common protocols and services. The corporate network is at the top and may span geographic and corporate boundaries, providing guaranteed, reliable message delivery and acknowledgment.

Down at the bottom are what have been up to now the islands of automation; highly tuned work-cell communications and process control. Normally special purpose, many will continue to be single vendor to provide the required cost and performance. The price is low because of limited capability and their proprietary nature. It may still make sense to implement them as islands of automation; however, you must plan to interconnect them from the beginning or they will remain islands forever.

Between the top and bottom are intermediate layers; the exact count will depend on who you talk to and what they are selling. The count which really counts is the functionality split which makes sense for your operation. These are the networks that link the manufacturing cells and those that link the various departments. Some may interconnect the plant-floor computers with supervisory workstations. One (usually the facility broadband cable plant) may provide wiring economy for widely distributed functions such as energy management and security. They all tend to be general purpose, fairly high speed, and very reliable because of the variety of users dependent upon them. At the same time they need to be flexible so that devices can be added and removed with little difficulty as needs and departments change.

Identifying Constraints

Most engineers, asked to identify the constraints the network is subject to, will immediately start considering topology, media, access method, and the like. However, the most important constraint is not technical, but political. The computer network must reflect management's beliefs and attitudes. The way the network is built and operated affects the way users approach their work. It dictates whether they are tightly bound to one another's actions or loosely coupled. It determines whether users are regimented into fixed groups or can adapt with fluid working teams as the need arises. The network organization can promote hierarchy, heterarchy, oligarchy, or even anarchy. None is intrinsically better than the other, but each fits different organizations and their needs better.

The network needs to complement the organization. It needs to reflect the management's trust in the users. Each individual's work can be a guarded secret, or it can be open to all. Network controls can be flexible or rigid, centralized or distributed. Even the concept of user "ownership" of resources can be adjusted to meet organizational expectations. Again, there are neither right nor wrong answers; the perfect network for one organization may be a total disaster in another. Even within a single organization there are differences, departments can vary widely, and even individuals in the same group may disagree. The key is to know the users and understand their needs and expectations. If you do not get a match at this level, the technical constraints will not make much difference.

This is not to say that the technical constraints are not important; they are. It is just that the technical constraints should reflect the real user needs, which includes the organizational and management constraints within which they must work. Let us look at some of the technical constraints which need to be considered.

Topology considerations

One of the first considerations must be the topology used to connect the nodes of the network together. (The various topologies are defined in the last section of Chapter 2.) We must be careful to distinguish between the topology defined by the connectivity of nodes and that defined by the appearance of the wiring diagram. For example, MAP specifies IEEE 802.4, which is a bus topology from the standpoint of network nodes sharing a common medium, but the broadband cable plant itself is usually wired in a hierarchical tree pattern, with the head end at the top and splitters, taps, and amplifiers allowing the cable to branch out to cover all corners of the facility. Similarly, the IEEE 802.5 token ring is a physical ring, but the wiring to each node is brought to the wiring closet, giving it the appearance of a star. Actually, it does more than just give the network the appearance of a star; it also provides the user many of the benefits of a star and compensates for most of the weaknesses normally associated with a ring topology.

Most wide area networks, including X.25 public data networks, are based on the complex mesh topology. This allows optimization of the total number and capacity of links to the needs of the network, an important consideration in wide area networks in which the cost of the communications links is the dominant cost of providing the service. The only real alternative to the mesh where it is essential to minimize length and number of links is the hierarchical tree. The weakness of the hierarchical tree is that there is only one path between any two points, which makes it sensitive to failure. The need to work up the tree to get to the node which is common to both end node branches can also affect performance and network capacity. On the other hand, optimal hierarchical tree design can be performed using any of a number of well-defined algorithms. The mesh is a combinatorial nightmare (complexity on the order of the factorial of the number of nodes), and guaranteed optimal designs are computationally impossible for even relatively small networks of one or two dozen nodes.

The ring topology such as that used in IEEE 802.5 has the benefit of simple design and implementation. Each node on the ring has one receive line and one transmit line, there are no routing decisions required, and configuration changes are easy. Stations are added by breaking the ring and inserting the station. Station removal can be just as easy as long as there is some means of patching the ring together where the station used to be. The disadvantage, of course, is that the loss of any station or a break in any point of the ring can result in loss of all communications. Most of the complexity in ring implementation comes from the steps required to reduce this sensitivity to any single failure, such as automatic bypass of a user outlet when no user is plugged into it.

The star topology, commonly seen in telephone switching systems, has the advantage of concentrating all the complexity required in connecting one node to another in the single central node. The satellite nodes need only implement enough capability to inform the central switching node of the desired destination. Troubleshooting is simplified because a technician at the central node has access to all signals and wires in one location. Station and wiring failures only affect the single station. The disadvantages are the need to physically connect from each station to the central switch and the complexity (and hence cost) of that central switch. The complexity is further increased by the need to ensure that the central switch does not fail, as any failure there will prevent any stations from communicating.

The bus topology, used by IEEE 802.3 and IEEE 802.4, has the advantage that every station can directly communicate with every other station. This allows features such as broadcasting and multicasting to be efficiently utilized, and it eliminates any concern with routing or forwarding messages from user to user on the same network. Of course, it has its disadvantages as well. Some means of control is required to prevent more than one station from transmitting at the same time, as noise or unintentional transmissions from anywhere on the bus will disrupt everyone's communications. At the same time, because all users must share the common media, the capacity is limited to the sum of all users. This capacity sharing is also a major benefit of bus networks. As long as all users do not need to communicate at the same time, the few who are communicating get to share the full bandwidth available.

The chief disadvantage of the bus, however, is the restriction to media that are broadcast media. Fiber optics would be an ideal media for bus-oriented local area networks except that they are an inherently point-to-point communications medium and therefore unsuitable for a bus. The closest anyone has come so far is to lay the fiber optics in a star pattern, with an active repeater for the center of the star so that whatever signal any station puts on their fiber is broadcast by the hub to all stations. The high-performance fiber optics based Fiber Distributed Data Interface (FDDI) has been designed around a ring topology as a result.

When we start tying multiple networks together, we usually get the general tree topology. The networks being connected do not need to be bus networks (although they often are); they could just as easily be stars, rings, or any other topology. The tree approach to networks of networks allows each individual network to take advantage of the properties of its particular topology, yet not impose the restrictions of that topology on other networks. The biggest challenge in a tree network of networks is network management. The configurations must be managed so that conflicts (such as in naming or addressing) do not arise. When failures occur, management controls are needed to reconfigure the tree to remove the offending network with minimal disruption to users not on the failed network.

Access method considerations

We discussed token passing and CSMA/CD access methods in Chapters 7 and 8, respectively. Token passing, whether on a ring or on a bus, provides predictable delays and fair distribution of communications resources even under overload conditions. CSMA/CD provides access to the full bandwidth of the medium to whoever can use it and provides higher performance under light loading than is possible with token passing. When the instantaneous load exceeds about 50 percent of the available capacity, CSMA/CD starts slowing dramatically, and users will usually notice the degradation by the time loading gets above about 80 percent.

Point-to-point links, as used in mesh and hierarchical tree networks, are not shared, so media access is only a concern in bus and ring networks. Instead, the user has to be concerned with store and forward delay times (to get the data through the intermediate nodes between the two stations trying to communicate) and routing the packet from node to node on its way to the destination.

Token passing and CSMA/CD are not the only shared media access methods either. Other access methods have been invented and are available to meet specialized needs. It is even possible to get a CSMA/CD network which automatically switches over to token passing when loading exceeds a certain threshold. However, only the IEEE 802 token passing and CSMA/CD are embodied in international standards and commonly available from multiple vendors.

Media considerations

The range of media to choose from is wide even in the MAP/TOP world, and it will continue to expand as technology develops new alternatives. The need to match environmental needs such as distance, electromagnetic noise, and safety will always present a challenge to the network designer.

Broadband coaxial cable provides environmental ruggedness and multiple services on the same medium. However, it does so at the cost of expensive modems and lack of flexibility once installed. Baseband and carrierband coaxial cable get around some of these drawbacks, with low-cost access and ease of adding new stations, but at the expense of dedicating the cable to a single computer network.

Compared to coaxial cable in any form, twisted pair is a much lower-cost connection. Many offices already have all the cable plant they need installed and ready for networking use. Making up for the cost, of course, is the limited bandwidth and sensitivity to electromagnetic interference. In general, twisted pair only makes sense in the relatively benign environment of the office and is not a viable option for factory floor networks except for very low-speed (under 20 Kbps) point-to-point links.

Fiber optics have two characteristics which make them ideal for factory floor communications. They are totally immune to electromagnetic interference and can provide incredibly high data rates over long distances. Their usage today remains restricted because of their point-to-point nature. When a cost-effective fiber optic bus becomes available, there may finally be a competitor for broadband and carrierband on the factory floor. In the meantime, usage of fiber optics remains restricted to those situations which must have the high data rate or electromagnetic immunity of fiber optics.

There are specialized communications media as well. Radio links can provide communications across gaps where cable cannot go, such as where you lack a right-of-way between one building and another. Satellite links can provide long distance communications at high data rates at relatively low cost. Infrared transmitters and receivers are available to get across a city street. However, none is perfect. Radio spectrum space is hard to obtain in many areas, and that which is attainable may not be free of interference. Satellite links provide high data rates but require special protocols to get around the propagation delays (about 250 ms) introduced by the trip up to synchronous orbit and back. Infrared links can be lost because of rain, snow, and other conditions that block the line-of-sight transmission. However, like fiber optics, each has its uses, some of which can be done no other way.

Application considerations

The ultimate deciding factor is the applications being supported. An application may dictate a particular technology. If the requirement is to transfer a billion bits per second, fiber optics is an obvious choice. Similarly, an application which must be supported may eliminate some choices. Communication between robots doing arc welding on the production line is not going to be over radio or twisted pair wiring. Beyond the clear decisions, the question is more often a judgment call. The IEEE 802 standards are more than adequate for the vast majority of applications. Be wary before deciding that a custom solution is required. While you can always find a better fit than the standard, the loss of choice and multiple sources is a very high price to pay for the improvement. Make sure it is really worth the sacrifice.

Cost-Benefit Analysis

The financial impact of network decisions cannot be neglected either. Even pilot projects are sizable capital investments which should be examined for their impact on the bottom line. The fact that the main benefits of MAP/TOP and computer-integrated manufacturing are the hardest to measure (for example, engineering productivity and product quality) is not an excuse for ignoring the impact on the corporate bottom line.

Outline of a feasibility study

The normal instrument for measuring benefits and comparing alternatives is the feasibility study. Going back to our original user requirements questions in Chapter 9, we identified the problems we were trying to solve and some of the alternatives available for solving them. We have already translated those user requirements into technical networking needs, and now is the time to evaluate the cost of the alternative ways of meeting those needs.

The general technique is to determine all the incremental cash flows (revenues, expenses, and capital investments) both recurring and nonrecurring for each alternative. Each cash flow is discounted to its net present value, and each alternative is summed to obtain the difference in net present value of each alternative. (Some companies may request calculation of internal rate of return or some other financial measures;

the important point is that the value of each alternative should reflect the time value of money. Using net present value allows simplifications in the comparison which emphasize the difference between alternatives but would distort measures intended to indicate true return on investment.)

The final step is to select the alternative (which may be the "do nothing" one) that best meets your company's financial and operational objectives. The availability of believable financial analysis data makes it much easier to obtain the necessary approvals and set the selected plan in motion.

Determining cost elements and costs

The gathering of cost data can be simplified immensely by the expedient of only using incremental costs and omitting costs which are the same for all plans. This will emphasize the differences between alternatives. But watch out; huge percentage differences in the result may not represent that much difference in the total costs.

Picking the cost elements to include is critical. Obviously, key elements must be consistent between plans in order for them to be comparable. Be particularly careful of sensitivity to initial assumptions such as production rates, market size, and time required for installation.

There is a wide variety of typical cost elements to consider. Wages and salaries are important if labor savings are involved. Remember to include overhead and benefits. Computers and interfaces have many costs associated with them. There are the initial hardware purchase or lease costs; software licenses and development costs of custom software; maintenance costs in the form of technical support personnel or maintenance contracts; supplies such as tapes, disks, and printer ribbons; and any salvage credits at the end of the study period. Consider the tax implications of all costs and benefits. Building costs such as floor space and duct work may vary with each alternative. Communications services from broadband cable plant installation to phone lines to access the X.25 public data network need to be considered. And the cost of disruption of current operations during installation and maintenance is often significant.

Once the cost elements are decided, you can determine what the cost of each is. Some, like wages, salaries, and benefits, are easily obtained. Others, such as predictions of savings, can be extremely hard to quantify. When exact numbers are not available, try to determine the minimum, maximum, and most likely. Sensitivity analysis can then determine if they make that much difference. Other key factors to determine are the length of the study, compensation for inflation, and credit to give to "soft" factors such as work-force satisfaction (or dissatisfaction), keeping up with technology, and impact on your customers' perception of your products or your ability to deliver them.

On the feasibility of feasibility studies

There are many arguments both for and against doing feasibility studies. On the negative side is the realization that the real world seldom behaves as nicely as models. There is real danger of succumbing to paralysis of analysis, striving for so much detail and accuracy in the study that it is never completed. There is also the danger of simplifying reality so much that the results are meaningless. Balancing this is the realization that the alternative to a feasibility study is to fly by the seat of the pants, a technique which cost many early aviators their life. When flying blind with the horizon invisible, almost any instrument is better than none.

Available MAP/TOP Components

It seems that every major computer and controller vendor has announced commitment to MAP and TOP compatible components, and several companies have been formed just to serve the market. So why not just order a MAP/TOP network, install it, and enjoy the benefits? There are a number of reasons, not the least of which is the fallacy that all it takes to integrate a factory is a MAP/TOP network. That belief is the equivalent of handing a person the keys to a Ferrari and telling him or her to race it at LeMans. The vehicle is only a small part of the requirement. The driver needs training, there is the support crew required to keep the vehicle running during the race, there is even the need to get the car to the race course to begin with. A MAP/TOP network in isolation is similarly inappropriate.

The network does not provide any software on the communicating systems to accomplish the application. That must be provided. System software takes time to develop, especially if it is to be done so that the implementation can be effectively migrated from MAP 2.1 to MAP/TOP 3.0, or from one vendor's machine to another's. Just as in process engineering, users are discovering that bench-top pilots do not always scale well to dozens or hundreds of nodes. The small delays and defects which were imperceptible in the pilot can grow to prevent successful operation at full scale.

Continuing our race car analogy, there remains a severe shortage of pit crew personnel. The test equipment and technicians required to build and maintain complex networks are a scarce resource. Throughout 1986, the Industrial Technology Institute remained the only facility for testing and certifying MAP/TOP components, and few other companies were even trying to get into the market. The cost of testing has kept many vendors away. The lack of guarantees that a tested product will interoperate even if tested has led users to depend on vendor commitments to fix defects rather than third-party test results. The user with production halted by an incompatibility needs it fixed, which is something no test result can do. The development and demonstration of useful interoperability testing is one of the key MAP/TOP contributions to open systems networking and the work will continue long after the release of MAP/TOP 3.0.

Typical components available

A wide variety of MAP and TOP components and systems are available on the market today. These range from integrated circuit chips for custom building an interface card to complete hardware and software packages provided by the computer or controller vendor. Machines with standard backplane interfaces such as Unibus and VMEbus have a wide range of plug-in cards to choose from, ranging from broadband and carrierband modems to complete implementations including application layer services.

For the system without a standard bus, the alternatives are more restrictive. Usually the choice comes down to accepting whatever the system vendor offers, designing and building a custom solution, or using a stand-alone network interface unit which goes from a standard interface on the system such as RS-232 or IEEE 488 to the MAP connection on the other side. This was a very common solution in the early days of MAP 2.1 when the only way to guarantee interoperability was to buy all the network interface units from one vendor. In articles describing early pilot implementations you will often see references to "TIMs" (Token Interface Modules), which is Concord Data Systems' trade name for their stand-alone box, one of the more popular interface units.

One problem which surfaced quickly as soon as off-the-shelf solutions became available for MAP 2.1 was the need for standard interfaces for application programs to use to access the network services. The ISO OSI model does not specify how to access network services; it only specifies what the network services are. This can be a problem when trying to implement applications which must run on multiple machines. Each vendor provided its own interface to the network and unwary users would find themselves rewriting their applications for each new machine. The MAP/TOP 3.0 specification alleviates the problem by also specifying standard interfaces to some of the network services. The safest solution is to access operating system and network services through your own interface module so that the application is not only insulated from any discrepancies in the service provider but can also be used with nonstandard services if desired. Even in the world of MAP/TOP, it may be desirable at times to take advantage of proprietary, higher-performance, lower-cost solutions. This will be particularly important in the early releases of MAP/TOP 3.0 and as new services are added. It takes time to tune up network software implementations, and you can expect MAP/TOP implementations to be slower than mature proprietary network services in a homogeneous environment. Even when MAP/TOP is fully mature, you will still find performance differences because of the extra protocol overhead required for heterogeneous communication. But in that heterogeneous environment, MAP/TOP could be an order of magnitude slower and still be the best available because in many cases it will be the only commercial network solution.

The MAP/TOP Product Directory

The Society of Manufacturing Engineers (SME) and the Industrial Technology Institute (ITI) joined forces in 1986 to publish a directory of MAP/TOP products and services. Aimed at the intense need for current information by implementors and users of MAP/TOP networks, the directory is published twice a year in hard-copy form, and a continuously updated on-line database is maintained for subscribers. The agreement has ITI responsible for developing and maintaining the database and for producing the camera-ready contents from it. SME handles the printing, marketing, and distribution.

The directory covers the entire spectrum of MAP/TOP products and services. The six categories of entries are end systems, intermediate systems, OEM products, gateways, network products, and network services. Each entry specifies the vendor contact for the product, protocols implemented, the intended operating environment, environmental specifications on operation, MAP/TOP version conformance, availability of conformance test results (and who performed them), the product's physical parameters, the date the first product was shipped, the number of installed sites, availability, and pricing. Directory users must be aware, however, that the information is supplied by the vendor, so its accuracy cannot be guaranteed. It also does not provide any indications of customer satisfaction among users; that information you need to get from users' group meetings and other sources.

Some checklist items

When putting together your network, there are a number of items you want to be sure you do not overlook. These are components which are normally required but are not part of the MAP/TOP specification. Gateways to other networks are frequently required. This includes not only MAP-to-MAP and MAP-to-TOP gateways, but also gateways to connect existing proprietary networks in the plant to the MAP/TOP network. If the broadband is being used to provide point-to-point terminal connections, protocol converters may be desirable so that users can access both IBM and other hosts from the same terminal. If the network is expected to exceed the capacity of a single 802.4 channel, remember to include bridges between the channels.

Other components are less obvious because they are not required to get the network running. A network control center may be desirable to keep track of network activities and to concentrate the directory servers and network monitoring in one location so that personnel do not have to range about the plant to get routine network maintenance accomplished. The exact equipment required in the network control center will depend greatly on the implementation specifics of the network as well as on its complexity. Some vendors design their equipment for centralized control (for example, frequency-agile modems which respond to control signals on the broadband cable); others tend to be more distributed. You need to make sure it is physically possible for the person or people responsible for keeping the network running to access the key control mechanisms. It is not safe to assume that all maintenance can be done over the network, as the most critical maintenance is restoration of the network after a failure has occurred which makes the network disfunction.

A software maintenance facility may be required to allow user applications to be tested without affecting ongoing operations. If any of the protocols or system integration is done in house, you will need a facility in which to test your work and track down defects as problems arise in operation. Even if all software is off the shelf, it can help to be able to try out new releases from the vendor before risking your users on them.

You may also want to specify special requirements on the interface units or for network management controls. For example, are plug-in cards required or are external interface units acceptable? What protocols must be provided in the interfaces and which must be provided in the station? Putting the protocols on the interface card avoids consuming host resources for network support. On the other hand, putting the protocols on the host allows access to resources that do not fit on a small printed circuit board. Be very careful about what protocols are provided to access the MAP/TOP protocols in the interface. If the interface is an external box, how well is the means of connecting it to the host supported by the host and what performance limitations are there?

Network management has a wide range of requirements not covered by the MAP/TOP specifications. We will discuss the needs in much greater detail in the next chapter, but you will want to keep at least the following capabilities in mind: configuration control, accounting, network interface unit diagnostics, packet monitoring, channel traffic statistics, RF diagnostics, redundant servers, directory services, channel balancing, trouble ticket databases, and per-user access control.

Generating an Effective Request for Proposals

Vendors for computer networks, whether MAP, TOP, or any other kind, are difficult to select, and the process is fraught with dangers. Start-up companies may have the best capabilities, but they may not be around when you need upgrades or repairs a few years later. Of course, there is no guarantee that the old reliable firm will continue to be there in the future either. It is not even safe to assume a well-known trademark means superior technology. The investment required to develop MAP/TOP hardware and software is large enough that many computer and controller vendors are reducing their risks by repackaging and reselling the offerings of component vendors such as Concord Data Systems (CDS) and Industrial Networking Incorporated (INI).

The best way to select a vendor is to base the choice on evidence that its life-cycle cost will be the lowest of all the competition. In other words, having chosen the highest payoff with a feasibility study, maximize that payoff with a life-cycle cost analysis. The probability for success is far higher than basing the decision on criteria such as "we have always bought from this company" or "the salesperson was very persuasive" or "they have the lowest-priced hardware" or "ABC company uses this brand and prefers it."

Preliminary screening

Since a full life-cycle study is time consuming and expensive for both you and the vendors, you want to screen out the obvious misfits before starting. For example, you will want to eliminate from consideration any products made or sold by companies that you would not deal with under any circumstances. Screen out any which do not meet your basic requirements, such as no service available in overseas locations or not conformant with the appropriate revision level of MAP/TOP. You can use a request for information to get price and technical information on products which provide the features identified in the feasibility study. Even at this stage, make it clear that nonconformers will not be considered further to avoid a flood of useless information and to keep the responses focused on your needs.

The life-cycle study process

Once the field of contenders is narrowed down to a reasonable size, you can initiate the life-cycle study. The initiation phase of the life-cycle study is a three-step process consisting of requirements determination, cost and benefit factors determination, and preparation of the request for proposals.

The starting step of determining requirements is the most critical step. After all, if you do not know where you are going, how do you expect to get there? You need to convert your networking plans and the work study and feasibility study results into actual equipment and performance requirements. This is the technical part of the process.

The second step is more business oriented. The various cost and benefit elements that will make up the life-cycle study need to be selected. The challenge is to make sure that the factors selected are both relevant and measurable. If too many relevant factors are not measurable, the outcome will be suspect and you need to either figure out how to make them measurable or find another way to evaluate vendors. Many of the cost factors will be the same ones used in the planning feasibility study; however, some are more elusive, such as when a manufacturer will declare a product obsolete and cease to support it.

The final preparatory step is the actual preparation of the request for proposals or request for price quotations. Include all the factors identified in the previous step in the request, such as purchase price of the equipment, maintenance and repairs, materials and supplies, and special equipment and training.

Key factors in the request for proposals

You can save yourself much work if you keep a few key items in mind as you prepare the request for proposals. For one, you want to let the vendor do as many of the calculations as possible so you do not have to do them. Let the vendors know that they will be evaluated on life-cycle cost, not just purchase price, and encourage alternate, more cost-effective proposals. However, make sure you require at least one proposal conforming to requirements so that you have a common basis for comparing vendors. Most important, make sure you get all the costs. If possible, write the request for proposals so that the vendor is required to make the system function as an integrated whole. If your system is inherently multivendor, adjust the requirement as required but maintain some leverage over each vendor for adequate performance of the whole or you will find that no one will accept responsibility. You do not want to find yourself stuck with islands of automation isolated by incompatible MAP/TOP implementations.

Another key time-saver is to provide your own forms to shape the vendors' responses. For example, separate equipment costs into units. This prevents bundling an expensive item with an inexpensive accessory which is not what you really want but does fit the letter of the requirement. Do the same for failure rates and other vital information. You want to avoid having to sort out the significant information from the averages. Time spent preparing and organizing here can repay itself many times over later in the process, particularly if you discover a need to change how the pieces fit together based on better understanding of user requirements or implementation possibilities.

The cover letter used to distribute the request for proposals is important, too. Make it clear that proposals will be evaluated in a life-cycle study and not on the basis of lowest price. Set a deadline for replies and reserve the right to reject any and all proposals. Repeat the invitation to submit alternate proposals in addition to one which conforms to the basic requirement. Finally, inform the vendors that any terms of their submission may later be negotiated into a contract. You do not want to find out later that the features which led you to select any particular vendor are not really available after all.

Evaluating Vendor Proposals

The evaluation of all the proposals obtained from the request for proposals can be almost as much work as figuring out what the users wanted in the first place. Before starting your evaluation, there are three guidelines to keep in mind. All data used in the evaluation should be reliable data from consistent sources. The world of computer networking is filled with hype and empty promises. You certainly do not want to reject a vendor who was honest enough to reply realistically rather than echo back what they thought you wanted to hear but have no way of really providing. Look for inconsistencies in pricing structure; it may be that the low bidder plans to use lower-grade cable, which while adequate for most installations does not have the noise immunity required in your environment, or the low bidder has found some other loophole in your specifications.

The second rule is to organize the data so that each entry can be traced to its source. That way, when you are further into the evaluation and discover a discrepancy, you can trace it to the original data and determine what other numbers are affected by the bad data and change them. Finally, for the evaluation to be meaningful and worth the effort, you need to evaluate the proposals with a systematic process. The following process, while not unique, is one way to proceed.

Organize vendor responses

The first step in the proposal evaluation process is to organize the vendor responses so that they are comparable. If you took the time in developing the request for proposals to shape the responses, this step will be much easier. You need to check each proposal for accuracy, reasonableness, and redibility. This is where your knowledge of MAP/TOP networking and the components available can help. Review each proposal for conformance and either fix, get fixed by the vendor, or discard any that do not meet your requirements. If you are working with good vendors, keep an open mind when evaluating alternative proposals and judge them on how well they meet user needs rather than your translation of those needs into networking requirements. The vendor may have seen an opportunity you have overlooked.

Once the data is consistent, you can rank and weight all features. Using a spreadsheet will allow you to modify assumptions fairly easily. The ranking and weighting used must be realistic; the purpose is to provide a measure of comparable benefit for each given alternative before looking at the cost of providing each benefit.

The life-cycle study

Before you can run the actual life-cycle study, you need to verify one last time that you have included all appropriate life-cycle considerations. Factors include the length of the study, the cost of money, the inflation rate, salvage value, tax effects, and revenues. Numbers which are uncertain can be replaced with ranges giving the minimum, maximum, and most likely values. Part of the life-cycle study will include a sensitivity analysis, at which time the impact of incorrect estimates can be evaluated.

The first time through the life-cycle study, keep the analysis at a high level. Look at just the major impacts, such as recovery from failures and reduced staffing. Develop a feel for each proposal's intangible benefits and costs as well, and try to quantify them in addition to the straight-forward summaries of cash flows.

As you get deeper into the study, you will also want to make sure that nothing significant has been overlooked as a potential differentiater between choices. Equipment costs include not only the purchase price and installation expenses, but also shipping, sales tax, and delivery. Software costs should include the cost of upgrades throughout the life-cycle period. Repair costs are not just the cost of repairing the failed unit but also the loss of production while waiting for the repair to be completed. In mixed vendor networks with no single vendor having overall responsibility, allocate time for your staff to referee the shifting of blame whenever the faulty behavior could be caused by defects or faults in more than one vendor's equipment.

Use sensitivity analysis

One thing that can make the life-cycle study worth the effort all by itself is the ability to perform sensitivity analyses on the data. As you are putting the data together and calculating the life-cycle costs, you will have many questionable numbers and assumptions. The sensitivity analysis is just running the life-cycle cost calculations with the different assumptions to see what the effect is on the bottom line. Computerized spreadsheets can be ideal for this kind of "what if" analysis. What if the failure rate does not meet the predictions? What if the savings in operator labor do not materialize? What if a better product comes out in 2 years and the system is upgraded 3 years earlier than planned? This is the time to test the impact of your initial assumptions as well. What if the production volume is only half of forecast or competition forces you to reduce your prices by 20 percent? You may find that the impact is negligible, in which case you do not have to worry as much about the absolute accuracy of the estimate. On the other hand, you may find that a relatively minor discrepancy between prediction and reality can make the difference between profit and loss, in which case you will want to check and recheck the assumptions before continuing.

Choosing the product

The final step is to choose the optimum vendor and product. All the math and spreadsheet analysis are only aids. You can always find ways (whether consciously or subconsciously) to make any product the "right" choice. Good selection requires application of judgment, knowledge, and experience as well as numbers. Be particularly wary of speculating on futures. Even companies with the purchasing clout of a General Motors have been stung by vendors unable or unwilling to deliver on promises. Remember the old maxim that 90 percent of the work on a software project occurs after it is 90 percent complete. If you can, wait for the second release of any product so that the defects uncovered by the early users have had a chance to be repaired.

Once you have made your choice, approach the preferred vendor and start negotiating before you commit to buying. You can often get further concessions in exchange for your business. When negotiating the purchase agreement, always keep in mind who the vendor's standard contract protects. Look for clauses which conflict with the written response and be sure they do not negate any factors key to your choosing the vendor in the first place.

Recap of Key Issues

Selecting MAP/TOP for your network architecture can considerably simplify the network specification problem, but it does not eliminate it completely. Even with a MAP/TOP network, there is considerable complexity involved in obtaining the network components that best meet your needs, and attention to detail is required. Any individual who believes that all that has to be done is to specify MAP/TOP, install it, and sit back and enjoy it is in for a rude awakening. Nor is MAP/TOP the only solution available. If a single-vendor solution meets all the present and future needs, the overhead and complexity of MAP/TOP today may not make sense, and a proprietary network may be a better solution.

11

Network Installation and Management

The objective of all the network requirements planning, specification, and selection is to install and use the network. In this chapter we will start with a look at some key considerations in installing a broadband cable plant. Then we will examine some important aspects of installing any network, followed by a discussion of some of the unique aspects of network management encountered in the MAP/TOP industrial environment. We will conclude with a brief diversion into another aspect of network planning, a look at the need of the network planner and manager to consider the marketing aspects of their job.

Cable Plant Design

The cable plant provides the raw communications foundation upon which the network is built. Regardless of the type of network—a broadband MAP network, a twisted pair TOP network, or a fiber optics one—there are the three Rs of cable plant design to consider: redundancy, reliability, and repairability. These are the three metrics which determine the availability of communications service to the users. How one is traded off against another is one of the tasks of the network designer.

Chapter 7 already discussed the need to have a qualified designer engineer the broadband cable plant. That design consists of three distinct elements: the site survey, the design process, and the documentation of the design. Let us look at each.

Site survey

The first step in generating a good design is the site survey. The designers come to your facility and walk around the areas in which the network is to be installed. The idea is to locate and identify potential problems to allow the cable plant to be designed around them. The designers should be familiar with all fire, electrical, and other safety codes and should know what can and cannot be done in normal environments that are similar to yours. It is up to you to ensure that they are aware of your unique requirements and are cognizant of the impact. For example, if exposure to an explosive atmosphere is possible, you need to make them aware of that fact, and they should know what restrictions that places on the cable plant design. It may be possible to design around a particular area of the plant, such as a clean room, that is especially sensitive to potential disruptions during installation. The restrictions may be more mundane as well, such as identifying heat sources to avoid locating sensitive electronic components in overly harsh environments.

Good designers will take a complete look around the facility. If you ask to have the cable run through existing conduit, they will look into the conduit to verify that there really is enough room. The same is true for locating the room which will house the head end. Is there adequate floor space, load bearing capacity, and power available? Is there room inside the ceiling or walls for amplifiers, splitters, and taps? It is not a case of the designer not trusting you; it is just that over the years, good designers have learned never to make assumptions. The consequences of invalid ones are too costly.

The site survey requires your cooperation in many ways. Not only do you need to show them around your plant, but you also need to work with them so they understand your expectations. Good designers will ensure that they understand your architecture and the impact it may have on their design.

Design checklist

There are a number of items you need to communicate to the cable plant designers. They need to know your expectations to start. The media you have in mind, whether broadband, carrierband, fiber optics, or something else, provides the starting point. The type of interface units planned, stand-alone boxes or plug-in cards, will help determine space requirements in the area of each user. The services expected have tremendous impact. IEEE 802.4 only, voice and data, video and data, IEEE 802.4 and point-to-point data, all of the above—each desire has an impact on the cable plant design.

Your choice of cable plant architecture also has its impact. Is the system single cable or dual? Midsplit, high split, or custom split all imply different requirements. Selection of a primary and secondary redundant system will require routing considerations not required in a conventional single system. After all, the benefits of redundancy are only realized to the extent that cables will not be damaged by the same physical accident or power loss.

The coverage required from the cable plant is another major consideration. There are big differences between an isolated pilot system, a backbone trunk interconnecting access networks running on various media, and a full coverage system with an outlet within 5 m of any location on the plant floor. What allowances are to be made for future expansion? It may be desirable to locate the head end in the computer room for ease of access, or it may be possible to locate it for maximum cable plant efficiency.

Finally, you need to discuss your expectations for cable plant management and any value-added features you feel desirable. What status monitoring features will be provided? You may want to take advantage of remotely addressable amplifiers and taps. The increased availability provided by redundant amplifiers and uninterruptible power supplies may be all that is required to meet your system availability requirements, or they could be a waste of money. The cable plant designers can only take your specific needs into account to the extent you communicate them.

Documentation requirements

Since the cable plant designers are not the ones who install and maintain the cable plant, the documentation provided by them to describe their design is critical. Items which should appear on all drawings include a list of symbols used and the part numbers associated with each, the system design frequencies for both forward and return paths, the types of cables selected and their associated loss, level settings for both trunk and distribution amplifiers, the method to be used to align the cable, the minimum outlet and tap signal levels at all design frequencies, and which outlets (if any) are to be terminated.

Head end details should include the signal level outputs of any video processors, frequency translators, and 802.4 remodulators. Vendor limitations on power levels must be noted, as well as any ac power blocks to be used.

The physical aspects of the cable plant also need to be documented as does the location of any extra cables pulled for redundancy or spares so that they can be located and identified when and if needed. The routing of the trunk cables and how to locate them should be specified. The attenuater and equalizer settings for each amplifier should be calculated, along with the length of every cable and the associated loss in each in both forward and reverse directions. The location and identification of manholes, raceways, conduits, and cable trays will be invaluable when maintenance is required in the future and the individuals associated with the original installation are no longer available.

Finally, do not forget the designer's name, address, and telephone number, along with a bill of materials. Expect and demand written consistency throughout the entire process and all documentation. All of this should be standard operating procedure for a good designer. Designing a multipurpose MAP broadband cable plant is one place where it does not pay to cut corners. You certainly do not want to be in the position of the anonymous university researcher heard mumbling, "We actually thought cable TV guys could handle this stuff!"

Network Implementation Planning

There are a number of considerations which must be kept in mind when planning the physical installation of the network. While such decisions as whether to do it yourself or contract the installation out and whether to phase in the implementation or do it all at once are important, they pale in comparison to the human side of the equation. While often considered in the office automation context, the people needs are just as important in a totally automated factory; they just may not be as obvious. In the case of pilot implementations, in which traditional and automated methods may be coexisting and competing for approval, the human aspects can overwhelm any technological advantages and make the difference between success and failure.

People aspects

The people aspects are really a reminder that good management practices are required in network installation the same as they are needed in all other phases of operations. Network benefits require the operation to be organized to benefit from the communications capabilities. Neither centralizing nor decentralizing is a universal solution. Each has its advantages. A good starting point is to consider centralized guidelines and standards (for example, data to be shared will be maintained in standard file formats) with decentralized control and operation (for example, access to shared data is controlled by the owner of the data). Someone must be responsible for administering the network so it does not go to waste. Common sense should prevail. Making the network so difficult to use that nobody does is as ineffective as making access so easy that everyone uses the network and those who really need the communications cannot get the capacity they need.

If organizational changes are required to take advantage of the new technology, make the changes early. If a reorganization is required, do it before the equipment arrives so the disruptions caused by reorganization are not blamed on the arrival of the new technology. While you cannot avoid the disruption associated with a reorganization, you can pick the time and place of its occurrence for minimal impact.

Along those lines, if new operating procedures will be needed, develop them in advance. For example, if a move to Just in Time (JIT) manufacturing is part of the plan, design your cards in advance and have them ready for use. Decide upon default values to use in any operation for which they are available and have them ready to install. Create address codes for messaging and electronic mail, and set up your local naming authorities and have address codes for users and stations ready for use. This includes not only their initial assignment but also procedures for additions, updates, resolution of conflicts, and directory maintenance, publication, and distribution.

Train early and thoroughly. If people do not know how to use the system, they will experience trouble and reduced productivity and will blame it on the new system. Users and managers should be trained not only in how to use the system but also in the benefits. This includes not only the productivity benefits but also what they can get out of the system to help them with their jobs. Develop assistance methods to help people who are having difficulty with the new system, as well as those looking for ways to expand the benefits.

Finally, install and cultivate feedback mechanisms. Let people express their opinions and ideas through some procedure. You may not like what you hear and it may not be true, but it will express genuine concerns. And it does not have to be limited to complaints. Some of the best ideas will be developed by the people who use the system every day. If your procedures include appropriate feedback, you can encourage the generation and flow of ideas, and benefit accordingly.

Make or buy

The make or buy decision is often a hard one. Except in the case of corporate edicts which demand one or the other, the choice is rarely an obvious one. Installing the hardware yourself has major benefits. No one knows your plant and its operations better than you do, and the experience gained will simplify future maintenance and expansion. On the other hand, paying someone else to do it should result in getting it done right the first time, and you gain the benefits of their experience. Of course, the degree of benefit gained will be directly proportional to the competence of the installer, so choose carefully.

Phasing of the installation

The timetable for implementation also provides options. Assuming you have taken the rational approach to computer-integrated manufacturing, you have already mapped out a set of incremental steps to get from where you are today to your ultimate vision for the future. Each intermediate step can optionally be broken down further to allow controlled phasing-in of the step. This provides a number of advantages, all of which are similar to the reasons for doing pilot projects in the first place.

The biggest advantage of a phased installation is the ability to try out each piece and fix it before proceeding on to the next. This avoids the situation of having to make the same change to all 500 units that were installed incorrectly rather than reworking the first 10 and changing the procedure for the remaining 490. There is less pressure when delays occur, helping to avoid the perennial dilemma of never having time to do it right but always having to find the time to do it over. There is less disruption to ongoing operations, as the impact is more isolated at any one time. Troubleshooting is simplified, as there is less equipment, less complexity, and fewer interactions to worry about.

Phasing the installation has its limits as well. The try it and fix it approach only works to the extent that enough pieces are installed to allow trying it. The ease of troubleshooting is only beneficial to the extent that there are problems and in the case of networking may be misleading. It is quite common for defects in one location not to show up at all until the network is further expanded. The fact that the network stopped working when the latest piece was added is no guarantee that the defect is associated with the new piece.

Other trade-offs revolve around the disruption of current operations. Phasing the installation often spreads out the disruption over a longer period of time, which you have to weigh against the greater control provided. When the new way is incompatible with the old, it may not be possible to gracefully phase in the new methods, and the goal must be to get it over with as quickly as possible. These are all value judgments with no hard and fast rules. The best you can do is have a well-thought-out master plan which exposes those affected to the issues and gains their support.

Gaining work force support

Unless your organization is so deeply into theory X management that the individual workers are considered totally mindless automatons, you need the support of the work force that will be using the network. Encourage participation in the development and specification process. Whether or not you sought out the inputs of everyone affected when initially determining user requirements (discussed in Chapter 9), you want to give everyone a chance to ask questions and offer suggestions. It is part of human nature for people who feel they have had a part in the birth and delivery of a system to be more interested in and motivated toward its success. It is to your benefit to have that support behind your network rather than opposing it.

One good technique is to form a users' group. While the formal makeup of the group will vary with the size of the organization, the idea is to get representatives of major users together periodically to discuss problems and benefits and generally help the system manager understand how to improve the system. This can be particularly beneficial in pilot projects, in which the users' group representatives can also serve as ambassadors to pave the road to acceptance for the full-scale capability. Conversely, they can provide the feedback required to limit the damages to the pilot test and prevent disaster.

One factor that seems to always arise in discussions about automation is job loss. People who feel their livelihood is threatened will resist. Sabotage does not have to be as obvious as a sledgehammer buried up to the handle in the top of a controller to be just as effective. Nor is it limited to "lower-level" workers. The executive who, because of a lack of belief in computers, refuses to initiate action when quality assurance data indicates a potential problem can be just as damaging. If nothing else, avoid tying any layoffs to the arrival of new equipment and be honest about the corporate strategy for handling any work-force surplus.

Network Management Planning

Managing a MAP/TOP or other local area network presents a number of challenges and opportunities which are different from the network management needs associated with the large-scale electronic data processing networks familiar to the data processing department. The number of autonomous stations can range from under 10 to several thousand. The physical portability of many types of attached equipment can lead to frequent configuration changes and varying traffic patterns. The stations are often relatively low cost, making it difficult to justify complex or expensive network management tools. Individual stations may not even have complete protocol stacks, further complicating the situation.

Local area network management has some aspects that are simpler than its data processing center equivalent. The stations, the network, and all the communications are usually owned by the organization, simplifying access control and administration. Unlike wide area nets, the link-level communications are generally reliable, and efficient link-level broadcast is available on all IEEE 802-based local area networks. This makes some operations practical which could never be considered on a wide area network, such as a station broadcasting a request for service rather than always going to a fixed address for it.

The technical viewpoint

The most common approach taken to specifying network management needs is the technical approach. These needs are the easiest for the technical person specifying the network to understand, and they include the critical day-to-day operational requirements that keep the network functioning. They can be roughly broken into four categories: configuration and change management, fault management, performance management, and capacity, usage, and accounting management.

Configuration and change management is a requirement from the viewpoint of all network layers. The network implementor and later the manager need the ability to establish and modify operating parameters. At the lower layers this can involve the ability to set and adjust parameters such as network and link addresses and retransmission timeouts and limits. It is equally critical at higher levels, such as regulating the services provided and keeping track of what hardware and software versions are in use at all locations. Just keeping track of what users are connected at what locations on the network can be a major challenge, let alone keeping track of who has access to what services on what machines.

Once the network is functional, fault management usually gets the most attention because of the visibility of failures. Fault management needs to provide for both detecting and correcting faults. This may include receiving and responding to error reports as well as performing confidence and diagnostic tests. As was mentioned earlier, the biggest challenge once the evidence of a fault is detected is often to track down just what and where the fault is. For example, a lapse in configuration management can cause a system which used to work to suddenly stop working, not because of a failure in that system but because a station with a conflicting address assignment was added to the network as part of another system.

After the necessities of configuration management and fault management are met, attention can be expanded to accounting management and performance management. Which receives the higher priority will usually be determined by corporate policy. Performance management has the highest payoff for users while accounting management allows recovery of costs based on need and usage.

Performance management provides the means to monitor network performance. It may also include functions normally considered part of configuration management to allow performance to be adjusted as well as measured. The key, of course, is that if you cannot measure network performance, there is no way to determine if the adjustments made are for better or for worse. Critical performance metrics will include response time, throughput, error rate, and availability. The specific metrics will depend on the type of network; for example, an IEEE 802.3 network will probably monitor collisions, whereas an IEEE 802.4 would keep track of lost tokens.

Capacity, usage, and accounting management have two distinct uses. First of all, you need the tools to determine individual usage of network resources so that users can be assessed their fair share of the network operating expenses. Many companies find it more cost effective in local area networks to consider the network part of overhead rather than attempt to bill for individual usage. It all depends on the management philosophy and how much money is really under consideration. However, even if detailed billing information is not required, proper network management requires at least spot testing of actual usage to determine any trends and forecast future unmet needs in time to react to them. In this role, capacity management is being used to identify limitations before they show up in performance management metrics.

The management viewpoint

Network management provides more than the technical means of keeping a network functioning. It also must meet management's needs for justifying the network's existence and maximizing benefit to expenditure ratio. Some of these needs overlap with the technical needs just discussed; others are independent. Part of your specification task is to ensure that the technical tools can meet management's needs as well as operational ones.

Management needs which overlap technical needs include such tasks as measuring system availability, monitoring system response time, and coordinating software changes. Some of the needs unique to management are functions such as monitoring work-force levels, controlling operational costs, monitoring data communications costs, following through on training, and tracking productivity improvements. You really need to consider management as just another of the network users you must satisfy and include their needs (whatever they happen to be) into the networking requirements. The biggest challenge will be translating the needs as expressed by management (whether explicitly or implicitly) into technical networking requirements.

Network security

One aspect of network management that has been deliberately ignored by MAP/TOP is security. The problem is endemic to networking in general and is much more than just a question of encryption. In most environments, security in terms of protection of data from industrial spies is the least significant aspect of network security needs. Security should be considered in the much broader context of controls that prevent the loss of capability. Threats range from fire and flood to hackers and human error. Security considerations range from hoods for on/off switches so equipment cannot be powered off accidentally to purchase of site licenses for personal computer software so that operations are not disrupted by a lawsuit over pirated copies of a program.

There are many factors which will influence security needs. The management style of the company will have a major impact on what capabilities and data are considered critical and which should be more open. The reliability of the employees and the sensitivity of the information being handled make a big difference. Some companies have gone to the extreme of removing the floppy disk drives from their personal computers to prevent illicit copying of data and software. Some data, such as personnel records and classified information, must be protected by law. Other data, such as financial results and new product development progress, may have a direct impact on the company's competitive position if disclosed.

Many in industry dread the prospect of a security audit; however, one can be beneficial. Particularly in the realm of networking, the auditors always seem to want more controls in place. The key is to listen carefully when they identify a "problem." Like your users, they will rarely express a perceived need as a need but rather will present their favorite solution. Always try to determine the causes for each request. The problem may be a misunderstanding, in which case you will want to refine your documentation and procedures. Or there may be more effective solutions to the problem identified that can be developed if the mood is one of cooperation.

Network management realities

The biggest challenge you will face in the network management aspects of your job is the tremendous gap between what you need to effectively manage the network and what is available to do it. Networks today are characterized by diverse standards, incompatible applications, and vocal users. Even in the relative haven of the MAP/TOP world, much of the network management is vendor proprietary and only the most basic functions are covered by the specification. Among the international standards under development, those associated with network management are years behind the rest.

One of the problems you will face with today's tools is the realization that monitoring a network is not equivalent to managing it. The frustration of watching your monitors as they give you a 5-min warning of a pending crash that you are powerless to prevent is hard to describe. There is a desperate need to automate today's control procedures so that the network can respond with or without operator intervention to correct problems before they affect user operations or, if that is impossible, at least minimize the impact on critical operations. Part of the challenge will be avoiding the Three Mile Island syndrome, where the alarms, indicators, and displays did more to confuse the operators than help them.

One trend that will help is the extension of remote test and control capabilities to more and more components in the network. We started out with basic components such as modems and amplifiers with the ability to monitor, self-test, and diagnose problems in their own operation. Once the basic capability was available, it was only a matter of time before the ability to exercise the capabilities and report the results using out-of-band signaling on the link to an attached network monitor became available. The current phase has this capability being extended beyond the limits of the link so that all operations may be controlled from a remote network control center. This can allow a large corporation to concentrate its network maintenance personnel at one site yet effectively work on problems anywhere in the world. It also makes more timely response by contract maintenance possible by eliminating the need for travel time. As the number of skilled network technicians continues to lag the number of networks installed and operating, the ability to maximize their effectiveness can justify significant increases in purchase costs, as your life-cycle study will prove.

Marketing Your Network

While it may seem strange in a technical book on networking, one of the most important factors in your success as a network designer is your marketing ability. To quote the famous management consultant Peter Drucker, "Marketing is so basic that it cannot be considered a separate function. It is the whole business seen from the customer's point of view."[1] Your network, whether it is three programmable logic controllers on a carrierband segment or total computer-integrated manufacturing for the entire company, will succeed or fail as the users perform. The technical merits of the network will be lost if the users do not perceive it to be to their benefit to utilize them.

One of the most important questions you need to answer then is who are your customers. Unless you are extremely lucky, you will find that you have many and that their needs and desires are not only widely varying but sometimes even contradictory. Some of them will be users in the traditional sense, but some will not. Upper management is one of your customers, but what they want is improved productivity and bottom-line financial impact. The programmers who develop the applications software are another of your customers. They require networking services which are easy to use and which allow them to build the applications programs which will satisfy their customers. The most important customers in the computer-integrated manufacturing environment may be the individuals who do not even realize they could be. These are the engineers in quality assurance who can now have access to up-to-the-minute production quality reports or the sales representative in the field who can now add value to the product by quoting delivery dates that reflect reality rather than wishful thinking or cautious pessimism. There is nothing in your job contract which says that you cannot seek out these opportunities and expand the benefits of factory automation and computer-integrated manufacturing beyond the immediate statement of work.

Step by step to success

Success requires attention to marketing at every step along the way. Start with informed management support so that the resources are available to allow successful implementation. Set up a task force with representation from all affected groups. Networking is difficult enough without having to contend with saboteurs in the form of groups considering themselves victims rather than partners. Study and understand the user requirements. Work to get them committed to working with you to solve their problems. Your goal should be to define the network which best meets their needs, and they need to know that. Finally, you can work with your "customers" to define the implementation schedules and actually start to implement solutions.

---

[1]*Info Systems,* July 1986.

This may seem like a lot of work, and it is. The payoff is a network that is useful and profitable rather than a showcase of technology. If MAP/TOP fits, use it. If it does not, find something that does. Any competent engineer can install a computer network; the differentiator is in how well it fits the needs of the users.

Recap of Key Issues

There are many factors which influence how you plan the installation and management of a MAP/TOP network. Broadband cable plant design is not trivial. Using the cable for multiple purposes only makes the design more difficult. Similarly, network management requires a great deal more than monitoring signal levels and analyzing an occasional packet or two. Beyond the technical concerns, the successful network planner will always keep in mind the people concerns as well, from the workers on the production line to the executives in the corporate offices.

12

Trends and Challenges

There are many technologies critical to the future of MAP/TOP which were still in the developmental stages when this book was written. Based on past history, some of these technologies will be in the developmental stages long after this book is out of date. Others may be mature by the time you read this. All have the potential to become a major influence in the development or application of computer-integrated manufacturing, computer networking in general, and MAP/TOP in particular.

Network Standards Development

The year 1986 witnessed the attainment of the long-sought goal of computer networking standards development. For the first time since the International Organization for Standardization introduced the Reference Model for Open Systems Interconnection, there was a consistent set of draft or final international standards approved for all seven layers. The year 1987 should more than double the number of available standards both at the application layer, where all the services provided to the user are defined, and at the physical layer, where the critical cost-effectiveness trade-offs affecting network installation must be made. This pleasant state of affairs can be attributed to a number of factors.

The increasing role of users

The explosion in the availability of application-level protocols was not possible until the underlying protocols they depend on for services were stabilized in 1986. Another contributing factor has been the demand by users for usable, multivendor protocols. The MAP/TOP community is not the only force in the world pushing for open systems. It just happens to be the most successful to date.

MAP/TOP supporters have been demanding (and, even more important, receiving) respect and approval from the various standards organizations. The Corporation for Open Systems (COS) has opened its membership to user corporations as well as vendors. Major users have been paying for the privilege of demonstrating their concern about the future direction of networking standards. Users are joining standards committees, investing money and time to ensure that the standards being developed meet their needs as well as those of vendors who have traditionally dominated international standards efforts.

Vendors have been cooperating with this trend. They have witnessed users not only demanding off-the-shelf systems and software that can connect multiple vendors without compatibility worries but also willing to pay a premium to get it. Virtually all major vendors worldwide have announced products or made product commitments to open systems networking based on ISO OSI standards (including MAP and TOP). This includes computer giants such as IBM, DEC, and HP, as well as their peers in the controller industry such as Allen-Bradley, Gould, and Honeywell. It is important to note that with few exceptions these commitments are in addition to, rather than in place of, their current proprietary network solutions.

The Corporation for Open Systems (COS) has been enjoying phenomenal growth. Forty-five companies joined within its first 6 months of operation. The membership list reads like a who's who of computer networking vendors and users. With an annual budget of over $5 million, COS has opened membership to users and vendors worldwide, none of whom were willing to risk being left out of consideration in any developments.

Getting involved

Users who ask for standards but do nothing about developing them are in a poor position to complain about what they get. There are two primary ways to participate in the process: directly through membership in standards-making committees and indirectly through users' groups and associations.

The direct route is to join the standards committees working on the standards that concern you. The primary challenge with this approach is the cost. International standards committees meet several times a year at locations around the world. Participation requires a substantial travel budget to attend meetings and a major time commitment to study and prepare between meetings. Although all committees are open to anyone who wishes to volunteer, the politics are much easier to handle in groups which are newly formed or not the center of public attention. The probability of successfully affecting any outcomes is substantially greater if you avoid the politically sensitive committees.

The user whose needs are more varied or who does not have a large travel budget can take the indirect approach. Users' groups such as the MAP/TOP Users' Group have volunteer company members on standards committees to provide liaison and lobbying. You receive coverage of the happenings in many more committees. Your impact is reduced to the extent it differs from the needs of the other members of the users' group, but at the same time it is increased to the extent your goals and the group's agree. After all, there are many more users than vendors, and to the extent vendors believe the users will purchase in accordance with their demands, they will promote useful standards for their own profit.

Protocol certification

Conformance testing of protocols to prove they are implemented in accordance with the specifications is critical to making compatible and interoperable protocol implementations possible. Interoperability testing of protocol implementations to prove that two implementations on a network can effectively communicate is critical to making off-the-shelf multivendor networking possible. Both are being pursued by treating the protocol implementation under test as a finite-state machine and verifying proper response to test stimulation. Practical limits on the time needed to test an implementation require the tests be effective with only a few hundred test cases out of the millions possible for most protocols.

Successful testing depends on more than just a suite of tests. The protocol being tested must be precisely defined to eliminate any questions of interpretation. Second, the precise specification must be validated to prove that the protocol meets its objectives and is implementable. Only then does implementing any tests make sense. This drive for precise protocol specification to allow conformance and interoperability testing is having a major impact on the standards defining the protocols.

Most ISO OSI protocol standards have been written as prose specifications. Since natural language prose is not suited for formal, mathematically provable logic specifications, the prose versions are being rewritten using formal description languages. The formal versions of the protocols are then reviewed by the originators of the protocol to ensure proper interpretation of the prose. This is a major improvement because it eliminates the need for each implementor to interpret the prose individually, sometimes with incompatible results. The formal versions become the official protocol standard while the original prose versions are retained as tutorial supplements.

Once a standard has been formally described, comprehensive test criteria, methodology, scenarios, and environments can be compiled and standardized by the test-process working group. After the responsible protocol working group reviews the completed test documentation, it is possible to have a standard, repeatable test for protocol implementation compliance.

Conformance Testing

The Industrial Technology Institute offers conformance testing services to vendors through their Network Evaluation and Testing Center. The test center has been in operation since September 1985. Other test centers are under development in the United Kingdom and West Germany. The procedure followed in all test centers is specified by the MAP/TOP Users' Group which claims all authority to approve and recognize conformance tests for MAP/TOP. The tests are divided into two parts, a static conformance test and dynamic tests.

The static conformance test starts by documenting the options the implementation under test (IUT) is supposed to support. Based on these options, a suitable set of test scenarios is selected. The final stage of static testing is verification and documentation of the ranges and accuracy of timers, counters, and the like.

The dynamic tests begin with a basic functionality test. This is a very simple and limited test sequence to confirm that the implementation under test can communicate with the test equipment. Assuming that the basic functionality test succeeds, the full dynamic conformance test is run. This phase is the bulk of the testing activity, as large numbers of test sequences are tried to verify correct operation. This includes proper handling of defective data as well as normal operation. If problems are encountered at any time, most test centers allow the vendor to purchase optional diagnostic testing to help determine what may be causing the failure.

The final step is generation of the formal test report. The test report describes which tests were run, the results for each, and any tests which were not run. These test reports are treated by the test center as confidential. However, the vendors may do whatever they like with them. The expectation of ITI was that users would request them from the vendors, creating a booming test business. Through 1986, the response has been weak because of the lack of a complete suite of tests. While tests were available for link level, internet, transport, session, and CASE, useful tests for network management, directory services, FTAM, media access control, carrierband, and broadband remained unavailable until 1987. Without an ability to test an entire protocol stack, the results of conformance testing were only useful if they were negative. A positive report did not guarantee that the untested layers would not introduce problems.

There is no work in MAP/TOP technical committees progressing or supporting the ISO conformance testing methodology work. However, ITI, the National Bureau of Standards, the Corporation for Open Systems, and other conformance test developers are following ISO's work. All are hard at work developing the missing tests required to make conformance testing of MAP/TOP and other ISO OSI networks meaningful. Given results to date, you can expect MAP/TOP 3.0 to experience the same delays waiting for useful conformance tests once the protocols themselves become available. The lifetime of MAP 2.1/TOP 1.0 (and MAP 2.2) may be much longer than predicted just because they may be the only multivendor protocols which can offer proven conformance for some time.

Interoperability testing

In the world of MAP/TOP, the goal of testing extends beyond conformance. The real need is to have repeatable, meaningful interoperability testing. It is not enough to know that a protocol adheres to the specification. What is required is knowledge that two implementations from arbitrary sources can function correctly together. This is a much more difficult problem than testing conformance. The NBS Implementation Workshops have been in progress for years negotiating the details that allow two conforming protocol implementations to communicate with each other.

The ultimate success of MAP/TOP depends on the availability of meaningful, cost-effective interoperability testing. Users and vendors need to be able to determine if different vendors' protocol implementations communicate correctly and reliably with each other. The availability of effective third-party testing is the key. The success of work by ITI, COS, NBS, and others will be seen at the 1988 MAP/TOP 3.0 exposition, where interoperability will be demonstrated to the world.

New Network Media

In Chapters 7 and 8 we discussed two of the IEEE local area network standards, 802.3 and 802.4. Two other media options which could have a major impact on MAP/TOP are the IBM token ring (IEEE 802.5) and Fiber Distributed Data Interface (FDDI).

IEEE 802.5

IEEE 802.5 is the standard for token-ring local networks. The specific ring standardized is the physical and media access layers of the IBM token ring introduced in 1985. The IBM Systems Network Architecture protocols which IBM uses for the upper layers in their proprietary implementations are not included. Standardization of the physical and MAC layers provide the ability for other manufacturers to connect their machines to the same ring without interfering with other users. However, it does require common upper layers to allow any communications to occur between users.

The ring is wired with twisted pair wiring in a star configuration from a central hub to the individual stations. The hub then connects the attached devices to form a ring. This provides the simplicity of token passing on a ring with the fault-finding convenience of a star. A technician in the wiring closet in which the hubs are located can verify the signals sent to and received from each device without physically going to each device location. The token-ring hub has the capability to remove a failed device from the ring, restoring operation.

Standard speed on the token ring is 4 Mbps. A 16-Mbps version is under development. The influence of IBM is expected to make the token ring an extremely popular networking choice. Some market analysts are predicting over half the local area networks installed by 1990 will be IBM/IEEE 802.5 token rings. Since it is an IEEE class network, other IEEE 802-based networks such as MAP/TOP can also function on the same wiring if suitable physical layer software and hardware are provided.

Fiber Distributed Data Interface

Fiber Distributed Data Interface, FDDI, is a token-passing ring network based on IEEE 802.5. The differences from 802.5 are designed to support efficient, high-speed operation over extended distances without giving up the advantages of compatibility with 802.2 link-level protocols. The FDDI ring uses fiber optics for the medium, transmitting data at a rate of 100 Mbps. The network is intended for use on a scale ranging from connecting several mainframe computers in a single room to tying up to a thousand nodes with a total ring circumference up to 200 Km.

An FDDI network consists of two independent rings. The primary ring transmits in one direction while the secondary ring transmits in the opposite direction. This dual ring architecture allows recovery from fiber failure or station failure. Both rings can also be used together to provide 200 Mbps of total communications bandwidth. The dual rings define two station types. Class A stations connect to both primary and secondary rings. Class B stations connect to only one ring. Hubs are also defined. A hub connects to the ring as a class A station and allows multiple class B stations to connect without affecting the ability of the main rings to reconfigure. Reliability and robustness of the overall network werre two of the prime considerations in the architecture's design.

FDDI includes standards for media access control, station management, physical layer protocol, and physical media. All are being developed under the auspices of the American National Standards Institute X3T9.5 working group. Since FDDI is the only viable international standard for fiber optics currently under development, it is receiving excellent support from the fiber optics industry, computer vendors, and potential users. FDDI should be the first network standard specifically designed to optimize the capabilities available from fiber optics.

New Technologies

There are a number of technological developments that could have a major impact on the future directions of MAP/TOP, CIM, and office automation. Continued progress in very large-scale integrated-circuit implementation of MAP/TOP protocols will continue to reduce the cost of network connections. Multimedia messaging and integrated voice and data promise improved office communications. Personal computers are getting more powerful, more sophisticated, and lower in cost every day. At the same time as the price of computer power is decreasing, expert systems are developing which can extend the use of computers into applications only dreamed of in the past. Let us look at each in turn.

VLSI implementation

The availability of network functions in integrated-circuit chips is reducing the cost of networks in general and having a profound impact on the MAP/TOP market. All the IEEE 802 protocols which have been approved as standards, with the exception of broadband modems, are available in integrated-circuit form from one or more vendors. Single-chip computers and low-cost memory allow the implemention of higher-level protocols on plug-in interface cards. This trend is seen by many as one possible way to overcome the performance limitations inherent in the complexity of open system protocol architectures such as MAP/TOP. As the prices for integrated solutions continue to plummet, any extra cost of implementing a MAP/TOP protocol rather than a proprietary one will not make much difference when the numbers involved are only a few dollars instead of the hundreds or thousands currently the case.

The degree of functionality currently available is illustrated by Motorola's IEEE 802.4 media access control chip. This integrated circuit is typical of the capabilities available from most major vendors and illustrates what can be done when a protocol is well defined and has a large enough market to justify integrating the functions. On a single integrated circuit, Motorola has integrated all IEEE 802.4 media access control functions plus station management functions such as initialization, setting and reading parameters, group address recognition, and station management data service. The chip even includes a complete station management to physical layer interface with functions like reset, transmitter disable, and transmitter fault state sensing.

The physical characteristics taken for granted in these devices are impressive. The chip supports serial data rates up to 10 Mbps, the 802.4 specification. To access the data at full speed, the chip provides four channels of direct memory access transfer with data transfer and management based on shared memory using fully linked data structures. Network flexibility is enhanced by support of the 802.4 real-time extensions, all four priority classes, and network monitoring and diagnostic aids. An integrated-circuit vendor cannot afford to exclude any implementation options. The chip supports 8-bit and 16-bit data transfers; priority interrupt request, vectoring, and control; and handles all popular modes of ordering and addressing bytes in word-wide memory.

What is amazing is not that so much capability is stuffed into a single integrated circuit but rather that so much capability must be included to even be considered competitive! As MAP/TOP becomes more popular, we might see all the ISO layers available in integrated-circuit chip form. The technology exists; the only piece missing is the market to justify the investment required to implement it.

Multimedia messaging

The introduction of message-handling systems and document exchange in TOP 3.0 is just the beginning. Expansion will occur in two dimensions: more media and more uses. Text and graphics could soon be supplemented with voice. Multimedia messages which include voice are a natural in the executive suite. Many managers desire the advantages of electronic documents but are unwilling or unable to learn how to type. Multimedia allows the executive to dictate a response that can be included with the document and listened to by the recipient. Multimedia voice and graphics may also be seen in applications in which literacy of the user is a problem.

The proliferation of personal computers and other low-cost, high-powered workstations is breaking down the traditional barriers that have prevented multimedia messaging in the past. Graphics capability in computer displays is being taken for granted, and voice and facsimile are available as reasonably priced options. The biggest challenge is getting the information into the computer and manipulating it once there. Using voice and handwritten documents to enter data into a computer is still beyond the state of the art except in a few limited applications. However, the computer can provide a very effective delivery system for both (via voice messaging and facsimile) even if it cannot decipher any of the meaning and must use millions of bits to encode only a few words' worth of information.

Integrated voice and data

Another potential major force in office-oriented networks is integrated voice and data. Here the same wiring is used for telephone and computer communications simultaneously. Voice and data switches have been introduced in a wide range of sizes. Units are available to meet needs ranging from small departments of 10 to 20 users up to entire companies requiring thousands of lines. The Northern Telecom Meridian DV-1 is a typical voice and data switch designed for offices with 10 to 50 users. Each twisted pair connected to the switch provides two voice channels and a 2-Mbps-plus data channel.

The problem so far has been the lack of a common standard for integrating voice and data. Multivendor connectivity is available only for voice signals and then only between switches. The only data channel standard available has performance too low to be competitive in the office automation local area network market. The Integrated Services Digital Network (ISDN) standard is targeted at making universal, worldwide, all-digital telephony possible. Unlike the office voice-data switch, which can specify the quality of cabling used, ISDN must function over the telephone wiring already installed on poles and under streets around the world. As a result, its performance is limited to one voice channel and 64 Kbps of data over the same twisted pair cable that proprietary solutions can use for two voice channels and over 2 Mbps of data.

The basic user service under ISDN is called 2B + D. Each B channel provides 64-Kbps switched circuit communications and can be used for either digitized voice or computer data. The D channel provides a 16-Kbps channel for system signaling and control. Two B channels and one D run over the single twisted pair previously used for analog voice. While there have been numerous pilot implementations, ISDN has not yet achieved widespread acceptance or implementation. Each pilot has used variations on the standard. The North American and European phone systems have had trouble agreeing on implementation details. Time will tell if ISDN will become popular and be installed widely.

Personal computers

Personal computers are ubiquitous. They are used in homes, offices, and even on the factory floor. They provide tremendous amounts of computing power at low cost. As better software becomes available, PCs will challenge many traditional minicomputer and mainframe applications. An entire industry has developed to provide software and hardware accessories for the IBM/PC compatible machines. The number of units in use around the world today ensures a market for almost any accessory or software package imaginable.

The newer, high-powered versions based on the Intel 80386 chip and its successors promise to bring computing power only dreamed of a few years ago to PC users. This can be seen in the software already available on PC- and AT-class machines. What is important on a personal computer is how easily the user can take advantage of the machine, not how efficiently the machine is used. Indeed, one of the dangers with the introduction of multitasking operating systems on the personal computers is that the ability to "waste" processor capacity on making an application usable may be considered undesirable. The future of personal computers still resides in making them personal by using the low-cost computing power to make life easier for the user rather than more complex.

The dangers inherent in personal computers are also well known. Quality, service, and support can range from superb to nonexistent because the vendor cost of entry into this market is almost zero. Selection of vendors can be critical. High price does not necessarily imply high quality. In many ways, the IBM/PC compatible marketplace resembles what General Motors originally dreamed MAP/TOP would be like—a wide range of vendors and products to choose from, all of which can plug together and interoperate regardless of who made what.

Expert systems

After 20 years of struggling in the laboratories, artificial intelligence is entering the real world in the form of expert systems. This is because of the convergence of two trends. The first trend is the incredible amounts of computer power becoming available in reasonably priced packages. The second trend is the lowering of user expectations for expert systems to a level attainable by today's knowledge processors. An expert system can be very effective as an assistant to an expert even if it cannot be considered a replacement for the expert.

The successful applications use expert systems to capture and disseminate the experts' knowledge and to help others benefit from that knowledge. By handling the routine cases which normally take up the majority of the experts' time, expert systems allow experts to concentrate on the situations that truly require an expert. More widespread usage still requires major improvements in the efficiency of moving expert system development out of the R&D laboratory and into production. Developing systems capable of handling nontrivial problems is still an extremely expensive proposition. The solutions available today are all one-of-a-kind specials, but several seem to be paying off well. For example, Digital Equipment Corporation is using an expert system to help configure VAX systems, reducing the number of incorrectly configured orders and increasing the percentage of orders that have no missing or extra pieces when delivered. Experience with expert systems has shown that maintenance and upgrade plans for the knowledge base are vital for success. Much the same as developing a human expert, the development of the expert system is only part of the task. Keeping the expert current can be even more difficult.

For More Information

The MAP and TOP specifications are available from:

The Society of Manufacturing Engineers
One SME Drive, P.O. Box 930
Dearborn, MI 48121

Copies of ISO standards (including proposed and draft standards and approved international standards) can be obtained from the International Organization for Standardization; contact:

Central Secretariat
1, Rue de Varmebe
CH-1211 Geneva, Switzerland-40

Copies are also available in most countries from the national representative to ISO. For example, in the United States, contact:

American National Standards Institute
1430 Broadway
New York, NY 10018

There are many other sources of information on networks and MAP/TOP in particular. Many books have been published about networking in general. Probably the best all-around treatment of computer networking theory is Tanenbaum's *Computer Networks* (Prentice-Hall, 1981). Although very technical, *Distributed Databases: Principles and Systems* (McGraw-Hill, 1984) by Ceri and Pelagatti is one of the best books on distributed databases, and it includes coverage of concurrency control. Champine's *Distributed Computer Systems: Impact on Management, Design, and Analysis* (North-Holland, 1980) presents a good mix of technical and management issues. *Tutorial: Distributed Processing* (IEEE Press, 1981) compiled and edited by Liebowitz and Carlson is an interesting collection of articles, many of which are dated because of their emphasis on hardware which is not as significant today as it was just 5 years ago. However, you may be surprised by how many supposedly new problems have been around since the 1970s.

While there are a large number of magazines and journals which occasionally carry articles about MAP and TOP, there is none (as of early 1987) which is MAP/TOP specific. Figure 12.1 lists some of the many magazines which occasionally publish articles which may be of interest. It is worth checking their tables of contents when they come into the library.

The best source of up-to-date information on MAP/TOP and related issues is the MAP/TOP Users' Group, which meets three times a year. Complete proceedings are published, transcribed from tape recordings made at the conference. The availability of these proceedings is a great convenience. They allow you to catch up on missed parallel sessions and to devote your time to making personal contacts to find out what others' experiences have been. SME also publishes a quarterly newsletter, *MAP/TOP Interface*, which provides general news of interest to the MAP/TOP community.

Timely MAP/TOP information is also published by several consulting firms. For example, the Industrial Technology Institute (ITI Information Systems Center, P.O. Box 1485, Ann Arbor, MI 48105) publishes *Gateway, The MAP Reporter* bimonthly. Issues are around 30 pages long and are dedicated to covering news and information specifically related to MAP/TOP.

General coverage on Open Systems Interconnection standards is provided by Omnicom, Inc. (501 Church Street NE, Suite 304, Vienna, VA 22180) in their monthly *Open Systems Communication*. These publications can be excellent if they provide the information you need in your work. There are a number of similar publications available to choose from, and the selection will expand further as MAP/TOP becomes more popular. Subscription costs are high, so read an issue or two before subscribing to ensure the coverage is suitable for your needs and your technical abilities.

Those wishing a more personal touch may choose from the many short courses available. Courses range from general introductions to the ISO OSI model to coding details for a particular manufacturer's interface card. Courses also vary widely in quality of content and presentation. You need to exercise diligence to insure that you are getting a course which meets your needs.

ACM Transactions on Computer Systems
ACM Transactions on Database Systems
ACM Transactions on Office Information Systems
CIM Technology
Communications of the ACM
Computer
Computer Decisions
Computer Design
Computer Networks and ISDN Systems
Computing Surveys
Data Communications
Datamation
Electronic Engineering Times
Electronics
IEEE Communications
IEEE Journal on Selected Areas in Communications
IEEE Spectrum
IEEE Software
IEEE Transactions on Communications
IEEE Transactions on Computers
IEEE Transactions on Software Engineering
Infosystems
Journal of Parallel and Distrubuted Computing
Mini-Micro Systems
Proceedings of the IEEE
SIGCOM Computer Communications Review
SIGOPS Operating Systems Review

Figure 12.1 Some magazines and journals which may carry networking and MAP/TOP related articles.

For those needing more personal attention, many consultants are available. Consultants can also be useful if you lack the time or resources to develop your own staff. However, as anyone who has used consultants to augment staffing will tell you, consultants can break your project as well as make it, so careful selection is a must.

The Future of MAP/TOP

As I am writing this (January 1987), the future of MAP/TOP is looking better than ever. This may seem like a strange statement since progress has slowed because of the increasingly large number of people involved and the first demonstration of MAP/TOP 3.0 capability has been postponed until sometime in 1988. However, these are not really set-backs. The delays are part of the reality of bringing a major state-of-the-art project on the frontiers of technology to market and are actually hastening the availability of a mature MAP/TOP 3.0 specification and the availability of useful MAP/TOP 3.0 conforming products. The lessons learned developing the MAP 2.1/TOP 1.0 specification have been heeded.

MAP/TOP 3.0 will not have all the features originally hoped, but that is not a problem. The foundations are being laid so that all desired features can be added in the future without affecting compatibility with existing systems. The experience gained from implementing the first subsets will provide guidance to the standards developers and superior product capabilities for MAP/TOP 3.X. MAP/TOP 3.0 will not be the ultimate MAP/TOP network any more than a CIM pilot is the ultimate CIM system. MAP/TOP 3.0 is just the beginning.

The needs which started General Motors, Boeing Computer Services, and others on the path to MAP/TOP over 10 years ago have not changed. The price of MAP/TOP may be higher than desired and the performance may be lower. The problem is one of impatience rather than lack of desire. MAP 2.1 and 2.2 along with TOP 1.0 meet real needs and have a place in factory floor automation and computer-integrated manufacturing. MAP/TOP 3.0 products will be available when the specifications and testing are solid enough to support multivendor interoperability. MAP/TOP may not be the only manufacturing network in the future, but it will be there meeting the need for useful multivendor communications.

MAP/TOP and the panoply of open systems networking services based on international standards are the future of computer networking. The only question is the time frame. In the meantime, though your job is made more difficult by the need to balance the cost effectiveness of proprietary solutions with the connectivity of open systems solutions, we can all continue to push to make MAP/TOP live up to its potential as a common solution to networking needs. There is no alternative.

Glossary

ABM Asynchronous Balanced Mode (HDLC specific)

Access points The end points at each end of a connection

ACK See acknowledgment

Acknowledgment An indication that a "message" was received without error

ACSE Association Control Service Elements (ISO)

AD Addendum, ISO standard status

ADCCP Advanced Data Communication Control Procedure

Address A coded representation of the origin or destination of data

Addressing Specifying the source and/or destination

AFI Address Format Identifier

ALOHA An experimental radio broadcast network

Alternating Mode Half-duplex, send-receive operation

AM See amplitude modulation

American National Standards Institute The coordinating organization for voluntary standards in the United States

Amplitude modulation Varying the carrier amplitude in accordance with the signal

Analog transmission Signal encoding by means of continuously variable physical quantities

ANSI See American National Standards Institute

Application layer The top layer of the ISO OSI model where the user's work is done

ARPA Advanced Research Projects Agency—now DARPA, for Defense Advanced Research Projects Agency

ARPANET An early experimental packet switching network still in use

ASCII American Standard Code for Information Interchange

ASN.1 Abstract Syntax Notation One (ISO)

Async See asynchronous transmission

Asynchronous transmission Having an arbitrary time between characters

Attached processor A processor which communicates with a MAP node that does not have its own end-to-end service component

Backbone A network used to connect subnetworks

Balanced (1) Electrical—differential signals; (2) link layer—no master-slave

Band The frequency spectrum between two defined limits delimiting a channel

Bandwidth The information capacity of a channel

BAS Basic Activity Subset (CCITT session layer)

Baseband Transmission of a signal at its original frequency, without modulation

Baud rate Modulation rate (not necessarily the same as bits per second)

BCS Basic Combined Subset (CCITT session layer)

Binary exponential backoff   Algorithm used to reschedule transmissions after a collision

Binary Synchronous Communications   IBM link protocol from the 1960s

Bisync   See Binary Synchronous Communications

Bit transfer rate   The number of bits transferred per unit of time

BIU   Bus Interface Unit

Blocking   (1) PBX—not being able to provide a path for a connection; (2) ISO OSI layer—combining several SDUs into one PDU

Bps   Bits per second

Bridge   Devices used to connect segments of a LAN at the link level

Broadband   Use of multiple channels over the same media via frequency division of the bandwidth

Broadcast   Transmission of a message to multiple destinations

BSC   See Binary Synchronous Communications

BSS   Basic Synchronized Subset (CCITT session layer)

Buffer   A block of memory for temporary storage

Burst errors   Several sequential bits in error

Bus   A shared communications channel in the form of a single cable

Byte   A unit of data, usually 8 bits

Cable   A transmission medium consisting of one or more conductors within a protective sheath

Carrier   Modulated signal that carries information

Carrier band   Modulation technique used for small factory floor networks

Carrier-sense multiple access   Listening before sending

CASE   Common Application Service Elements (ISO)

Catanet   An interconnected set of networks using bridges, routers, and/or gateways

CATV   Community Antenna TV (Cable TV)

CBX   Computerized Branch Exchange

CCITT   International Consultative Committee on Telegraph and Telephony (Comité Consultatif Internationale de Télégraphique et Téléphonique); division of the International Telecommunications Union which sets standards

CCR   Commitment, Concurrency, and Recovery (ISO)

CGI   Computer Graphics Interface (ISO)

CGM   Computer Graphics Metafile (ISO)

Channel   A path along which signals can be sent

Character   A transmission symbol (usually 7 or 8 bits)

Checksum   A form of error check

Choke packet   A flow-congestion control mechanism

CIM   Computer-Integrated Manufacturing

Cipher text   Encrypted text

Circuit-switching   Providing a fixed path for messages

CIU   Communications Interface Unit

Clear   To close a connection

CLNS (also CL NS)   ConnectionLess Network Service

Close   To terminate a connection

Coaxial cable   A cable consisting of one conductor surrounded by an insulated shield

Collision   When two users send at the same time

Communicating entity   (1) Any program, state machine, or automation of some form capable of communicating on a network; (2) CCITT—(N) entities with (N − 1) connections between them

Communications   The transfer of information between the origin and receiver

Concentrator   Combining several users' data on one link

Congestion control   Relieving an excess of traffic in the network

Connection   A logical relationship between two end points

Connectionless   Message transmission without establishing a circuit

Connection-oriented   Message transmission with sequenced, error-free delivery

Connectivity   A characteristic of open systems such that they have the ability to pass data from one to another

Contention   To attempt to gain control of a shared communication channel

CNC   Computer Numerical Control

CR   Carriage Return character

CRC   See cyclic redundancy check

Cryptographic   Security protection by encryption

CSA   Client Service Agent (MAP directory service specific)

CSMA   Carrier Sense Multiple Access

CSMA/CA   CSMA with Collision Avoidance

CSMA/CD   CSMA with Collision Detection

Cyclic redundancy check   An error checking method

DA   Destination Address

DAD   Draft ADdendum, ISO standard status

DARPA   See ARPA

Data Circuit-terminating Equipment   The functional unit of a data station that establishes, maintains, and releases connections and otherwise interfaces data terminal equipment to a data transmission line (CCITT)

Data communication   An (N) function which transfers (N) protocol data units according to an (N) protocol over one or more (N − 1) connections (CCITT)

Data Encryption Standard   U.S. (NBS) encryption standard

Datagram   An independent unit of data

Data link   A logical connection between two stations on the same circuit

Data link layer   The layer of the ISO model responsible for reliable node-to-node communications

Data terminal equipment   Subscriber equipment that serves as a message source or message sink (CCITT)

Data units   Messages passed over connections

DBX   Digital Branch Exchange; see private branch exchange

DCE   See data circuit-terminating equipment

DDCMP   Digital Data Communication Message Protocol (DECnet)

DDN   Defense Data Network; the DDN Program Management Office sets U.S. Department of Defense networking standards

Deadlock   Not being able to progress for lack of resources

DECnet   Trademark for Digital Equipment Corporation's network architecture

DES   See Data Encryption Standard

DIB   Directory Information Base or Directory Database (MAP specific)

Dibit   Handling 2 bits at a time

Digital interface unit   Equipment which permits a DTE to connect to a public data network

Directory services   Network system function to provide required addressing given a global name

DIS   Draft International Standard, ISO standard status
DIU   See digital interface unit
DLC   Data Link Control
DLE-doubling   Transparency control on character-oriented link protocols
Domain (of NM)   The physical devices and resources under the control of a network management entity
DP   Draft Proposal, ISO standard status
DP1   First ballot of the draft proposal
DP2   Second ballot of the draft proposal
DS   Directory Service
DSA   Directory Service Agent (MAP directory service specific)
DSMDU   Directory Service Message Data Unit (MAP directory service specific)
DTE   See data terminal equipment
Duplex transmission   Data transmission over a circuit capable of transmitting in both directions at the same time
Duplicate   A second copy of a message
EBCDIC   Extended Binary-Coded Decimal Interchange Code (IBM character set)
ECMA   European Computer Manufacturers Association
EDIF   Electronic Design Interchange Format
EIA   See Electronics Industries Association
Electronics Industries Association   A U.S. manufacturer's group which sets some interface standards
Elements (of NM)   Abstractions used to describe and categorize the responsibilities of network management
Encryption   Making data unreadable except by those authorized to receive it
End user   The source or destination of data sent through a network
Entity   An abstract or concrete thing in the universe of discourse (CCITT)
EPA   Enhanced Performance Architecture (MAP)
Error   One or more bits of a message being wrong
Error control   The part of a protocol controlling the detection, and sometimes correction, of errors
ESTELLE   A formal description technique based on an extended state transition model (ISO)
Ethernet   A local area network based on CSMA/CD
Euronet   The European (Common Market) network
FADU   File Access Data Unit
FCS   See frame check sequence
FDM   See frequency division multiplexing
Fiber optics   An alternative medium for communications which uses optical rather than electrical signals
FIPS   Federal Information Processing Standards
Flag   (1) A character which indicates the occurrence of some condition; (2) indicator that identifies the start of a frame in bit-oriented link protocols
Flooding   Routing by sending out on all paths
Flow control   Procedure for regulating the flow of data between two points
FM   See frequency modulation
Four-wire circuit   A two-way communications circuit using two independent paths, one for each direction (telephony)
FPDU   FTAM Protocol Data Unit

Fragmentation Splitting a message into pieces
Frame A unit of information at the link protocol level
Frame check sequence The error check on a frame
Frequency division multiplexing Sharing a channel by dividing its frequency (bandwidth) into pieces
Frequency modulation Method of information transmission in which the frequency of the carrier wave is modulated by the signal
Frequency shift keying Modulating a digital signal onto a carrier by varying the frequency
Front-end computer A communications computer associated with a host computer
FSK See frequency shift keying
FTAM File Transfer, Access, and Management (ISO)
FTP File Transfer Protocol (ARPA/DDN)
Full duplex Simultaneous transmission in both directions on a connection
Gateway Devices to connect different network architectures using different protocols by providing protocol translation
GKS Graphic Kernel System (ISO)
GKS-3D Graphic Kernel System—three dimensional
Global address A unique address for each communicating entity among all communicating entities that are able to communicate
Global name A unique name for a specific communicating entity among all communicating entities regardless of its global address or location
Half-duplex Transmission in one direction at a time
Handshaking Exchange of predetermined signals during communications
HDLC See high-level data link control
Head end The location in a broadband system where the inbound signals are transformed to outbound signals
Header The control portion of a message
Hierarchical network A structure with the most control at the top
High-level data link control An ISO link layer protocol
High split Mode of operation for a broadband cable plant
Hit A transient disturbance to a communications medium
Host computer A computer primarily providing services such as computation or database access
Host-to-host protocol End-to-end (transport) protocol
ICST Institute for Computer Science and Technology (of NBS)
IEEE Institute of Electrical and Electronics Engineers
IEEE 802 Project to develop local area network standards
IEEE 802.1 High-level interface (architecture, internetworking, and management)
IEEE 802.2 Logical link control
IEEE 802.3 CSMA/CD networks
IEEE 802.4 Token bus networks
IEEE 802.5 Token ring networks
IEEE 802.6 Metropolitan area networks
IEEE 802.7 Broadband technical advisory group
IEEE 802.8 Fiber optics technical advisory group
IEEE 802.9 Integrated data and voice networks
IGES Initial Graphics Exchange Specification (ANSI)

IMP   Interface Message Processor (ARPANET)

In-band control   Sending messages over the same channel as the data

Information frame   A frame containing data

Integrated services digital network   A network in which the same digital switches and paths are used to establish connections for voice and data (CCITT)

Interface data unit   The total unit of information transferred across the service access point (OSI)

International Organizationfor Standardization   Voluntary coordinating group for development of standards in any field for international use; the primary source of MAP/TOP networking protocols

International Standards Organization   Another name for the International Organization for Standardization

Internet   (1) Consisting of two or more nets; (2) ISO network layer protocol

Internetwork   Between networks

Intranetwork   Within a single network

IP   Internet Protocol (ARPA/DDN)

IPC   InterProcess Communication

IPDU   Internet Protocol Data Unit

IPL   Initial Program Load

IRDS   Information Resource Dictionary System (ISO)

IS   International Standard, ISO standard status

ISDN   See Integrated Services Digital Network

ISO   See International Organization for Standardization

ISO646   Seven-bit ASCII standard

ISO Reference Model for Open System Interconnection   A layered protocol model

JTM   Job Transfer and Manipulation (ISO)

Kbps   Thousand bits per second

Kermit   Personal computer protocol for file transfer over an async channel

LAN   See local area network

LAP   Link Access Protocol

LAPB   Link Access Protocol—balanced

Layer   The overall networking architecture as defined by ISO is subdivided into "layers"; each layer provides a set of network-related services to the layer above.

Leased line   A dedicated telephone channel

LED   Light Emitting Diode

LF   Line Feed character

Link   The interconnection between two nodes on a network

LLC   Link Layer Control

Local area network   A high-data-rate network covering a small geographic range

Local loop   The line from a subscriber to the telephone company central office

LOTOS   A formal description technique based on temporal ordering of observational behavior (ISO)

LPDU   Link layer Protocol Data Unit

LRC   Longitudinal Redundancy Check

LSAP   Link layer Service Access Point

LSDU   Link layer Service Data Unit

MAC   See media access control

Manchester encoding   A signaling method used for transmission of data

MAP   Manufacturing Automation Protocol

MAP network   A set of MAP network segments connected via bridges viewed logically as a single network

MAP network segment   A single physical medium system supporting MAP (see subnetwork)

MAU   Media access unit

Mbps   Million bits per second

Media access control   Methodology by which a node gains access to the network to transmit a message

Message   A collection of data considered a single logical unit

Metropolitan area network   An extended LAN serving a city

Midsplit   Mode of operation for a broadband cable plant

Migration path   Methodology to allow a practical implementation of MAP specified functionality as it is developed

MiniMAP   MAP subnetwork using EPA protocols

Modbus   Modicon LAN product

Modem   Contraction for MOdulator-DEModulator, a device which converts digital signals to analog for transmission (and back)

Modulation   Converting signals from one form (digital) into another (analog)

MMFS   Manufacturing Messaging Format Standard (MAP 2.X)

MMS   Manufacturing Messaging Service (ISO)

MTBF   Mean Time Between Failures

MTTR   Mean Time To Repair

Multidrop   See multipoint

Multiplexing   Division of a communications facility into two or more channels

Multipoint   Having several units sharing a line, usually with a master

NAPLPS   North American Presentation-Level Protocol Syntax

NAK   Negative AcKnowledgment

NBS   National Bureau of Standards (USA)

NC   Numerical Controller

NCC   (1) Network Control Center; (2) National Computer Conference

NCP   Network Control Protocol (ARPANET and IBM SNA)

NDL   Network Data Language

Network interface sublayer   Provides a mapping function between the facilities of the actual network and the services required by layer 4

Network layer   The ISO model layer covering the services across a network

Network management   The facility by which the network communication is observed and controlled

Network management entity   A logically singular instance of a network manager

Network manager   The consciousness of the network management facility; may be human or machine

NFT   Network File Transfer

NISL   See Network Interface Sublayer

NIU   Network Interface Unit

Node   The processor component

Node address   A unique address for each machine on the LAN where local control of addressing is maintained

NPAI   Network Protocol Address Information

NRM   Normal Response Mode (HDLC specific)

NSAP   Network Service Access Point
NSDU   Network Service Data Unit
Null layer   A layer which provides no additional services
Octet   An 8-bit data unit
ODA/ODIF   Office Document Architecture/Office Document Interchange Format (ISO)
ODIF   See ODA/ODIF
OEM   See original equipment manufacturer
1base5   StarLAN IEEE 802.3
Open systems interconnection   Connecting systems from different manufacturers
Original equipment manufacturer   A manufacturer who buys equipment from other suppliers and integrates it into a single system for resale
OSI   Open Systems Interconnection
Out of band   Using a separate channel for control signals
PABX   Private Automatic Branch Exchange; see private branch exchange
Pacing   SNA term for flow control
Packet   A small segment of information for transmission across the net
Packet assembler-disassembler   Provides packet switched network access for asynchronous terminals (CCITT)
Packet frame   A data structure, according to a protocol, that contains predetermined fields for user data and control data
Packet switching   A mode of data transmission in which messages are broken up into smaller units called packets and each packet is transmitted independently
Packet switching network   A network using packet switching for communications
PAD   See packet assembler-disassembler
Parity   A simple 1-bit error check
PBX   See private branch exchange
PCM   See pulse code modulation
PD   See programmable device
PDES   Product Data Exchange Standard (ANSI)
PDN   See public data network
PDU   See protocol data unit
Peer entity   A logical equal
Peer network device   Any device directly attached to a MAP LAN which contains a system manager and has transport layer functionality
Peer protocol   A protocol for interaction between corresponding layers
PGI   Parameter Group Identifier
Phase modulation   Modulation by changing the phase of the carrier signal
PHIGS   Programmer's Hierarchical Interactive Graphic System (ISO)
Physical layer   The lowest layer of the ISO model
PI   Parameter identifier
Piggybacking   Carrying ACKs, etc., with a message
Pipelining   Having several messages "in flight"
PLC   Programmable Logic Controller
PM   See phase modulation
Point-to-point   A link usable for communication between two and only two data stations

Polling   Link control by a master station inviting data stations to transmit one at a time

Port   A logical entry-exit point from a software process

Presentation layer   The ISO model layer that converts the representation of data

Private branch exchange   A telephone switching device serving a specific customer; often owned by the customer and located on the customer's premises

Private line   Same as leased line

Programmable device   Plant floor devices such as PLCs, robots, CNC machines, etc. (MAP)

Propagation delay   The delay caused by the finite speed of electronic transmission

Protocol   A set of rules and formats for communications

Protocol data unit   Information that is delivered as a unit between peer entities and that contains control information and address information, and may contain data

PTT   Post, Telegraph, and Telephone

Public data network   A network established and operated to provide data transmission services to the public

Public key   An encryption method in which the encrypt key is known publicly

Pulse code modulation   A method used to transmit voice in digital form

Q bit   Qualified data; an X.25 flag that indicates how the data packet is to be interpreted

Query   A request for service

Queue   A waiting line

RDA   Remote Data-Access protocol

RDBA   Remote Data Base Access

RDR   Request Data with Immediate Reply (IEEE 802.2)

Reassembly   Putting fragments back together

Redundancy check   A check for errors using extra data inserted for that purpose

Remote job entry   Submission of jobs through an input unit connected to the computer by a data link

Repeater   A signal regenerator

Reverse channel   A channel in the opposite direction

RFA   Remote File Access

RFC   Request For Comments; a set of on line documents providing information about ARPAnet protocols (ARPA/DDN)

Ring network   A LAN with a circular topology

RJE   See remote job entry

RNR   Receiver Not Ready (HDLC specific)

Router   Devices similar to bridges except that they require going up through the first three layers of the OSI model

Routing   Finding a path across the network

RPC   Remote Procedure Call

RPM   Remote Process Management

RR   Receiver Ready (HDLC specific)

RS-232   Standard for connecting DTE to DCE (EIA)

RS-511   Standard for manufacturing messaging (EIA)

RSCS   Remote Spooling and Communications Subsystem (IBM protocol)

SA Source Address
SAP See service access point
SASE Specific Application Service Element
Scroll mode terminal A terminal in which the data passes by a line at a time and only data on the current line may be modified
SDA Send Data with immediate Acknowledge (IEEE 802.2)
SDL Specification and Description Language (CCITT formal description technique)
SDLC See synchronous data link control
SDU System Data Unit
SEAP Service Element Access Point
Secondary The "slave" end of a link
Serial transmission Sending signals a bit at a time
Services The functions offered by an open system to communicating entities in adjacent layers
Service access point The access means by which a pair of communicating entities in adjacent layers use or provide services
Session layer A layer of the ISO model
SGML Standard Generalized Markup Language (ISO)
Signal Waves propagated along a transmission channel which convey some meaning to the receiver
Simplex Transmission in a single predetermined direction only
Sliding window A mechanism which indicates the frames that can currently be sent
Slotted ring A LAN architecture in which a constant number of fixed-length slots circulate around a ring
SMTP Simple Mail Transfer Protocol (ARPA/DDN)
SNA See systems network architecture
SNACF Subnetwork Access Facility (ISO)
SNDCF/SNDCP Subnetwork Dependent Convergence Facility/Protocol (ISO)
SNICF/SNICP Subnetwork Independent Convergence Facility/Protocol (ISO)
SNPA Subnetwork Point of Attachment
Socket A network-wide name for an entry or exit point at a process
Source routing Determining the path (route) at the source of the message
SPDU Session Protocol Data Unit
SQL Structured Query Language
SSAP Session Service Access Point
Star Type of tree network in which there is exactly one intermediate node
Start-stop Character asynchronous transmission
Statistical multiplexer Sharing a link by only sending data when it is available
STEP Standard for the Exchange of Product Model Data (ISO)
Stop and wait protocol Wait for an ACK before sending the next message
Store and forward Store the message (or packet) before sending it on
Subnetwork (MAP) A MAP compatible, bridge accessible subnetwork; logically both the backbone and the subnetwork look like one network
Subsplit Mode of operation for a broadband cable plant
Supervisory frame A control frame
SVC Switched Virtual Circuit
Switched connection A mode of operating a data link in which a dedicated circuit is established between data stations

Synchronous data link control A form of data link control (IBM)

System manager Resides in all MAP nodes and is responsible for interfacing with network management

Systems network architecture IBM's proprietary network, introduced in 1974

T1 carrier A telephone facility (1.544 Mbps in the USA, 2.048 Mbps in Europe)

TAC Terminal Access Controller (ARPA/DDN)

TCP Transmission Control Protocol (ARPA/DDN)

TDM Time Division Multiplexing

10base2 CheaperNet IEEE 802.3

10base5 High-performance IEEE 802.3

10broad36 AUI-compatible broadband IEEE 802.3

Terminal (1) A point in a communications network at which data can enter or leave; (2) a device which provides the human/system interface

Timeout Waiting for a timer to expire before taking action

TLV Type, Length, and Value; the three components of a data element

Token A recognizable control mechanism used to control access to a network

Token bus A network architecture based on a bus topology and using a token-based media access method

Token ring Network architecture using a ring topology and a token-based media access method

TOP Technical and Office Protocols

Topology The structure of a network

TP, TP0-TP4 Transport Protocols (ISO)

TPDU Transport Protocol Data Unit

Traffic analysis Determining the traffic level of a network

Transceiver Transmitter-receiver

Transparency The mechanism providing the function is hidden from the user

Transport layer The layer of the ISO model for host-to-host communication

Trunk The circuits connecting PBXs and central offices to each other

TSAP Transport Service Access Point

TSDU Transport Service Data Unit

Turnkey An installation in which the user receives a complete running system that is ready to be used

Twisted-pair cable Interconnection cable consisting of pairs of wires twisted together

Two-wire circuit A metallic circuit formed by two conductors (usually twisted pair) simplex, half-duplex, or full-duplex communications

UDP Uniform Datagram Protocol (ARPA/DDN)

Umodem Personal computer protocol for file transfer over an async channel

UNDEF Octet format

Unnumbered frame A control frame

User address A unique address for each communicating entity on the LAN where local control of addressing is maintained

User friendly Systems designed to be easily understood and used by the user

User program A computer program running in a processor that performs information processing for some specific use.

UUCP UNIX to UNIX CoPy

VAN Value Added Network

VARCRLF Text format

VDI Virtual Device Interface, see CGI

VGI   Virtual Graphics Interface, see CGI
VRC   Vertical Redundancy Check
V series standards   CCITT standards for the connection of digital equipment to public telephone (analog voice) networks
Virtual circuit   Provides sequenced, error-free delivery
Virtual terminal   Terminal to remote host connection over a network
VLSI   Very Large-Scale Integration
Voice Grade Line   The standard telephone channel
VT   See virtual terminal
WD   Working Draft, ISO standard status
Wide area network   A data communications network designed to serve large geographic areas
Window   The allowable messages (sequence numbers) that can be sent
Workstation   A computer system designed for use by an individual; often connected to other workstations by a LAN
X series standards   CCITT standards for the connection of digital equipment to a public data network
XID   Exchange ID (IEEE 802.2)
Xmodem   Personal computer protocol for file transfer over an async channel
XNS   Xerox Network System
X.25   CCITT communications recommendation defining the connection of a computer to a packet-switched network
X.121   CCITT standard for international X.25 addressing
X.400   CCITT E-mail standard
X.409   CCITT message-handling syntax
X.410   CCITT remote operations protocol
Ymodem   Personal computer protocol for file transfer over an async channel
Zero insertion   A transparency method for bit-oriented link protocols

Index

ABOUT THE AUTHOR

Vincent C. Jones has been active in the field of computer networking for more than 15 years, including 6 years as a Hewlett-Packard Research and Development project manager and as a frequent seminar leader for Integrated Computer Systems. Work experience with the U.S. Air Force and the University of Illinois has ranged from analysis of secure data handling techniques for packet switched networking to demonstration of robot control systems based on artificial intelligence. A graduate of Rutgers University and the University of Illinois in electrical engineering, an active member of IEEE, and a registered professional engineer, Dr. Jones lives in Fort Collins, Colorado.